Population Genetics

THE COLLEGE LIBRARY OF BIOLOGICAL SCIENCES
Edited by Ralph Buchsbaum

Population Genetics

By

CHING CHUN LI

THE UNIVERSITY OF CHICAGO PRESS

CHICAGO AND LONDON

THE UNIVERSITY OF CHICAGO COMMITTEE
ON PUBLICATIONS IN BIOLOGY AND MEDICINE

Library of Congress Catalog Card Number: 55-5134

THE UNIVERSITY OF CHICAGO PRESS, CHICAGO & LONDON
The University of Toronto Press, Toronto 5, Canada

To
the memory of
JEFF

Preface

POPULATION genetics is neither so new nor so formidable a discipline as is often supposed. Many of its most important theorems were worked out in the period 1908-32, but the findings of those early years did not become generally known until much later. The gap between theoretical advance and experimental research, owing partly to the abstruse mathematical language used by the theoreticians, barred the understanding and thus spoiled the natural interest of most students of biology in this field of investigation. Yet this subject was too challenging and important to be long neglected. Actual studies of natural populations began to appear in the late thirties and new results to unfold from then on.

In order to appreciate the recent advances in this field, the student will need a certain amount of background which textbooks of fundamental genetics do not provide. The writer has tried to provide such background, to reduce the mathematics involved to its simplest terms, and to present the subject in a systematic sequence, accompanied by numerical illustrations in each stage; so that any student of genetics who remembers something of his college algebra and has a rudimentary knowledge of statistics will be able to read with comparative ease.

To those intending to use this book as a teaching text, the writer wishes to make it clear that this small treatise is primarily an exposition of some of the fundamental principles and theorems established in this field—not an attempt to review the experimental results. The latter must be supplied by the teacher himself in his special field of interest or according to the demands of his audience. For a short introductory course, some of the sections may well be omitted without disturbing the general thesis of the book.

Furthermore, the statistical study of Mendelian consequences in populations is by no means all that might be included under the present title. For instance, the subject of quantitative inheritance dealing with polygenes, also known as biometrical genetics, has been barely touched upon here. To go into this field in the same systematic fashion as for the subjects presented here would probably double the length of the book. Fortunately, biometrical genetics recently has been well treated by other authors; and I have chosen to limit the scope of this book to the classical Mendelian aspects of the field. However, some of the elementary theorems concerning the inheritance of metrical characters are introduced in the third chapter, and a few others are given in later chapters. The important applications of the genetics of quantitative variability to plant

vii

and animal breeding must be left to special authorities, as in each field there are special problems and considerations, and they cannot be treated profitably in this more general treatise.

The present volume is based largely on a series of lectures given by the writer to students majoring in genetics at the University of Nanking and at the National Peking University prior to 1949. The lectures were published by the National Peking University Press in 1948. But many of the sections have been completely rewritten, and more than 20 per cent of the material is new. The "Notes and Exercises" at the end of each chapter, extensively revised and expanded, are an essential part of the book. They are intended to serve several different purposes and are thus of heterogeneous nature. First, there are numerical examples to provide the student with an opportunity to verify the theorems established in the text. Second, there are some further corollaries or deductions of the main theorem which can be worked out by the student himself. Third, there are mathematical details necessary to the demonstration of a theorem but too long to be included in the text without interrupting its general flow. Fourth, there are presentations of approaches alternative to those given in the text, since it is often instructive to arrive at the same result by different methods. Fifth, some materials give further treatment and provide additional information on the subject covered by the chapter. Because they often overlap, no attempt has been made to classify the various kinds of materials into the categories just listed, and they should be regarded as a flexible supplement to the main text.

The first chapter of the original Peking edition, that on the segregation of small families, has been omitted, because the nature of the subject is not quite the same as that of the rest of this book. However, the substance of that chapter has been recently expanded by the writer and published as a separate paper in *Methods of Medical Research*, Volume 6 (1954).

It is with pleasure and much gratitude that I make the acknowledgments to those who aided in the production of this book. First of all, I wish to thank Professor H. J. Muller of Indiana University for his warm personal encouragement, without which I probably would never have undertaken such a task. Early in 1949, when the Peking edition first reached this country, Professor J. L. Lush of Iowa State College kindly sent me, through my brother, a list of corrections to be made in later editions. In the spring of 1952 Professor Howard Levene of Columbia University made some of his lecture notes on inbreeding populations available to me. Professor J. F. Crow of the University of Wisconsin read the manuscript with the utmost care and offered a detailed list of suggestions, criticisms, corrections, and even some new demonstrations, as well as made his unpublished lecture notes available to me. His generous help deserves very special mention. Professor A. B. Chapman of the same school has kindly read and criticized the two chapters (12 and 13) on path coefficients. Professor Sewall Wright of the University of Chicago, one of the most prolific architects of this field, scrutinized the manuscript from beginning to end and made many valuable criticisms and corrections. Finally, I wish to record my appreciation to Professor Ralph Buchsbaum of the University of Pittsburgh and to Mrs. Buchsbaum for editorial help which renders the passages more readable than they would otherwise be and for their supervision of the artist, Mr. Bernard Garnett, in his execution of the diagrams.

C. C. Li

PITTSBURGH, PENNSYLVANIA

Table of Contents

CHAPTER 1

Large Random-mating Populations

SEARCHING for the mechanism of heredity, geneticists at the turn of this century discovered and established the Mendelian principles from studies at the familial level—limiting their investigations to the alikeness or unlikeness between specified parents and their offspring. In a simple Mendelian study they might cross a purple-flowered plant with a white-flowered one and examine the proportions of the kinds of plants arisen from the seeds. Population genetics, on the other hand, is concerned with the statistical consequences of Mendelism in a *group* of families or individuals; it studies the hereditary phenomenon on a *populational level*. The mechanism of heredity is presumed to be what Mendelian genetics has described. And the population geneticist then goes on to investigate the proportions of purple- and white-flowered plants in a given region, the frequencies of the various types of crosses in such a regional population, the proportions of the various kinds of plants from each type of cross, and the genetic composition of one generation as compared with that of the next under various circumstances.

The life of an individual is limited in length of time, and his genetic makeup is fixed throughout his life, barring mutations. In contrast, a population is practically immortal, may be large or small in size, may be distributed over a wide or limited area, and may change in genetic composition from generation to generation, suddenly or gradually. The study of population genetics is thus inevitably related to that of organic evolution, which, from the genetical viewpoint, is but a process of cumulative change in the heredities characteristic of species. In the study of the Mendelian consequences in a continuous population, certain principles or laws have emerged; and we shall deal with those that have become well established.

We shall begin our study with the simplest but most frequently encountered case—that of autosomal genes of diploid organisms practicing bisexual reproduction in a large population mating at random. The first law to be established for such a population was an important landmark in population genetics, and it will be the main content of this chapter. Before we discuss the law itself, it is necessary to explain a few terms which are not always mentioned in ele-

1

mentary genetics textbooks but which we shall use constantly throughout this book.

§ 1. *Gene Frequency*

In what follows we shall assume that there are only two alleles (A, a) at a particular locus. We shall suppose that there are N diploid individuals, of which D are dominant (AA), H are heterozygous (Aa), and R are recessive (aa), where $D + H + R = N$. To designate such a group of individuals, we shall subsequently adopt, for the sake of brevity, the following symbol:

$$(D, H, R),$$

where the three numbers are always understood to be in the order of AA, Aa, aa. Although there are three types of individuals in this group, there are only two kinds of genes: A and a. These N individuals have $2N$ genes altogether. Since each AA individual has two A genes, and each Aa individual has one A gene, the total number of A genes in this group is $2D + H$. Therefore, the *proportion* of A genes in this group is

$$p = \frac{2D + H}{2N} = \frac{D + \frac{1}{2}H}{N}.$$

This proportion is known as the *gene frequency* of A in this group. Similarly, the frequency of the gene a in this group is $q = (H + 2R)/2N = (\frac{1}{2}H + R)/N$, so that $p + q = 1$. For example, in a group of 40 individuals: $(2, 12, 26)$, $p = (2 + 6)/40 = 0.20$ and $q = (26 + 6)/40 = 0.80$.

Frequently the three genotypes are given in percentages instead of in actual numbers, especially when the group is large. Then we may let $D + H + R = 1$, where D is now the *proportion* of AA individuals in this group, etc. Hence, $p = D + \frac{1}{2}H$ and $q = \frac{1}{2}H + R$. Adopting this notation, our previous population $(2, 12, 26)$ takes the form $(.05, .30, .65)$, in which $p = 0.05 + 0.15 = 0.20$ and $q = 0.15 + 0.65 = 0.80$, as before. In subsequent sections we shall deal with large populations and use D, H, R to denote the proportions of the three genotypes in the population.

§ 2. *Random Mating*

Many organisms in nature, both animals and plants, seem to mate at random or nearly so. The formal definition of random mating is that, in the case of bisexual organisms, any one individual of one sex is equally likely to mate with any individual of the opposite sex. In other words, the frequency of a certain type of mating is dictated by chance. Thus, if the mating is completely at random in the population (D, H, R), the frequency of $AA \times AA$ would be D^2 among all matings, assuming that genotypic proportions in both sexes are the same. The various types of matings and their frequencies are shown in Table 1.

It should be emphasized, however, that the theoretical frequencies will be realized only in very large populations.

The term "panmixia" is sometimes used as a synonym of random mating, and then the population is said to be *panmictic*.

TABLE 1

RANDOM-MATING FREQUENCIES

FEMALES		MALES		
		AA D	Aa H	aa R
AA	D........	D^2	DH	DR
Aa	H........	HD	H^2	HR
aa	R	RD	RH	R^2

§ 3. *The Hardy-Weinberg Law*

Let us consider a large panmictic population with p of A and q of a, where $p + q = 1$. If the proportions of the three genotypes with respect to this pair of genes in the population are

$$D = p^2, \quad H = 2pq, \quad R = q^2,$$

the genotypic proportions in the next generation will be the same as those in the preceding generation. The population $(p^2, 2pq, q^2)$ is then said to be in *equilibrium* under the system of random mating. By "equilibrium" we mean that there is no change in genotypic proportions in a population from generation to generation. This implies no changes in gene frequencies either. There are many possible types of equilibrium conditions, some of which we shall study in later chapters. The particular equilibrium condition under random mating is known as the *Hardy-Weinberg Law* because it was discovered independently by Hardy and by Weinberg in the same year, 1908. (For a historical note see Stern, 1943, in which an important section of Weinberg's original paper was translated into English.) This law is of such fundamental importance in population genetics that it shall be expounded in detail.

Since the matings are at random and since the population is assumed to be large, the frequencies of the various types of matings in the population may be obtained immediately in the manner shown in Table 1, substituting p^2 for D, etc. If we combine reciprocal crosses (because we are considering autosomal genes), the nine different kinds of mating may be collected into six types. The frequencies of each mating type and the corresponding proportions of their offspring are given in Table 2, from which it is seen that the offspring generation is also $(p^2, 2pq, q^2)$. It follows that in all subsequent generations the genetic composition of this population will remain the same provided that there are no disturbing forces at work. This equilibrium is due to the symmetry of the Mendelian mechanism for bisexual reproduction.

As a numerical example, consider a large random-mating population (.04, .32, .64) in which $p = 0.2$ and $q = 0.8$. Students who are encountering this equilibrium law for the first time should carry out the detailed numerical calcu-

TABLE 2

MATINGS AND OFFSPRING IN AN EQUILIBRIUM
RANDOM-MATING POPULATION

TYPE OF MATING	FREQUENCY OF MATING	OFFSPRING		
		AA	Aa	aa
$AA \times AA$.......	p^4	p^4	....	....
$AA \times Aa$.......	$4p^3q$	$2p^3q$	$2p^3q$	....
$Aa \times Aa$.......	$4p^2q^2$	p^2q^2	$2p^2q^2$	p^2q^2
$AA \times aa$.......	$2p^2q^2$	....	$2p^2q^2$	....
$Aa \times aa$.......	$4pq^3$	....	$2pq^3$	$2pq^3$
$aa \times aa$.......	q^4	....	....	q^4
Total.......	1.00	p^2	$2pq$	q^2

lation step by step according to Table 2 and convince themselves that the proportions of the three genotypes in the next generation do indeed remain the same as those of the parent-generation.

§ 4. *Establishment of Equilibrium*

Our previous theorem states that the population (p^2, $2pq$, q^2) is in equilibrium under random mating. But what happens to a population which is not in equilibrium proportions? Let us consider an arbitrary population (D, H, R), where D, H, R are any three positive numbers with sum unity. Referring to Table 1 for random-mating frequencies, and combining the reciprocal crosses and calculating their offspring in the same manner as we did in Table 2, we will find that the proportions of the three genotypes in the offspring generation are in the equilibrium state (see Table 3). Thus we have proved the second important theorem concerning large random-mating populations, viz., equilibrium is reached after a single generation of random mating regardless of the initial composition of the population (Wentworth and Remick, 1916). Symbolically, this theorem may be stated in the following form:

$$(D, H, R) \rightarrow (p^2, 2pq, q^2) .$$

It should be stressed that the genotypic proportions of an equilibrium population are entirely determined by its gene frequencies. Thus, on random mating the arbitrary initial population (.10, .20, .70), in which $p = 0.2$ and $q = 0.8$, becomes (.04, .32, .64) in the next generation, which from then on will remain the same in all subsequent generations as long as the system of random mating continues to hold. In fact, all populations with the same gene frequencies (though their genotypic proportions may be different) will attain the same equilibrium condition on random mating. Thus, the populations (.05, .30, .65), (.01, .38, .61), (.18, .04, .78), (0, .40, .60), (.20, 0, .80), etc., will all become (.04, .32, .64) in the next generation on random mating. Students are advised to take any one of these arbitrary populations and carry out the arithmetic of Table 3 to see that this is actually the case. Since the equilibrium condition is immediately established under random mating, it is justifiable in most cases

TABLE 3

ESTABLISHMENT OF EQUILIBRIUM UNDER RANDOM MATING

Type of Mating	Frequency of Mating	Offspring		
		AA	Aa	aa
$AA \times AA$	D^2	D^2	. . . .	. . . .
$AA \times Aa$	$2DH$	DH	DH	. . . .
$Aa \times Aa$	H^2	$\frac{1}{4}H^2$	$\frac{1}{2}H^2$	$\frac{1}{4}H^2$
$AA \times aa$	$2DR$	. . . .	$2DR$	. . . .
$Aa \times aa$	$2HR$	. . . .	HR	HR
$aa \times aa$	R^2	. . . .	. . . .	R^2
Total	1.00 or	$(D+\frac{1}{2}H)^2$ p^2 .04	$2(D+\frac{1}{2}H)(\frac{1}{2}H+R)$ $2pq$ .32	$(\frac{1}{2}H+R)^2$ q^2 .64

to consider a natural population to be in equilibrium condition if random mating is taking place. This justification is important in practical applications, as we shall see in the next chapter.

§ 5. *Random Union of Gametes*

The long demonstration of random mating and its resulting equilibrium was given partly for reasons of clarification and partly because we shall use some of it (particularly Table 2) to derive further results later on. As far as the Hardy-Weinberg equilibrium proportions are concerned, however, they may be obtained in a much shorter manner by using an important theorem concerning random mating. It should be clear (at least intuitively) that the total result of random mating between individuals, and the subsequent random union of gametes produced by the mates, is equivalent to complete random union of all the gametes produced by the population. This principle may be diagramed as shown in Figure 1.

This one principle will establish the results of the preceding two sections at the same time, for it shows that any population (D, H, R) becomes $(p^2, 2pq, q^2)$

in the next generation with random mating and that this status remains constant thereafter.

Later we shall make frequent use of this principle when dealing with multiple alleles, polyploids, and sex-linked genes and whenever more than one pair of genes are involved and a complete enumeration of all possible genotypic mat-

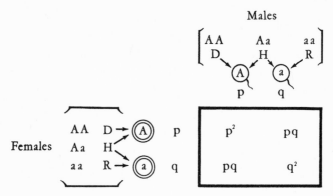

Males

Females

FIG. 1.—The establishment of equilibrium in one single generation of random mating between individuals which is equivalent to random union of male and female gametes.

ings would be very tedious. By the use of this principle, all we have to do in order to determine the composition of any generation is to find the total gametic output of the parent-generation and unite the gametes at random.

§ 6. *Parental Combinations of Recessives*

Up to this point we have been concerned with the frequencies of the various types of matings and their corresponding offspring in a random-bred population. Now let us consider a sort of inverse question: Given a group of individuals of a certain genotype, what are their possible parental combinations and their frequencies? As an example, let us consider the parents of aa individuals. They can only be $Aa \times Aa$, $Aa \times aa$, or $aa \times aa$. An examination of the last column of Table 2 shows that these three parental combinations are of the following frequencies:

PROPORTION	PARENTAL COMBINATION			TOTAL
	$Aa \times Aa$	$Aa \times aa$	$aa \times aa$	
Among all matings.....................	p^2q^2	$2pq^3$	q^4	q^2
Among matings producing aa offspring.....	p^2	$2pq$	q^2	$1\ 00$

The last row happens to be the same as the genotypic proportions in the population. A practical conclusion derived from this is that, when recessive individuals are rare in the general population, the great majority of them will be the off-spring of $Aa \times Aa$ matings. For example, human albinism is thought to be a simple recessive trait. Its general incidence is found to be approximately 1 in 20,000 ($q^2 = 0.00005$) in some European countries. Hence the frequency of the recessive albino gene is approximately $q = \frac{1}{140} = 0.007$. The proportion of heterozygotes in the population is, however, much larger, being $2pq = \frac{1}{70}$, ap-proximately. Among all the albino individuals, $(.993)^2 = 98.60$ per cent will be the offspring of $Aa \times Aa$, where both parents are normal.

The above results may be arrived at entirely from probability considerations without referring to Table 2. Since the occurrence of an aa individual implies that each of his parents must have at least one a gene, we know immediately that his parents are of the type $Xa \times Xa$, where X stands for the unknown gene. Now the probability that a random gene should be A is p and that it should be a is q. Hence, the probability that the two unknowns are both A is p^2, etc. Thus we see how the use of gene frequencies as probabilities can shorten our calculations in many genetic problems—a convenience we shall appreciate again and again in later chapters.

§7. *Some Properties of Equilibrium Populations*

In a diploid population the proportion of heterozygotes is $H = 2pq$, the value of which never exceeds 0.50. Putting

$$\frac{dH}{dq} = \frac{d}{dq} \, 2q \, (1 - q) = 2 - 4q = 0 \, ,$$

we see that the maximum value of H is 0.50 when $q = p = \frac{1}{2}$. H could be greater than either D or R, as in the population (.36, .48, .16), but never greater than $D + R$. If the frequency of one gene is more than twice that of the other, the proportion of heterozygotes is intermediate between those of the two homozy-gous types. For instance, when $p > 2q$, that is, when $p > \frac{2}{3}$, we have

$$p^2 > 2pq > q^2 \, .$$

Another property of an equilibrium population is that the proportion (or number) of heterozygotes is twice the square root of the product of the two homozygous proportions (or numbers), that is,

$$\frac{H}{\sqrt{(D \times R)}} = 2 \, .$$

This property offers us a simple test for equilibrium—a test that has the ad-vantage that the ratio 2 is independent of the gene frequencies of the popula-tion. The above property may also be written in the form

$$4DR = H^2 \, .$$

Any population (D, H, R) may be represented by a point in an equilateral triangle. (The first to use homogeneous coordinates to represent a Mendelian population was B. de Finetti, 1927, cited by Haldane and Moshinsky, 1939.) Let XYZ be an equilateral triangle (Fig. 2), the altitude of which we take as unity. A population may then be represented by a point P inside the triangle such that the perpendiculars from the point P to the three sides are equal to D, H, R. (Students may recall that the sum of the three perpendicular distances to the sides of an equilateral triangle is equal to its altitude, which we take here

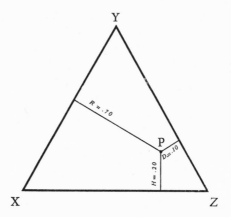

FIG. 2.—Homogeneous coordinates of a population point $P = (D, H, R)$

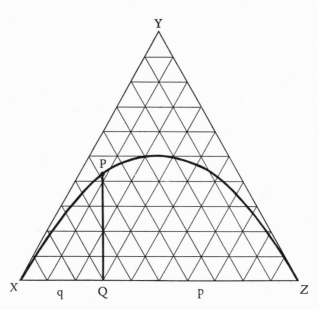

FIG. 3.—The parabola represents the locus of equilibrium population points. The projection point Q divides the base in the ratio of gene frequencies.

as unity.) It is convenient to take the perpendicular distance from P to the base XZ (opposite the vertex Y) as the proportion of heterozygotes, H; and take the distance from P to YZ (the side opposite to X) as D, the proportion of AA. Thus, in Figure 2, the point P represents the population (.10, .20, .70).

As already mentioned, for equilibrium populations under random mating the values of D, H, R can be related by the equation $4DR = H^2$. Therefore, the points representing equilibrium populations lie on the parabola $4DR - H^2 = 0$ (Fig. 3). For example, the particular point P on the parabola shown in Figure 3 represents the population (.49, .42, .09). Any equilibrium population corresponds to a point on the parabola. Furthermore, if Q is the projection point of P on the base XZ, then the two segments of the base will be proportional to gene frequencies, because

$$XQ:QZ = R + \tfrac{1}{2}H:D + \tfrac{1}{2}H = q:p \,.$$

All the preceding properties are concerned with the genotypic proportions of an equilibrium population. We may consider here one property concerned with the frequencies of matings. Inspection of the second column of Table 2 shows that the frequency of $Aa \times Aa$ matings is twice that of $AA \times aa$, a relation entirely independent of gene frequencies in the population. We shall see later that this is true for any kind of equilibrium population, not for random-mating populations alone (Chap. 11, § 5).

Notes and Exercises

1. W. E. Castle (1903) and Karl Pearson (1904) showed that if the F_2 individuals from an original cross $AA \times aa$ are allowed to mate at random, the composition of the next generation would be the same as that in the F_2, viz., $(\tfrac{1}{4}, \tfrac{1}{2}, \tfrac{1}{4})$. This is simply a particular case of the Hardy-Weinberg proportions with $p = q = \tfrac{1}{2}$. The De Finetti point representing this population is the vertex (maximum point) of the parabola shown in Figure 3.

2. *Gene frequency ratio.*—Let $u = p/q$ and divide the Hardy-Weinberg proportions by q^2 throughout; an equilibrium population then assumes the form

$$(u^2, 2u, 1) \,.$$

The sum of these three proportion numbers is $(u + 1)^2$, instead of unity. As p varies from 0 to 1, the ratio u varies from 0 to ∞ (always positive). It is seen that $p = (u^2 + u)/(u + 1)^2 = u/(u + 1)$. Similarly, $q = 1/(u + 1)$. Also $p:q = u:1$. Using this notation, and with $u = 0.2/0.8 = \tfrac{1}{4}$, the population (.04, .32, .64) assumes the form $(\tfrac{1}{16}, \tfrac{1}{2}, 1)$. All the properties concerning large random-mating populations described in the text may just as simply be shown in terms of u. Much of Haldane's earlier work dealt with u rather than with p and q. In some genetics problems, particularly those concerning natural selection, the formulas take a simpler form in terms of u than in terms of q.

3. If the frequency of one gene is very low, so that the frequency of the other allele is close to unity, the Hardy-Weinberg proportions take *a limiting form*. Suppose q is so small that q^2 is negligible; then the equilibrium population is very close to $(1 - 2q, 2q, 0)$. Nearly all the recessive genes are in the heterozygous condition, and the proportion of heterozygous individuals is approximately twice the recessive-gene frequency (Haldane, 1927; Moree, 1950). For human albinism if $q = 0.007$, the proportion of heterozygotes is approximately $H = 0.014 = \frac{1}{70}$, as was pointed out in the text.

4. What will be the composition of the next generation under the system of random mating if the initial population is (.16, .48, .36)? Calculate by the long method, as shown in Table 2.

5. Find the proportions of the three genotypes in the next generation for the following populations whose individuals mate at random:

$$(.25, .10, .65) ; \qquad (.30, 0, .70) ; \qquad (0, .60, .40) .$$

6. Check the following populations which are in equilibrium and calculate the equilibrium proportions for those which are not:

$$(.50, 0, .50) ; \quad (25, 10, 1) ; \quad (.36, .15, .49) ; \quad (1, 1, \tfrac{1}{4}) ; \quad (.09, .10, .81) ;$$

$$(.45, .45, .10) ; \quad (.22, .36, .42) ; \quad (.5625, .3750, .0625) .$$

7. If we let $v = 1/u = q/p$, show that an equilibrium population will assume the form $(1, 2v, v^2)$.

8. Show that the maximum value of $H = 2u/(u + 1)^2$ is attained when $u = 1$.

9. What percentage of a random-mating population showing 5 per cent recessives is heterozygous?
   ANS.: $2(1 - \sqrt{.05})\sqrt{.05} = 34.7$ per cent.

10. If there were 5 per cent dominants in the population, what would be the percentage of heterozygotes?
    ANS.: $H = 2(1 - \sqrt{.95})\sqrt{.95} = 2(.02532)(.97468) = 4.936$ per cent, while the proportion of AA is only $(.02532)^2 = 0.064$ per cent. Thus we see that the great majority of dominants are heterozygotes and that therefore $Aa \times aa$ matings will be far more numerous than $AA \times aa$.

11. Calculate the genotypic proportions of equilibrium populations with $q = .1, .2, \ldots, .9$ and plot these points in an equilateral triangle as shown in Figure 3.

12. Romashov and Ilyina (1942) collected 14,345 foxes, of which 12 were black, 678 intermediate, and 13,655 red. Find the frequencies of the black and the

red genes in this fox population. Are the observed numbers consistent with those expected from the Hardy-Weinberg Law? (See next chapter for statistical test.)

13. With $p + q = 1$, verify the following relations:

(i) $\quad p + 2q = 1 + q = 2 - p$;

(ii) $\quad 1 - 2q = p - q$;

(iii) $\quad p^2q + pq^2 = pq = q - q^2$;

(iv) $\quad (1 - 2q)^2 = (1 - 2p)^2$;

(v) $\quad q^3 + pq^2 = q^2 = (1 - p)^2$;

(vi) $\quad p^2 - q^2 = p - q$;

(vii) $\quad p(1 + q) = 1 - q^2 = p(2 - p)$;

(viii) $\quad \dfrac{1 - 2p}{pq} = \dfrac{1}{p} - \dfrac{1}{q}$.

14. Let x, y, z be the proportions of AA, Aa, aa, respectively, in a population where $x + y + z = 1$. Show that

$$(2x + y)(y + 2z) = 4xz - y^2 + 2y .$$

If it is a random-mating population, so that $4xz - y^2 = 0$, what will be the value of $(2x + y)(y + 2z)$?

15. If we were to let $2y$ denote the proportion of Aa in a population ($x + 2y + z = 1$), many of the expressions in this and later chapters would usually take a simpler form. Thus, $p = x + y$ and $q = y + z$. The equation of the parabola representing equilibrium populations in Figure 3 would then be $xz - y^2 = 0$. It is worth noting that this equation may be written in a more generalized form:

$$\frac{x}{x + y} + \frac{z}{y + z} = 1 .$$

$\dfrac{p^2}{p} + \dfrac{q^2}{q} = p + q = 1$

The fraction $x/(x + y)$ is that proportion of an allele which is in homozygous condition. We shall see that this form may readily be extended to the case of multiple alleles (Chap. 4).

CHAPTER 2

Applications and Extensions of the Equilibrium Law

THE Hardy-Weinberg Law was treated algebraically in the last chapter, and readers may wonder how it applies to practical problems. Now we shall consider a few examples of its applications to show its validity in nature and then deduce some further theorems that follow from the fundamental law.

§ 1. *Without Dominance*

The simplest case is one in which the three genotypes are directly distinguishable, such as the human M-N blood types. Let a, b, c be the observed numbers of genotypes A_1A_1, A_1A_2, A_2A_2, respectively, in a random sample of $G = a + b + c$ individuals. This is equivalent to a random sample of $2G$ genes, of which $2a + b$ are observed to be A_1 and $b + 2c$ to be A_2. Therefore, the estimates of the proportions of A_1 and A_2 genes in the population are, respectively,

$$p = \frac{2a+b}{2G}, \qquad q = \frac{b+2c}{2G}, \tag{1}$$

with sampling variance

$$V(p) = V(q) = \frac{pq}{2G}. \tag{1V}$$

This is also the maximum likelihood estimate (Ex. 1). To determine whether the observed numbers of the three genotypes are consistent with those expected on the basis of the Hardy-Weinberg Law, we may use the chi-square test, where the expected numbers are $a' = Gp^2$, $b' = 2Gpq$, $c' = Gq^2$. Thus,

$$\chi^2 = \frac{(a-a')^2}{a'} + \frac{(b-b')^2}{b'} + \frac{(c-c')^2}{c'} \tag{2}$$

with *a single degree of freedom* (because we used up one degree of freedom in making $a' + b' + c' = G$ and another one in estimating p).

Since the zygote A_1A_1 may be regarded as an attribute satisfying the condition that both the female and the male gametes which united to produce it are A_1-carriers, the observed numbers of the three kinds of zygotes may be arranged in the form of a 2×2 contingency table from which the value of chi square may be calculated.

	A_1	A_2	
A_1	a	$\frac{1}{2}b$	$a+\frac{1}{2}b$
A_2	$\frac{1}{2}b$	c	$\frac{1}{2}b+c$
	$a+\frac{1}{2}b,$	$\frac{1}{2}b+c$	G

$$\chi^2 = \frac{(ac - \frac{1}{4}b^2)^2 \cdot G}{(a+\frac{1}{2}b)^2(\frac{1}{2}b+c)^2} = \frac{(4ac - b^2)^2 \cdot G}{(2a+b)^2(b+2c)^2}. \tag{2'}$$

That the two expressions (2) and (2') for chi square are identical may readily be verified by the substitutions $a' = Gp^2$, where $p = (2a + b)/2G$, etc.

As a numerical example, we may cite the results of L. Ride (1935; cf. Haldane, 1938), who tested the blood of more than one thousand Chinese in Hong Kong with the following results:

NUMBERS	BLOOD TYPES			TOTAL
	M	MN	N	
Observed....	342	500	187	1029
Expected....	340.6	502.8	185.6	1029

$p=0.5753, \quad q=0.4247, \quad \chi^2=0.032, \quad P=0.85$

The almost perfect agreement between observed and expected numbers shows how closely a biological phenomenon may obey a mathematical law. This example, simple as it is, should be sufficient to show the importance of analytical treatment of genetical data.

§ 2. *Exact Formula for Small Samples*

The effective size of any sample is partly related to the magnitude of gene frequencies. If a gene frequency is very low, so that q^2 is a very small fraction, we would need a very large sample to include some aa individuals. A moderately sized sample might not include any aa individuals at all. The method described earlier for taking $a' = Gp^2$, etc., can be used only for large samples or for gene frequencies of moderate magnitude. It cannot be used if the gene frequency is so low that $Gq^2 < 1$; that is, if $q < 1/\sqrt{G}$.

Levene (1949a) developed the following formula for calculating the expected numbers of the various genotypes for small samples. For the sake of brevity, we write $g_1 = 2a + b$ and $g_2 = b + 2c$, where $g_1 + g_2 = 2G$. The expected numbers of the various genotypes *under the condition* that there are g_1 A_1-genes and g_2 A_2-genes are (for derivation see "Notes and Exercises" at end of chapter):

$$\frac{g_1(g_1-1)}{2(2G-1)}, \qquad \frac{g_1 g_2}{2G-1}, \qquad \frac{g_2(g_2-1)}{2(2G-1)}. \tag{3}$$

It is left to the student, as an exercise, to show that the sum of these three expected numbers is G, as it should be. Note that, if there is only one A_1-gene in the sample ($g_1 = 1$), formula (3) gives the expected number of $A_1 A_1$ individuals as zero, which is evidently correct.

The expected number of homozygotes given by (3) is always smaller than that calculated by the usual procedure of taking $a' = Gp^2$, etc., but the difference is very small for large samples with gene frequencies of moderate values. In our previous example, that of M-N blood types of Hong Kong Chinese, $g_1 = 1184$, $g_2 = 874$, and $2G = 2058$. The expected numbers of M, MN, N individuals under this condition are, respectively, 340.46, 503.07, 185.46, which differ very little from our previous results. Levene's formula may be readily extended to the case of multiple alleles (with which his original paper dealt) and is particularly useful when we are interested in the total number of the various kinds of homozygotes.

§ 3. *With Dominance: Snyder's Ratio*

When there are only two distinguishable phenotypes, dominants and recessives, the estimation of gene frequencies from a sample of a random-mating population is very simple. Let D and R be the observed numbers of dominants and recessives in a sample of G random individuals ($D + R = G$). Then our estimate of the recessive-gene frequency is

$$q^2 = \frac{R}{G}, \qquad\qquad q = \sqrt{\left(\frac{R}{G}\right)}; \tag{4}$$

$$V(q^2) = \frac{q^2(1-q^2)}{G}, \qquad V(q) = \frac{1-q^2}{4G}. \tag{4V}$$

Note that the expressions (4) are true only when the population is a large random-mating one; for, otherwise, the proportion of recessives, R/G, would not provide an estimate of q^2 at all. This is different from (1), which is true whether matings are at random or not.

When dominance is present, the testing of the hypothesis that a certain trait is controlled by one pair of autosomal genes usually requires data covering two generations. (It is also possible to test the hypothesis on the basis of one-generation data, i.e., sib-pairs, as pointed out by Cotterman, 1937*b*, and Rife, 1938. Their methods will be mentioned later in this chapter.) When there is dominance, there are only three distinguishable types of mating. Referring to Table 2, we see that the first three types of mating are Dominant $\times$ Dominant, while the fourth and fifth are of the type Dominant × Recessive. The two columns under AA and Aa offspring may also be combined to give the proportion of dominants. Thus, that table will assume the form of Table 4, from which it is seen· that among Dominant × Dominant families the ratio of dominant offspring to recessives is $(1 + 2q):q^2$ and that among Dominant × Recessive families the ratio is $1:q$. The proportion of recessives among the offspring of the two types of families are, respectively,

$$S_2 = \frac{q^2}{(1+q)^2}, \qquad S_1 = \frac{q}{1+q}. \qquad (5)$$

These ratios are from Snyder (1932), and the student may find it helpful to remember that S is the initial of Snyder, while its subscript indicates the number

TABLE 4

TYPES AND FREQUENCIES OF MATING AND OFFSPRING IN A PAN-
MICTIC POPULATION WHEN THERE IS DOMINANCE

TYPE OF MATING	FREQUENCY OF MATING	OFFSPRING	
		Dominants	Recessives
Dom×Dom.......	$(1-q^2)^2 = p^2(1+q)^2$	$p^2(1+2q)$	p^2q^2
Dom×Rec........	$2q^2(1-q^2) = 2pq^2(1+q)$	$2pq^2$	$2pq^3$
Rec×Rec........	$(q^2)^2 = q^4$	0	q^4
Total.........	1.00	p^2+2pq	q^2

of dominant parents in the family. The proportions (5) are pooled averages of several different Mendelian ratios. For instance, S_2 contains the recessives due to the 1:0 and 3:1 segregation types, but each is weighted by its corresponding frequency of mating. The resultant proportion of recessives is a function of the gene frequency in the population, because the frequencies of mating are functions of gene frequencies. It is evident that $S_2 < \frac{1}{4}$ and $S_1 < \frac{1}{2}$, because only a portion of Dom × Dom families would give $\frac{1}{4}$ recessive offspring, while the rest would give none at all, etc. The proportions S_2 and S_1 vary from trait to trait in the same population, and from population to population for the same trait, in contrast to the Mendelian ratios, which are constants for all traits and for all populations. Snyder (1947) properly called S_2 and S_1 "population ratios."

Once the value of q is determined (estimated from a sample), the theoretical proportions of recessive offspring from the two different types of families may be calculated and compared with the observed values to test if the hypothesis for one pair of autosomal genes with dominance is true.

The sampling variances of S_2 and S_1 may be found very easily by the "delta method," remembering that $V(q) = (1 - q^2)/4G$ as given by (4V). Now,

$dS_2/dq = 2q/(1+q)^3$; and $dS_1/dq = 1/(1+q)^2$. Hence, for large samples,

$$V(S_2) = \left(\frac{dS_2}{dq}\right)^2 V(q) = \frac{q^2(1-q^2)}{G(1+q)^6};$$
$$V(S_1) = \left(\frac{dS_1}{dq}\right)^2 V(q) = \frac{1-q^2}{4G(1+q)^4}. \qquad (5V)$$

It should be recognized that these expressions are identical with those given in various papers of Snyder. The only comment that need be made in connection with (5V) is that G denotes the number of independent individuals used in estimating q.

As a numerical illustration of Snyder's method we may cite the inheritance of human ability to taste phenylthiocarbamide (PTC). The 1600 parents (Table 5)

TABLE 5

INHERITANCE OF THE ABILITY TO TASTE PHENYLTHIO-
CARBAMIDE (PTC) IN MAN

(Snyder, 1932)

No. and Type of Mating	No. of Offspring		
	Taster	Nontaster	Total
425 (Taster×Taster)..........	929	130	1059
289 (Taster×Nontaster).......	483	278	761
86 (Nontaster×Nontaster)....	(5)*	218	218
800 families.................	1412	626	2038

* May be due to illegitimacies, adoptions, errors in diagnosis, etc., and omitted from the analysis.

are unrelated individuals, but their 2038 children are neither independent of each other (because some of them are sibs) nor independent with respect to their parents. Therefore our sample is equivalent to one consisting of more than 1600 and yet less than 3638 independent individuals. For our present purpose, however, and using the data of Table 5 (where the numbers and sizes of separate sibships are not given), we may adopt an approximate method of estimating q based upon the total 3638 individuals. There are $2(86) + 289$ recessive parents and 626 recessive children. So we may take $q^2 = 1087/3638 = 0.2988$, yielding $q = 0.5466$. Substituting in (5), we obtain the expected proportions

$$S_2 = 0.125, \qquad S_1 = 0.353,$$

while the observed values are, respectively (Table 5),

$$\tfrac{130}{1059} = 0.123, \qquad \tfrac{278}{761} = 0.365,$$

in close agreement with those expected. This supports the hypothesis that the ability to taste PTC is a simple dominant Mendelian trait. (For qualifications of this test see Chap. 8 and Li, 1953d.)

§ 4. *Mother-Child Combinations*

Since we are dealing with autosomal genes, the four kinds of relationships—father-son, father-daughter, mother-son, and mother-daughter—are all the same; and the most general term for this kind of relationship is parent-offspring (PO). Here, however, we use the term "mother-child" (MC), because most of the published data of this kind are concerned with mothers and their children, and it is convenient to specify the parent.

For one pair of genes without dominance it might be thought that there are nine MC combinations. But the two combinations, mother AA–child aa and mother aa–child AA, are impossible; so that there are actually only seven different combinations. The frequencies of these seven combinations in a random-mating population may be obtained in various ways. The most straightforward method is to rewrite Table 2, distinguishing the reciprocal crosses between the parents so that there will be nine different crosses in the table, and then collecting them into three groups according to one (say, the mother's) parental genotype. The resultant table will be our Table 6. Students should perform this operation as an exercise.

When A is dominant to a, there will be only four phenotypic MC combinations. The frequencies of these are given in Table 7, which is obtained by pooling the phenotypically indistinguishable cells of Table 6. An alternate form of Table 7 is given in Exercise 10.

TABLE 6

FREQUENCIES OF MC COMBINATIONS
IN A RANDOM-MATING POPULATION

MOTHER	CHILD			TOTAL
	AA	Aa	aa	
AA.....	p^3	p^2q	......	p^2
Aa.....	p^2q	pq	pq^2	$2pq$
aa......	......	pq^2	q^3	q^2
Total.	p^2	$2pq$	q^2	1.00

TABLE 7

FREQUENCIES OF MC COMBINATIONS
WITH DOMINANCE

MOTHER	CHILD		TOTAL
	$A-$	aa	
$A-$....	$p(1+pq)$	pq^2	p^2+2pq
aa......	pq^2	q^3	q^2
Total.	p^2+2pq	q^2	1.00

§ 5. *Estimating Gene Frequency from MC Data*

Suppose that we have in Table 8 data concerning human M-N blood types, where the a's denote the observed numbers of MC *pairs*, and $\Sigma a = G$ the total number of MC *pairs* (involving $2G$ individuals with $4G$ genes). We may estimate the gene frequencies based upon the G mothers alone or upon the G children alone, but this procedure would throw away the information supplied by the other G individuals. Alternatively, we may estimate the gene frequencies from the pooled marginal totals of mothers and children and apply the method described in (1). This approach has the difficulty that the $2G$ individuals are not independent, and thus we do not have $4G$ independent genes in the sample; so that the variance of estimates is not $pq/4G$, as would be given by formula (1V). Since each child must share a gene with his mother, it is evident that there

TABLE 8

OBSERVED NUMBERS OF MC COMBINATIONS

MOTHER	CHILD			TOTAL MOTHER
	M	MN	N	
M..............	a_1	a_2	....	a_1+a_2
MN............	a_3	a_4	a_5	$a_3+a_4+a_5$
N..............	....	a_6	a_7	a_6+a_7
Total child....	a_1+a_3	$a_2+a_4+a_6$	a_5+a_7	G

are only three independent genes per MC pair (although four genes are apparently present).

The most satisfactory method of estimating gene frequencies from MC pairs is the maximum likelihood method applied to the individual combination numbers, $a_1, a_2, \ldots, a_7$, in connection with their corresponding probabilities given in Table 6. Thus,

$$L = a_1 \log p^3 + (a_2 + a_3) \log p^2 q + a_4 \log pq + (a_5 + a_6) \log pq^2 + a_7 \log q^3.$$

This expression can be greatly simplified because of the fact that $\log p^2 q = 2 \log p + \log q$, etc., so that all the terms break down into components involving either $\log p$ or $\log q$. Collecting terms, we write

$$L = B \log p + C \log q,$$

where

$$B = 3a_1 + 2(a_2 + a_3) + a_4 + (a_5 + a_6)$$

and

$$C = \qquad (a_2 + a_3) + a_4 + 2(a_5 + a_6) + 3a_7.$$

Note that $B + C$ contains three of each of the a's except a_4, of which there are only two. Hence $B + C = 3G - a_4$. Putting $dL/dp = 0$ and solving for p, we obtain

$$p = \frac{B}{B+C} = \frac{3a_1 + 2(a_2 + a_3) + a_4 + (a_5 + a_6)}{3G - a_4}; \qquad (6)$$

$$V(p) = \frac{pq}{B+C} = \frac{pq}{3G - a_4}. \qquad (6V)$$

The expression (6) is instructive when we interpret it in terms of independent genes. For each mother M–child M combination there are three independent M-genes, yielding the term $3a_1$. For the mother M–child MN combination the M-gene of the child is necessarily derived from his mother, but his N-gene is an independent one. So there are two M-genes, out of the three independent genes of this pair, yielding the term $2a_2$, and so on. It should be noted, however, that the mother MN–child MN combination must be regarded as though there were only two independent genes, of which one is M, because in this combination we have no way of telling whether the M-gene or the N-gene of the child is from his mother (Cotterman, 1947). Now we see that expression (6) gives the proportion of independent M-genes among a total of $3G - a_4$ independent genes.

Since one MN-MN pair is worth two independent genes and its frequency in a random-mating population is pq, and since all the other kinds of pairs are worth three independent genes each, the *average* worth of an MC pair is

$$2 \times pq + 3 \times (1 - pq) = 3 - pq \text{ genes} . \tag{7}$$

The maximum value of pq is $\frac{1}{4}$; hence the minimum worth per MC pair is 3.00 $- 0.25 = 2.75$ independent genes. In the case of M-N blood types where the values of p and q are close to $\frac{1}{2}$, the MN-MN combinations are more frequent than any other combination in the population, thus lowering the average worth per MC pair close to its minimum value. When either p or q is small, the average worth per parent-child pair is very near three independent genes. In other words, a parent and a child are approximately equivalent to $1\frac{1}{2}$ independent individuals.

§ 6. *Types of Sib-Pairs*

The type of sib-pair is of course determined by the type of parental mating. For instance, in a mating of $AA \times Aa$, if the parents have two children, the probability of their producing an AA-AA, AA-Aa, Aa-AA, or Aa-Aa sib-pair is in each case $\frac{1}{4}$.

If we distinguish the order of birth of sibs (first child, second child), there will be nine types of sib-pairs in the general population; without distinguishing their order of birth, there will be six types of sib-pairs. The three types of family, $AA \times AA$, $AA \times aa$, and $aa \times aa$, can produce only alike sib-pairs, while $AA \times Aa$ and $aa \times Aa$ can produce four kinds of sib-pairs. The only type of family that can produce all nine types of sib-pairs is $Aa \times Aa$. The probabilities of these nine sib-pair combinations are given by the nine terms of $(\frac{1}{4}AA + \frac{1}{2}Aa + \frac{1}{4}aa)^2$. Hence, at the present stage of the student's knowledge about random-mating populations, the most direct way of calculating the frequencies of various types of sib-pairs in the general population is to adopt a modification of the scheme in Table 2. The three single-child columns, under the heading "Offspring," are replaced by nine (or six) sib-pair columns in which the frequencies of various sorts of sib-pairs are entered for each type of mating.

The totals of these sib-pair columns are their frequencies in the general population and are given in Table 9.

If A is dominant to a, there will be only three phenotypic types of sib-pairs, disregarding the order of birth. As dominance is frequently encountered in practical problems, the details of calculating frequencies for the three types of sib-pairs are given in Table 10, which also serves as an illustration of the procedure

TABLE 9

FREQUENCIES OF TYPES OF SIB-PAIRS IN A
RANDOM-MATING POPULATION

Full Sibs	AA	Aa	aa	Total
AA........	$\frac{1}{4}p^2(1+p)^2$	$\frac{1}{2}p^2q(1+p)$	$\frac{1}{4}p^2q^2$	p^2
Aa........	$\frac{1}{2}p^2q(1+p)$	$pq(1+pq)$	$\frac{1}{2}pq^2(1+q)$	$2pq$
aa........	$\frac{1}{4}p^2q^2$	$\frac{1}{2}pq^2(1+q)$	$\frac{1}{4}q^2(1+q)^2$	q^2
Total....	p^2	$2pq$	q^2	1.00

TABLE 10

FREQUENCIES OF SIB-PAIRS IN A RANDOM-MATING POPULATION WHEN THERE IS DOMINANCE

TYPE OF MATING	FREQUENCY OF MATING	TYPE OF SIB-PAIR		
		Dom-Dom	Dom-Rec	Rec-Rec
$AA \times AA$......	p^4	p^4	....	....
$AA \times Aa$.......	$4p^3q$	$4p^3q$	....	....
$Aa \times Aa$.......	$4p^2q^2$	$4p^2q^2 \cdot (\frac{3}{4})^2$	$4p^2q^2 \cdot 2(\frac{3}{4})(\frac{1}{4})$	$4p^2q^2 \cdot (\frac{1}{4})^2$
$AA \times aa$.......	$2p^2q^2$	$2p^2q^2$	....	....
$Aa \times aa$........	$4pq^3$	$4pq^3 \cdot (\frac{1}{2})^2$	$4pq^3 \cdot (\frac{1}{2})$	$4pq^3 \cdot (\frac{1}{2})^2$
$aa \times aa$........	q^4	....	....	q^4
Total......	1.00	S_{11}	S_{10}	S_{00}

described in the last paragraph. For an $Aa \times Aa$ family the probabilities of producing Dom-Dom, Dom-Rec, and Rec-Rec sib-pairs are $(\frac{3}{4})^2$, $2(\frac{3}{4})(\frac{1}{4})$, $(\frac{1}{4})^2$, respectively. Of course, the totals of the sib-pair columns (S_{11}, S_{10}, S_{00}) may also be obtained by pooling phenotypically indistinguishable cells of Table 9. The total frequency of aa-aa sib-pairs in the general population is

$$S_{00} = q^4 + pq^3 + \tfrac{1}{4}p^2q^2 = \tfrac{1}{4}q^2(1+q)^2,$$

in agreement with that given in Table 9.

When there is dominance, the frequency of phenotypically discordant (unlike) sib-pairs in the general population is

$$S_{10} = \tfrac{3}{2}p^2q^2 + 2pq^3 = \tfrac{1}{2}pq^2(3+q).$$

The maximum value of S_{10} is 0.272335, when $q = 0.686$. Therefore, the frequency of phenotypically concordant pairs is always higher than that of unlike pairs in the general population, whatever the gene frequency. The excess of the former over the latter is

$$S_{11} + S_{00} - S_{10} = 1 - 2S_{10} = 1 - pq^2(3 + q) . \qquad (8)$$

In Section 3 it was mentioned that traits due to one pair of autosomal genes with dominance may be analyzed on the basis of sib-pair data without knowing the parents (Cotterman, 1937b). To do this, we have only to compare the observed proportions of the three types of sib-pairs with their theoretical frequencies. Cotterman has also extended this method to sibships of larger sizes: trios, quartets, quintets, etc. In certain cases, however, this method cannot

TABLE 11

FREQUENCIES OF TYPES OF SIB-PAIRS IN A RANDOM-MATING POPU-
LATION WHEN THERE IS DOMINANCE
(Condensed from Rife, 1938)

q	S_{11}	S_{10}	S_{00}	Remarks
0.01.......	0.9998255	0.0001490	0.0000255	$S_{10}:S_{00} \doteq 6:1$
.10.......	.983025	.013950	.003025	
.20.......	.9344	.0512	.0144	
.30.......	.858025	.103950	.038025	
.40.......	.7584	.1632	.0784	
.50.......	.640625	.218750	.140625	
.60.......	.5104	.2592	.2304	←┐Nearly alike
.70.......	.374025	.271950*	.354025	with S_{11} and S_{00}
.80.......	.2384	.2432	.5184	←┘interchanged
.90.......	.111025	.157950	.731025	
0.99.......	0.0101	0.0196	0.9703	$S_{10}:S_{11} \doteq 2:1$

* Close to maximum value.

enable us to decide which phenotype is dominant. To illustrate this point there are listed in Table 11 a few numerical values of S_{11}, S_{10}, S_{00} for various values of q. Note that the relative frequencies of the three types of sib-pairs are almost similar for the cases $q = 0.60$ and $q = 0.80$, with values of S_{11} and S_{00} reversed, so that it is impossible to say which trait is dominant or recessive without knowing the parents.

It should be pointed out that there are only two types of matings, $Aa \times Aa$ and $Aa \times aa$, which can give rise to discordant sib-pairs when complete dominance is present (Table 10). This fact may be used to analyze the inheritance of *rare* traits (Rife, 1952). When a trait is rare, it is usually not feasible to collect the concordant sib-pairs, both members of which lack the trait, because the great majority of sibs are of this type in the general population. But it may be possible to compare the frequency of discordant pairs to concordant pairs possessing the rare trait. If the rare trait is recessive, practically all discordant sib-pairs are from the mating $Aa \times Aa$, which yields $2(\frac{3}{4})(\frac{1}{4})$ discordant pairs and $(\frac{1}{4})^2$ concordant pairs with the rare recessive trait (see Table 10). Therefore, the frequencies of these two kinds of sib-pairs in the general population should be approximately $6:1$ (see first line of Table 11 for the case $q = 0.01$). On the other hand, if the rare trait is due to a dominant gene, practically all discordant pairs will arise from $Aa \times aa$. Such matings produce $\frac{1}{2}$ unlike pairs and $\frac{1}{4}$ pairs with the rare trait, so that the frequencies of these two kinds of sib-pairs in the general population should be approximately $2:1$ (see last line of Table 11, where $q = 0.99$). Thus, the relative frequencies of discordant pairs to pairs *concordant with respect to the rare trait* would indicate whether the trait is dominant or recessive.

Notes and Exercises

1. Let p and q be the frequencies of a pair of alleles in a panmictic population. The probability of obtaining a sample of G random individuals (a, b, c) is

$$\frac{G!}{a!\,b!\,c!}\,(p^2)^a\,(2pq)^b\,(q^2)^c = \frac{G!\,2^b}{a!\,b!\,c!}\,p^{2a+b}q^{b+2c}.$$

To estimate the parameter p from the sample, we form the logarithm likelihood function:

$$L = (2a + b)\log p + (b + 2c)\log q + \text{const.}$$

$$\frac{dL}{dp} = \frac{2a+b}{p} - \frac{b+2c}{q} = 0; \qquad \therefore p = \frac{2a+b}{2G} \qquad \text{i.e., (1)}$$

$$\frac{1}{V(p)} = \frac{-d^2L}{dp^2} = \frac{2a+b}{p^2} + \frac{b+2c}{q^2} = \frac{2G}{pq}. \qquad \text{i.e., (1V)}$$

2. Before we derive Levene's formula (3), it is necessary to establish an identity between a binomial coefficient and the sum of certain multinomial coefficients. It is best to illustrate the situation with a numerical example first. Consider the binomial expansion $(x + y)^{12}$, which consists of thirteen terms. Let us concentrate on one of its terms, for instance $(12!/5!7!)(x^5 y^7)$. Now, suppose we expand the same expression in a different way, say, as a trinomial $(x^2 + 2xy + y^2)^6$. It consists of twenty-seven terms which represent a subdivision of the thirteen terms of the binomial. The following three terms of the trinomial expansion involve $x^5 y^7$:

$$\frac{6!}{0!5!1!}\,(x^2)^0\,(2xy)^5\,(y^2)^1 = \frac{6!\,2^5}{0!5!1!}\,x^5y^7,$$

$$\frac{6!}{1!3!2!}\,(x^2)^1\,(2xy)^3\,(y^2)^2 = \frac{6!\,2^3}{1!3!2!}\,x^5y^7,$$

$$\frac{6!}{2!1!3!}\,(x^2)^2\,(2xy)^1\,(y^2)^3 = \frac{6!\,2^1}{2!1!3!}\,x^5y^7.$$

The sum of these three terms must be equal to the corresponding term of the binomial. Hence, we obtain the relation

$$\frac{12!}{5!7!} = \frac{6!2^5}{0!5!1!} + \frac{6!2^3}{1!3!2!} + \frac{6!2^1}{2!1!3!},$$

that is,

$$792 = 192 + 480 + 120.$$

The identity we are trying to establish is simply an algebraic statement of the above relation. In expanding the binomial $(x + y)^{2G}$, let us concentrate on the term

$$\frac{(2G)!}{g_1! g_2!} x^{g_1} y^{g_2},$$

where g_1 and g_2 are *fixed* and $g_1 + g_2 = 2G$. On the other hand, in expanding the same expression as a trinomial $(x^2 + 2xy + y^2)^G$ whose general term is of the type

$$\frac{G!}{a!b!c!} (x^2)^a (2xy)^b (y^2)^c = \frac{G!2^b}{a!b!c!} x^{2a+b} y^{b+2c},$$

where $a + b + c = G$, the sum of those terms with $2a + b = g_1$ and $b + 2c = g_2$ is identically equal to the corresponding binomial term involving $x^{g_1} y^{g_2}$. Hence the identity:

$$\frac{(2G)!}{g_1! g_2!} = S\left(\frac{G!2^b}{a!b!c!}\right),$$

where S denotes the summation over all possible nonnegative integral values of a, b, c, which *conform with the conditions* $2a + b = g_1$ and $b + 2c = g_2$.

Being an identity, it is true for any value of G. If we replace G by $G - 1$ in the exponent of the trinomial, we should replace $2G$ by $2G - 2$ in the exponent of the binomial. In other words, g_1 may be replaced by $(g_1 - 2)$, or g_2 by $(g_2 - 2)$, or g_1 and g_2 by $(g_1 - 1)$ and $(g_2 - 1)$, respectively. Hence, the above identity may also be written as

$$\frac{(2G-2)!}{(g_1-2)!g_2!} = S\frac{(G-1)!2^b}{(a-1)!b!c!}; \quad \frac{(2G-2)!}{(g_1-1)!(g_2-1)!} = S\frac{(G-1)!2^{b-1}}{a!(b-1)!c!}.$$

We shall make use of these relations to derive the formula (3) in the next problem.

3. Suppose we have a random sample of G individuals (a, b, c). This is equivalent to a random sample of $2G$ genes, of which $g_1 = 2a + b$ are allele A_1, and $g_2 = b + 2c$ are allele A_2. Then we may ask what is the probability of observing a particular set of (a, b, c) *under the condition* that there are g_1 of A_1-genes and g_2 of A_2-genes (the values of g_1 and g_2 being held constant)? The probability is

$$P = \frac{G!2^b}{a!b!c!} \Big/ S\left(\frac{G!2^b}{a!b!c!}\right) = \frac{G!2^b}{a!b!c!} \times \frac{g_1! g_2!}{(2G)!}$$

by virtue of the identity we have just proved. For example, with $g_1 = 5$, $g_2 = 7$ given (fixed constants), the probability of obtaining $(1, 3, 2)$ is $\frac{480}{792}$. The expected value of a with the values g_1 and g_2 fixed is therefore

$$E(a) = S(aP) = S \frac{a \cdot G! 2^b}{a! \, b! \, c!} \times \frac{g_1! \, g_2!}{(2G)!}$$

$$= G S \frac{(G-1)! \, 2^b}{(a-1)! \, b! \, c!} \times \frac{g_1! \, g_2!}{(2G)!}$$

$$= \frac{G \cdot (2G-2)!}{(g_1-2)! \, g_1!} \times \frac{g_1! \, g_2!}{(2G)!} = \frac{g_1 (g_1-1)}{2 (2G-1)},$$

which is our formula (3). The expression for $E(c)$ is the same except for interchanging g_1 and g_2. The expected value of heterozygotes, $E(b)$, under the same condition may be found in exactly the same way. Thus,

$$E(b) = S(bP) = S \frac{b \cdot G! 2^b}{a! \, b! \, c!} \times \frac{g_1! \, g_2!}{(2G)!}$$

$$= 2G S \frac{(G-1)! \, 2^{b-1}}{a! \, (b-1)! \, c!} \times \frac{g_1! \, g_2!}{(2G)!}$$

$$= \frac{2G \cdot (2G-2)! \, g_1! \, g_2!}{(g_1-1)! \, (g_2-1)! \, (2G)!} = \frac{g_1 g_2}{2G-1}.$$

4. In a sample of D dominants and R recessives $(D + R = G)$, we have the estimate $q^2 = R/G$, as stated in Section 3. Show that

$$V(q) = \frac{1 - q^2}{4G} = \frac{q^2 (1 - q^2)}{4R} = \frac{D}{4G^2},$$

so that the standard error of q is

$$\sigma_q = \frac{\sqrt{D}}{2G}.$$

5. In estimating the gene-frequency ratio, u (see "Notes and Exercises" of Chap. 1), from a sample of G individuals (a, b, c), show that the maximum likelihood method leads to

$$u = \frac{2a + b}{b + 2c}, \qquad V(u) = \frac{u (1 + u)^2}{2G}.$$

Check the latter by the relation

$$V(u) = \left(\frac{du}{dp}\right)^2 V(p),$$

noting that $1/(1 - p) = 1 + u$.

6. Let D, H, R be the proportions of the three genotypes in a sample of G individuals. Then $\sqrt{D}$ and $\sqrt{R}$ will be the estimates of p and q, respectively,

if the population practices random mating, in which case $\sqrt{D} + \sqrt{R}$ should be close to unity. Whether or not this last is true would provide a test of the hypothesis of one pair of genes. The standard error of the sum $\sqrt{D} + \sqrt{R}$ is $\frac{1}{2}\sqrt{G}$ (Wiener, 1932). This method is, however, less efficient than the one described in Section 1. Furthermore, if the population is not a random-mating one, $\sqrt{D}$ and $\sqrt{R}$ would not be the estimates of p and q at all. But $D + \frac{1}{2}H$ and $R + \frac{1}{2}H$ would still give us the best estimates of gene frequencies *whatever the mating system*.

7. In most human races the frequency of the M-gene is higher than that of the N-gene, so that the gene-frequency ratio u is greater than unity but very seldom exceeds two. Ainus and Australian aborigines, however, have a very low frequency of the M-gene, while Eskimos and Hindus have a very low frequency of the N-gene. The following are the results of studies of pure Eskimos by Fabricius-Hansen in East Greenland (1939) and West Greenland (1940):

LOCALITY	BLOOD TYPE			TOTAL
	M	MN	N	
East Greenland.......	475	89	5	569
West Greenland......	485	227	21	733

Find the frequencies of the N-genes of these two Eskimo populations. Do they differ significantly?

8. The presence of antigen-P in human blood is a simple dominant Mendelian trait. We shall speak of those who possess this antigen as "positive" and those lacking it as "negative." Similarly, the presence of a group-specific substance in human saliva is also a simple dominant trait. Those whose saliva contains such a substance are known as "secretors" $(+)$, and those lacking it are "nonsecretors" $(-)$. The following are the pooled results of several authors (Wiener, 1943) in regard to these two traits. Calculate the expected values of S_2 and S_1 and compare with those observed.

INHERITANCE OF ANTIGEN-P

No. AND TYPE OF FAMILIES	CHILDREN	
	$(-)$	Total
249 $(+)\times(+)$........	79	756
134 $(+)\times(-)$........	179	465
34 $(-)\times(-)$........	94	94
417 families..........	352	1315

INHERITANCE OF SECRETOR

No. AND TYPE OF FAMILIES	CHILDREN	
	$(-)$	Total
150 $(+)\times(+)$........	33	274
62 $(+)\times(-)$........	67	170
18 $(-)\times(-)$........	42	42
230 families..........	142	486

9. Wiener (1950) reported the following frequencies of mother-child combinations with respect to M-N blood types:

MOTHER	CHILD			TOTAL
	M	MN	N	
M..........	93	74	0	167
MN..........	69	151	60	280
N..........	0	59	50	109
Total.....	162	284	110	556

Estimate the gene frequencies and calculate their standard errors from equations (6) and (6V).

10. Table 7 was obtained from Table 6 by pooling combination frequencies of cells of the same phenotype. However, it may be obtained in another manner, considering the fact that the marginal totals of that 2×2 table are fixed. If the mother is aa, the probability that her child should be aa is q under panmixia. Therefore the probability that mother-child should be aa-aa is q^3. The other three cell frequencies may be obtained by subtraction from the marginal totals. Then Table 7 assumes the following form:

MOTHER	CHILD		TOTAL
	$A -$	aa	
$A -$..........	$1-2q^2+q^3$	q^2-q^3	$1-q^2$
aa..........	q^2-q^3	q^3	q^2
Total.....	$1-q^2$	q^2	1.00

This is the form given by Fisher (1940), who first developed the maximum likelihood weights for MC pairs. The weight per pair is between 1 and 2, depending upon the value of q, but it is close to 1.5 for all values of gene frequencies. In other words, one MC pair is worth approximately 1.5 independent individuals in estimating the value of q.

11. The genetics of the Rh factor in human blood has advanced greatly in the last few years. For our purpose here, however, we may still treat it as though it were controlled by one pair of genes with dominance. Boorman (1950) reported the data on page 27 regarding MC combinations. Estimate q is based on mothers and children separately and then is based on mothers and children combined. In the latter case, $q^2 = 644/3980 = 0.1618$ and $q = 0.40225$. In calculating its variance, we may take $G = 1990 \times 1.5$

= 2985 *approximately* in our formula (4) for $V(q)$. (For more exact treatment see Fisher, 1940; Cotterman, 1947.)

| | RH Type of Child | | Total |
Mother	(+)	(−)	
(+)..........	1475	182	1657
(−)..........	204	129	333
Total......	1679	311	1990

12. Show that, when $q^2 = \frac{1}{2}$ and thus $q = 0.707$, the proportions of the two types of concordant sib-pairs are equal: $S_{11} = S_{00} = 0.3643$ and $S_{10} = 0.2714$.

13. Show that

$$S_{10} = \tfrac{1}{2}pq^2(3 + q) = pq^2(2 - \tfrac{1}{2}p) \; ;$$
$$S_{00} = q^2 - \tfrac{1}{2}S_{10} \; ;$$
$$S_{11} = 1 - q^2 - \tfrac{1}{2}S_{10} \; .$$

CHAPTER *3*

Genetic Variance and Correlation

THE inheritance of *metrical characters* in a Mendelian population is a field of such scope that adequate treatment would have to be comparable to that accorded here to the classical Mendelian principles. This brief account will serve as an introduction to the subject and as a background for the few other theorems, dealing with metrical characters, that will be given in later chapters.

§ 1. *Genetic Variance*

The three genotypes AA, Aa, aa will in general assume different values with respect to a metrical character (e.g., vitamin content of corn or tomatoes). Various authors have used different notations in dealing with quantitative inheritance. Some of the most frequently used ones are shown in Table 12 for the

TABLE 12

VALUES OF A METRICAL CHARACTER OF VARIOUS GENOTYPES
WITH ADDITIVE GENIC EFFECTS

GENOTYPE	FRE-QUENCY	GENERAL NOTATION	MEASURED FROM SMALL HOMOZYGOTE		MEASURED FROM HETEROZYGOTE		MEASURED IN UNITS OF GENIC EFFECTS	
		(1)	(2)	(3)	(4)	(5)	(6)	(7)
AA	p^2	G_{AA}	$g+2a$	$2a$	$g+a$	$+a$	2	$+1$
Aa	$2pq$	G_{Aa}	$g+a$	a	g	0	1	0
aa	q^2	G_{aa}	g	0	$g-a$	$-a$	0	-1

case of no dominance—when the heterozygote's measurement is exactly at the mid-point between those of the two homozygotes. The intermediate nature of such a heterozygote may be described as follows:

$$G_{Aa} = \tfrac{1}{2}(G_{AA} + G_{aa}) ; \qquad (1.1)$$

$$a = G_{AA} - G_{Aa} = G_{Aa} - G_{aa} = \tfrac{1}{2}(G_{AA} - G_{aa}) . \qquad (1.2)$$

The quantity a represents the effect of each gene substitution and may be

28

called the *genic effect* on a metrical character. Thus, no dominance is synonymous with *additive* genic effects.

To find the variance of a metrical character, it is convenient to take the values of AA, Aa, aa as $2a$, a, 0, respectively, since variance is independent of origin. Thus, in a random-mating population, the mean and the variance of the character are

$$\bar{G} = 2pa, \qquad \sigma_G^2 = 2pqa^2. \qquad (2)$$

The latter is known as the *genetic variance* of the population, because the variation of G is due entirely to the differences between genotypes in the population. Note that the mean is proportional to the frequency of the "positive" gene and that the variance is proportional to the frequency of heterozygotes in the population. A generalization of (2) to cases involving more than one pair of genes is given in Chapter 9.

In many problems it is convenient to take the genic effect as the unit of measurement (i.e., to take $a = 1$). Then, the G values will be 2, 1, 0; and

$$\bar{G} = 2p, \qquad \sigma_G^2 = 2pq. \qquad (3)$$

For one pair of genes the G values 2, 1, 0 may also be interpreted as the number of A-genes in a genotype.

§ 2. *Dominance Deviation*

If any degree of dominance is present, the variance of the character in the population will change accordingly. Let the actual (phenotypic) value of a genotype be represented by Z. Then the actual variance is σ_Z^2. To determine the effect of dominance on the variance, we fit a set of hypothetical G values for which the effect of each gene substitution is constant (like the case treated in the preceding section). The difference between the actual and the fitted values, $D = Z - G$, is called the *dominance deviation*. A numerical example of this scheme is given in Table 13 and illustrated in Figure 4, while the theoretical setup of this method is given in Table 14. Studying Table 13, we see that the G

TABLE 13

ANALYSIS OF GENETIC VARIANCE INTO AN ADDITIVE
GENIC COMPONENT AND A COMPONENT DUE TO
DOMINANCE DEVIATION

Genotype and Frequency, f	Actual Value Z	Fitted Value G	Dominance Deviation $D = Z - G$
AA, .36........	8.0	8.8	−0.8
Aa, .48........	7.0	5.8	+1.2
aa, .16........	1.0	2.8	−1.8
Mean........	$\bar{Z} = 6.4$	$\bar{G} = 6.4$	$\bar{D} = 0$
Variance......	$\sigma_Z^2 = 5.76$	$\sigma_G^2 = 4.32$	$\sigma_D^2 = 1.44$

values may be regarded as the theoretical values of Z without dominance in a population *with the same mean value* of the metrical character. Thus, $\bar{Z} = \bar{G}$ = 6.4, so that $\bar{D} = 0$. The theoretical (additive) genic effect is $8.8 - 5.8$ = $5.8 - 2.8 = 3.0 = a$. The actual genetic variance, $\sigma_Z^2 = 5.76$, may then be analyzed into two components—one due to the additive genic effects, σ_G^2 = 4.32, and another due to the dominance deviations, $\sigma_D^2 = 1.44$. These numerical results show that

$$\sigma_Z^2 = \sigma_G^2 + \sigma_D^2. \tag{4}$$

This important theorem was first established by Fisher (1918).

The reader may wonder how the numerical values of G and D have been

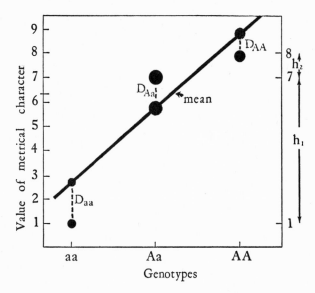

FIG. 4.—Fitting of theoretical genotypic values G (*gray dots*) based upon additive genic effects to actual values, Z (*solid dots*). The difference $Z - G = D$ is the dominance deviation. The fitted values are such that the sum of squares of the dominance deviations (weighted by their corresponding frequency, as indicated by their relative size) is a minimum. The data are taken from Table 13.

reached with the given values of Z in Table 13. The method used is similar to that of fitting a straight line to a set of observed points. Here, we want the G values to be as close to the actual Z values as possible; and by this we mean that we want the sum of squares of the dominance deviations to be a minimum. The quantity to be minimized is (see Fig. 4 and Table 14)

$$\Delta = \Sigma f D^2 = p^2 D_{AA}^2 + 2pq D_{Aa}^2 + q^2 D_{aa}^2. \tag{5}$$

Since Z's are given and $Z = G + D$, we may minimize the above quantity either by directly choosing a set of suitable D values or by choosing suitable values of g

and a. The algebraic details are given in the "Notes and Exercises" at the end of this chapter. The solutions are (Wright, 1952b):

$$D_{AA} = -q^2(h_1 - h_2), \quad D_{Aa} = pq(h_1 - h_2), \quad D_{aa} = -p^2(h_1 - h_2), \quad (6)$$

where

$$h_1 = Z_{Aa} - Z_{aa} \quad \text{and} \quad h_2 = Z_{AA} - Z_{Aa}.$$

Note that, if $h_1 = h_2$, the genic effects are additive and $Z = G$, so that $D = 0$. Therefore, the dominance deviations are functions of $(h_1 - h_2)$. Alternatively, the suitable values of g and a are found to be (Ex. 1)

$$g = \bar{Z} - 2pa, \quad a = ph_2 + qh_1. \quad (7)$$

The first expression simply indicates that $\bar{Z} = g + 2pa = \bar{G}$, so that $\bar{D} = 0$.

TABLE 14

ANALYSIS OF PHENOTYPIC VALUES OF A METRICAL CHARACTER INTO A COMPONENT OF ADDITIVE GENIC EFFECT AND A COMPONENT OF DOMINANCE DEVIATION

Genotype and Frequency f	Actual Value of Character Z	Fitted Value Based on Additive Effect G	Dominance Deviation $D = Z - G$
$AA, \ p^2 \dots$	$Z_{AA} = z + h_1 + h_2$	$G_{AA} = g + 2a$	D_{AA}
$Aa, \ 2pq \dots$	$Z_{Aa} = z + h_1$	$G_{Aa} = g + a$	D_{Aa}
$aa, \ q^2 \dots$	$Z_{aa} = z$	$G_{aa} = g$	D_{aa}

The second expression indicates that the theoretical additive genic effect is the weighted (by gene frequencies) average of the actual differences between the genotypes.

Analogous to the situation of fitting a straight line to a set of observed points, the estimated values G and the deviations D are independent, so that the relation (4) holds. With the solutions (6) and (7) and in view of (2), we obtain

$$\left. \begin{aligned} \sigma_G^2 &= 2pqa^2 = 2pq(ph_2 + qh_1)^2, \\ \sigma_D^2 &= D_{Aa}^2 = p^2q^2(h_1 - h_2)^2. \end{aligned} \right\} \quad (8)$$

With some algebraic manipulation it may be demonstrated that the observed variance σ_Z^2 is the sum of σ_G^2 and σ_D^2.

The *degree of dominance* may be conveniently measured by

$$\frac{h_1 - h_2}{h_1} = \frac{6 - 1}{6} = \frac{5}{6} \quad (9)$$

in the example given in Table 13. This quantity is 0 when the heterozygote is exactly intermediate ($h_1 = h_2$), is 1 when there is complete dominance ($h_2 = 0$), is greater than 1 with overdominance, and is 2 if there is "pure" overdominance ($h_1 = -h_2$, or $Z_{AA} = Z_{aa}$).

The additive proportion of the genetic variance is

$$\frac{\sigma^2_G}{\sigma^2_Z} = \frac{4.32}{5.76} = 75 \text{ per cent}$$

in our example, where the degree of dominance is very high. With moderate dominance this proportion is close to unity. Wright (1952b) has tabulated this proportion for various degrees of dominance and gene frequencies. The happy conclusion is that the effects of dominance on genetic variance are serious only when dominance is very nearly complete.

§ 3. *Correlation between Family Members*

The joint frequencies of parent-child combinations and those of sib-sib combinations (Tables 6 and 9) may be regarded as the "correlation tables" between the indicated relatives. With additive genic effects we may take the values of AA, Aa, aa as 2, 1, 0, respectively, since correlation is independent of origin and unit of measurement. Consider the parent-offspring correlation table first. The marginal frequencies of the parental variable G' and of the offspring variable G are the same in a random-mating population. The mean and variance are (see [3]): $\bar{G}' = \bar{G} = 2p$, and $\sigma^2_{G'} = \sigma^2_G = 2pq$. The parent-child covariance, $\sigma_{GG'}$, may be found from the cell frequencies of Table 6:

$$\sigma_{GG'} = 4p^3 + 4p^2q + pq - (2p)^2 = pq .$$

Thus, the product-moment correlation coefficient between parent and offspring in a random-mating population is

$$r_{PO} = \frac{\sigma_{GG'}}{\sigma_{G'}\sigma_G} = \frac{pq}{2pq} = \frac{1}{2} . \tag{10}$$

Similarly, the correlation coefficient between full sibs in a random-mating population may be calculated from Table 9. It turns out to be

$$r_{00} = \tfrac{1}{2} .$$

The student is advised to go through the calculation and verify this result. It is a remarkable fact that the genotypic correlation is solely determined by the "blood" relationship between individuals, being independent of the gene frequencies in the population. Another point to be noticed is that, although parent-offspring and sib-sib correlations are all equal to $\tfrac{1}{2}$ in a random-mating population, the frequencies of the various kinds of combinations (i.e., joint distribution) are entirely different for the two types of relatives.

If A is dominant to a, however, the correlation loses its simplicity and is no longer independent of gene frequencies. In the following we shall consider only the case of complete dominance. The phenotypic correlation between parent and offspring may be obtained from Table 7. For actual calculation it is much more convenient to assign the Z value 1 to *recessives* and 0 to *dominants*. With this scale it will be found that the mean $\bar{Z} = \bar{Z}' = q^2$, the variance $\sigma_Z^2 = \sigma_{Z'}^2 = q^2(1 - q^2)$, and the covariance $\sigma_{ZZ'} = q^3 - q^4$, so that the phenotypic correlation between parent and offspring in a random-mating population is

$$r_{PO}^* = \frac{q^3(1-q)}{q^2(1-q^2)} = \frac{q}{1+q}. \tag{11}$$

Similarly, the phenotypic correlation between full sibs may be obtained from a modified form of Table 9. Again, it is convenient to assign the Z value 1 to recessives and 0 to dominants. Then the correlation table and the correlation coefficient would be as follows (meaning of S_{11}, etc., is the same as that given in the preceding chapter):

	0	1
0	S_{11}	$\frac{1}{2}S_{10}$
1	$\frac{1}{2}S_{10}$	S_{00}

$$r_{\text{sibs}}^* = \frac{1+3q}{4(1+q)}. \tag{12}$$

With dominance, the correlations for parent-offspring and for full sibs are not the same any more. The latter, with a minimum value of $\frac{1}{4}$, is always higher than the former except in the trivial case $q = 1$.

§ 4. *Identity of a Gene*

So far we have studied only the correlations between immediate family members in a random-mating population. To pave the way for a study of more remote relatives, this section will introduce a fundamental concept about the identity of a gene. The problem of identical and independent genes came up in the preceding chapter when we tried to estimate gene frequencies from mother-child data. A more formal consideration of this subject is now in order.

Let X denote a gene of a locus. It may be A or a. We say that the gene X exists in two possible *states*, with a probability p that it is in state A and a probability q that it is in state a. If two genes of the same locus, X_1 and X_2, happen to exist in the same state (both A or both a), we say that these two genes are *alike in state*. The ordinary term "genotype" merely refers to the states in which an individual's two genes exist; it indicates nothing about the origin of the genes.

If one gene is derived from another, through division and subsequent transmission, we say that these two genes are *identical by descent*. For example, the child of parent X_1X_2 (whatever his genotype) necessarily receives either X_1 or X_2 (never both) from his parent. The X_1-gene of the child is derived from the X_1-gene of the parent; therefore, these two genes are identical by descent. Identical genes are necessarily in the same state, barring mutation. The identity of a gene may be traced through any number of generations.

Furthermore, if the parent X_1X_2 has two children, and each of the children has received the X_1-gene from the parent, then the two X_1-genes of the children are also identical by descent because they are both derived from the same X_1-gene of their parent.

Now, each diploid individual has two genes. Two "blood" relatives who can at most have one identical gene in common are called *unilineal* relatives. Parent and offspring always have one identical gene in common, and they are the most important kind of unilineal relatives. Grandparent-grandchild, uncle-nephew, first cousins, half-sibs, etc., are all unilineal relatives.

Two relatives who can have both genes identical by descent are called *bilineal* relatives; of these, the most important kind is the full sib. Suppose the parents are $X_1X_2 \times X_3X_4$ and their first child is X_1X_3. Their second child may also receive X_1 from the first parent and at the same time receive X_3 from the second parent, resulting in X_1X_3. In such an event these two sibs are just like "identical twins" as far as the X locus is concerned. On the other hand, if the second child receives X_2 from the first parent and X_4 from the second parent, resulting in X_2X_4, these two sibs are just like two independent individuals (with respect to the X locus) because they have no identical gene in common. Finally, if the second child is X_1X_4 or X_2X_3, the two sibs have one identical gene in common, a relationship similar to that of parent and offspring. The next important kind of bilineal relationship in a human population is that of double first cousins, whose parents are members of two sibships.

To summarize, unilineal relatives may or may not have one identical gene in common. Bilineal relatives may have both genes identical, only one gene identical, or no genes identical by descent. Diagrams of some of the more important kinds of relatives are given in Chapter 13 (p. 178), in which we will view the relationships from a different angle.

§ 5. *The* ITO *Method*

The derivation of the joint frequencies of parents and offspring (Table 6) is simple enough. The direct derivation of the frequencies of the various kinds of sib-pairs (Table 9) is straightforward but laborious. (Did you try it?) The direct method of obtaining the combination frequencies of relatives beyond the family circle, such as those for uncle-nephew, first cousins, etc., is very tedious. This section describes a method by which the joint frequency distribution for any type of relatives may be obtained in a very simple manner.

The foundation of this new method is the use of matrices of *conditional* probabilities. Of these, the following three are fundamental:

$$I = \begin{pmatrix} 1 & 0 & 0 \\ 0 & 1 & 0 \\ 0 & 0 & 1 \end{pmatrix}, \quad T = \begin{pmatrix} p & q & 0 \\ \frac{1}{2}p & \frac{1}{2} & \frac{1}{2}q \\ 0 & p & q \end{pmatrix}, \quad O = \begin{pmatrix} p^2 & 2pq & q^2 \\ p^2 & 2pq & q^2 \\ p^2 & 2pq & q^2 \end{pmatrix}. \quad (13)$$

The elements of each row, adding up to unity, are the conditional probabilities for a relative to be AA, Aa, aa, when the genotype of *the other relative is given*. The first row refers to the case in which one relative is given as AA; the second row, Aa; the third row, aa.

The I matrix gives the conditional probabilities when the two relatives have both genes identical by descent. Therefore, they are necessarily of the same genotype. The O matrix consists of the conditional probabilities when the two relatives have no genes identical by descent. In such cases, whatever the genotype of the given relative, the probabilities for the other relative to be AA, Aa, or aa are simply p^2, $2pq$, or q^2. Finally, the T matrix refers to the case in which the two relatives have one gene identical by descent. The derivation of one of its elements is given here to illustrate how T is obtained. Suppose the given relative is Aa. What is the probability that the other relative who has one identical gene in common should be AA? The probability that the other relative should have A in common is $\frac{1}{2}$, while the probability that his other (independent) gene should exist in state A is p; so that the probability that he should be AA is $\frac{1}{2}p$, which is the element in the second row and first column of T. Alternatively, since parent and offspring *always* have one identical gene in common, the T matrix may be obtained by dividing the first row of parent-offspring combination frequencies (Table 6) by p^2, the second row by $2pq$, and the third row by q^2. It should be emphasized, however, that the T matrix applies to any pair of relatives who *have* one identical gene in common.

The mathematical advantage of using the matrices of conditional probabilities is that they may be multiplied, either by themselves or by other matrices of similar nature, to form a "chain process," yielding a set of conditional probabilities at the end of the chain. For example, when one grandparent is given, the conditional probability for the grandchild to be AA, Aa, or aa will be the elements of the product matrix $T \cdot T = T^2$. Similarly, when one great-grandparent is given, the conditional probabilities for the great-grandchild will be the elements of the product matrix $T \cdot T \cdot T = T^3$, etc. Actual multiplication shows that

$$T^2 = \tfrac{1}{2}T + \tfrac{1}{2}O, \quad T^3 = \tfrac{1}{4}T + \tfrac{3}{4}O, \quad T^4 = \tfrac{1}{8}T + \tfrac{7}{8}O, \Big\}$$
$$T^n = (\tfrac{1}{2})^{n-1}T + [1 - (\tfrac{1}{2})^{n-1}]O, \quad \Big\} \tag{14}$$

where n is the number of generations between the two relatives. This result reduces the multiplication process to a simple addition process. Therefore, the conditional probabilities for any ancestor-descendant pair may be found according to (14). To convert these conditional probabilities into absolute frequencies in the population, we multiply the first row by p^2, the second row by $2pq$, and the third row by q^2, thus obtaining the "correlation table" for this type of relatives.

Note that T also gives the conditional probabilities for parent when the child is given. Therefore, T^2 also represents the conditional probabilities for *half-sibs*, who have one parent in common.

In expressions (14) the coefficient of T is the probability that the two relatives should have one identical gene in common, while the coefficient of O is the probability that they should have no identical gene in common.

Next, let us consider the conditional probabilities for full sibs. When the genotype of one sib is given, the probabilities that the other sib should have both genes, one gene, or no gene identical by descent are $\frac{1}{4}$, $\frac{1}{2}$, $\frac{1}{4}$, respectively. Therefore, the conditional probabilities of the other sib are the elements of the following matrix:

$$S = \tfrac{1}{4}I + \tfrac{1}{2}T + \tfrac{1}{4}O . \tag{15}$$

If we actually write out the nine elements of the S matrix and then multiply its rows by p^2, $2pq$, q^2 to convert it into a table of absolute frequencies in the population, we will find that it is exactly the same as Table 9.

With the help of S and T, the conditional probabilities for any type of relatives may be written down quite easily. For example, the uncle-nephew transition matrix is $ST = TS$. Since $IT = T$ and $OT = O$, we have the result

$$ST = TS = T^2 , \tag{16}$$

showing that the uncle-nephew relationship is the same as that of grandparent-grandchild or of half-sibs.

When a double first cousin is given, the conditional probabilities that the other cousin should have both genes, one gene, or no gene identical by descent are $\frac{1}{16}$, $\frac{6}{16}$, $\frac{9}{16}$, respectively. Hence, the transition matrix for double first cousins is

$$S^2 = \tfrac{1}{16}I + \tfrac{6}{16}T + \tfrac{9}{16}O . \tag{17}$$

Converting S^2 into absolute frequencies, we obtain the "correlation table" for double first cousins given by Fisher (1918), through the direct method of randomly mating the *sibships* of the population.

§ 6. *An Example: Single First Cousins*

The foregoing account of the ITO method should be clear even to students who do not know how to multiply matrices, because the final product matrix has been reduced to a linear combination of the three fundamental matrices. However, it may be helpful to illustrate the method for the case of first cousins. Since a first cousin is one's parent's full sib's child, the transition matrix is

$$
\begin{aligned}
TST = T^3 &= \tfrac{1}{4}T + \tfrac{3}{4}O \\
&= \begin{pmatrix}
\tfrac{1}{4}p + \tfrac{3}{4}p^2 & \tfrac{1}{4}q + \tfrac{3}{4}2pq & \tfrac{3}{4}q^2 \\
\tfrac{1}{4}(\tfrac{1}{2}p) + \tfrac{3}{4}p^2 & \tfrac{1}{4}(\tfrac{1}{2}) + \tfrac{3}{4}2pq & \tfrac{1}{4}(\tfrac{1}{2}q) + \tfrac{3}{4}q^2 \\
\tfrac{3}{4}p^2 & \tfrac{1}{4}p + \tfrac{3}{4}2pq & \tfrac{1}{4}q + \tfrac{3}{4}q^2
\end{pmatrix} .
\end{aligned} \tag{18}
$$

Multiplying the first row by p^2, the second row by $2pq$, and the third by q^2, we obtain the first-cousin combination frequencies in the population, as shown in Table 15. From the fact that $TST = T^3$ it follows that the first-cousin relationship is the same as that of great-grandparent to great-grandchild.

TABLE 15

FREQUENCIES OF PAIRS OF FIRST COUSINS (OR GREAT-GRAND-
PARENT AND GREAT-GRANDCHILD) IN A RANDOM-
MATING POPULATION

First Cousins	AA	Aa	aa	Total
AA	$\frac{1}{4}p^2(p+3p^2)$	$\frac{1}{2}pq(\frac{1}{2}p+3p^2)$	$\frac{1}{4}q^2(0+3p^2)$	p^2
Aa	$\frac{1}{4}p^2(q+6pq)$	$\frac{1}{2}pq(\frac{1}{2}+6pq)$	$\frac{1}{4}q^2(p+6pq)$	$2pq$
aa	$\frac{1}{4}p^2(0+3q^2)$	$\frac{1}{2}pq(\frac{1}{2}q+3q^2)$	$\frac{1}{4}q^2(q+3q^2)$	q^2
Total . . .	p^2	$2pq$	q^2	1.00

The conventional method of obtaining the correlation between first cousins is to assign the values 2, 1, 0 to AA, Aa, aa in Table 15 and to calculate the covariance. The next section gives a short cut by which the correlation between relatives, with or without dominance, may be obtained as soon as the final transition matrix is expressed in terms of I, T, and O.

§ 7. Correlation between Relatives

We will first make an observation concerning an additive property of the correlation coefficient under some restrictive conditions. Suppose that there are N_1 pairs of values (y, x) with a correlation coefficient r_1 in one population and N_2 pairs of (y, x) with correlation r_2 in another population. It may be shown that, if the mean and variances of x and y in these two populations are equal, then the correlation between x and y in the pooled population of $N_1 + N_2$ pairs is

$$r = \left(\frac{N_1}{N_1 + N_2}\right) r_1 + \left(\frac{N_2}{N_1 + N_2}\right) r_2 .$$

That is, the correlation in the pooled population is the weighted mean of the separate correlations. Or, in other words, the pooled correlation may be subdivided into two components, corresponding to the contributions of the component populations. This theorem may be extended to any number of component populations as long as the variables have the same mean and variance.

Now, the ultimate transition matrix for any kind of relatives may be written in the following general form

$$\text{(Conditional probabilities)} = c_I I + c_T T + c_O O , \qquad (19)$$

where c_I, c_T, c_O are probabilities that the two relatives should have both genes, one gene, or no identical gene in common ($c_I + c_T + c_O = 1$). The I component contributes perfect (unity) correlation between the relatives, while the O component contributes nothing. If r_T is the correlation in the T component population (to be calculated after converting T into absolute frequencies), then the correlation between the relatives in the general population will simply be

$$r = c_I + c_T r_T . \qquad (20)$$

Therefore, to calculate the general r, we need only to calculate the one basic value of r_T once and for all. For unilineal relatives, $c_I = 0$, so that $r = c_T r_T$. According to (10) and (11), we have, in the present notation, $r_T = \frac{1}{2}$ for the case of no dominance, and $r_T^* = q/(1 + q)$ for the case of complete dominance. In particular, for unilineal relatives with the transition matrix T^n, the correlations without and with dominance are

$$r = (\tfrac{1}{2})^{n-1}(\tfrac{1}{2}) = (\tfrac{1}{2})^n, \qquad r^* = (\tfrac{1}{2})^{n-1}\left(\frac{q}{1+q}\right). \qquad (21)$$

For bilineal relatives only one example will be given, that of the correlations between full sibs without and with dominance:

$$r_{\text{sibs}} = \tfrac{1}{4} + \tfrac{1}{2}(\tfrac{1}{2}) = \tfrac{1}{2}, \qquad r_{\text{sibs}}^* = \tfrac{1}{4} + \tfrac{1}{2}\left(\frac{q}{1+q}\right), \qquad (22)$$

the latter being identical with (12). The corresponding correlations for double first cousins may be calculated, as an exercise, by the student. These methods may be applied, with only slight modifications, to sex-linked genes; they are discussed in more detail in Li and Sacks (1954).

§ 8. *Allocation of Genetic Variance*

We close this chapter with a description of another property of the genetic variance in a random-mating population. The value $\sigma_G^2 = 2pq$, as given by (3),

TABLE 16

ALLOCATION OF GENETIC VARIANCE OF A
RANDOM-MATING POPULATION

FREQUENCY OF FAMILY PATTERN	PATTERN OF FAMILY			FAMILY MEAN	VARIANCE WITHIN FAMILY
	AA (2)	Aa (1)	aa (0)		
p^4	1	0	0	2.0	0
$4p^3q$	$\tfrac{1}{2}$	$\tfrac{1}{2}$	0	1.5	$\tfrac{1}{4}$
$4p^2q^2$	$\tfrac{1}{4}$	$\tfrac{1}{2}$	$\tfrac{1}{4}$	1.0	$\tfrac{1}{2}$
$2p^2q^2$	0	1	0	1.0	0
$4pq^3$	0	$\tfrac{1}{2}$	$\tfrac{1}{2}$	0.5	$\tfrac{1}{4}$
q^4	0	0	1	0	0

Summary $\begin{cases} \text{Variance within families} & = pq = \tfrac{1}{2}\sigma_G^2 \\ \text{Variance between families} & = pq = \tfrac{1}{2}\sigma_G^2 \\ \text{Total variance in population} = 2pq = \sigma_G^2 \end{cases}$

is the total genetic variance of the population as a whole. It may be subdivided into components, using the family as the criterion for grouping the individuals. Then every individual belongs to one of the six patterns of families listed in Table 2. The mean and variance in each type of family are given in Table 16.

The average value of variance (weighted by frequency of family pattern) *within* all families in the population is $p^3q + 2p^2q^2 + pq^3 = pq$. The variance *between the mean* values of families (i.e., 2.0, 1.5, 1.0, 1.0, 0.5, 0), also weighted by corresponding frequencies, is found to be pq. Thus, in a random-mating population half of the genetic variance is due to variations of individuals within families and half is due to variations between families. This allocation of the genetic variance is independent of gene frequencies in the population.

Notes and Exercises

1. The quantity to be minimized, as given by (5), and following the scheme of Table 14, may be written as follows:

$$\Delta = p^2(Z_{AA} - g - 2a)^2 + 2pq(Z_{Aa} - g - a)^2 + q^2(Z_{aa} - g)^2 .$$

Putting $\partial\Delta/\partial a = 0$ and $\partial\Delta/\partial g = 0$, we obtain the equations

$$p^2(Z_{AA} - g - 2a) + pq(Z_{Aa} - g - a) = 0 , \tag{i}$$

$$p^2(Z_{AA} - g - 2a) + 2pq(Z_{Aa} - g - a) + q^2(Z_{aa} - g) = 0 . \tag{ii}$$

The second equation says that $p^2 D_{AA} + 2pq D_{Aa} + q^2 D_{aa} = \bar{D} = 0$; or $\bar{Z} - g - 2pa = 0$. Canceling p from (i) and canceling q from the expression (ii)–(i), we obtain the following two equations:

$$p(Z_{AA} - g - 2a) + q(Z_{Aa} - g - a) = 0 , \tag{iii}$$

$$p(Z_{Aa} - g - a) + q(Z_{aa} - g) = 0 . \tag{iv}$$

Subtracting (iv) from (iii) and thus eliminating g, we obtain

$$a = p(Z_{AA} - Z_{Aa}) + q(Z_{Aa} - Z_{aa}) = ph_2 + qh_1 ,$$

which is our solution (7).

2. To obtain the explicit solutions (6) for dominance deviations, we may regard the D's as variables and differentiate the expression (5) with respect to D's. Since there are only two independent D values, we may express D_{Aa} in terms of D_{AA} and D_{aa}. Noting that $h_1 - h_2 = 2Z_{Aa} - Z_{AA} - Z_{aa}$, we have

$$Z_{Aa} = \tfrac{1}{2}[Z_{AA} + Z_{aa} + (h_1 - h_2)] ;$$

since

$$G_{Aa} = \tfrac{1}{2}[G_{AA} + G_{aa}] ,$$

$$\therefore D_{Aa} = Z_{Aa} - G_{Aa} = \tfrac{1}{2}[D_{AA} + D_{aa} + (h_1 - h_2)] .$$

Substituting this expression of D_{Aa} in (5), we arrive at the following equations:

$$\frac{\partial \Delta}{\partial D_{AA}} = 2p^2 D_{AA} + pq\,[D_{AA} + D_{aa} + (h_1 - h_2)] = 0,$$

$$\frac{\partial \Delta}{\partial D_{aa}} = 2q^2 D_{aa} + pq\,[D_{AA} + D_{aa} + (h_1 - h_2)] = 0.$$

It follows that $p^2 D_{AA} = q^2 D_{aa}$. Substituting and solving, we obtain the values of the D's as given by (6). As was pointed out in the text, the solutions (6) and (7) are equivalent, because when the D's are known, the G's are also known, and vice versa.

3. There is more than one way to demonstrate the truth of (4). One method is to show that the G and D values obtained above are uncorrelated; that is, the covariance $\sigma_{GD} = 0$. Another method is a longhand algebraic demonstration that σ_Z^2 is actually the sum of the expressions (8). Since variance is independent of origin, the algebra becomes much easier if we take the Z values of AA, Aa, aa as h_2, 0, $-h_1$, respectively.

4. When there is complete dominance, and we assign the value 1 to dominants and 0 to recessives, show that

$$\bar{Z} = 1 - q^2, \qquad \sigma_Z^2 = q^2(1 - q^2).$$

Also show that the genetic variance with complete dominance is maximum when $q = \sqrt{.50} = 0.707$.

5. The following is a numerical example of *overdominance*. The method of fitting the G values is the same as described in the text. Verify the results and draw a diagram similar to Figure 4.

f	Z	G	D
$p^2 = 0.36$......	4.0	4.8	-0.8
$2pq = 0.48$......	5.0	3.8	$+1.2$
$q^2 = 0.16$......	1.0	2.8	-1.8
Mean..........	4.0	4.0	0
Variance.......	1.92	0.48	1.44

$$\left.\begin{array}{l} h_2 = -1 \\[4pt] h_1 = 4 \end{array}\right\}\quad a = 1, \qquad \frac{h_1 - h_2}{h_1} = \frac{5}{4} = 1.25, \qquad \frac{\sigma_G^2}{\sigma_Z^2} = \frac{0.48}{1.92} = 25 \text{ per cent}.$$

6. According to (15), the sibling transition matrix is

$$S = \begin{pmatrix} \frac{1}{4} + \frac{1}{2}p + \frac{1}{4}p^2 & \frac{1}{2}q + \frac{1}{2}pq & \frac{1}{4}q^2 \\[6pt] \frac{1}{4}p + \frac{1}{4}p^2 & \frac{1}{4} + \frac{1}{4} + \frac{1}{2}pq & \frac{1}{4}q + \frac{1}{4}q^2 \\[6pt] \frac{1}{4}p^2 & \frac{1}{2}p + \frac{1}{2}pq & \frac{1}{4} + \frac{1}{2}q + \frac{1}{4}q^2 \end{pmatrix}.$$

It may also be obtained by considering the conditional probabilities of parental combinations when one child is given. We will derive the elements of its second row as an example. When the given child is Aa, the probabilities of his parental combinations and of his sib's genotype are as follows:

PARENTAL. MATING	CONDITIONAL FREQUENCY	SIB'S GENOTYPE		
		AA	Aa	aa
$AA \times Aa$........	p^2	$\frac{1}{2}p^2$	$\frac{1}{2}p^2$	0
$Aa \times Aa$........	pq	$\frac{1}{4}pq$	$\frac{1}{2}pq$	$\frac{1}{4}pq$
$AA \times aa$........	pq	0	pq	0
$Aa \times aa$........	q^2	0	$\frac{1}{2}q^2$	$\frac{1}{2}q^2$
Total......	1.00	$\frac{1}{4}p+\frac{1}{4}p^2$	$\frac{1}{2}+\frac{1}{2}pq$	$\frac{1}{4}q+\frac{1}{4}q^2$

7. Those who know the rules for multiplying matrices should verify the relation $ST = TS = T^2$ by actually carrying out the multiplication.

8. Calculate the correlation between first cousins from Table 15 by the product-moment method. Verify:

No dominance, $r = \frac{1}{8}$; complete dominance, $r* = \frac{1}{4}\left(\frac{q}{1+q}\right)$.

CHAPTER 4

Multiple Alleles

MANY of the theorems and corollaries given in the last three chapters may be applied also to problems involving multiple alleles. The case with only three alleles is the most important one in many applications, and in this chapter we shall devote most of our attention to it.

§ 1. *Equilibrium Proportions*

With three alleles, A, a', a, whose frequencies are p, q, r, respectively ($p + q + r = 1$), the proportions of the six genotypes, in a large random-mating population, are given by

$$\begin{pmatrix} A & a' & a \\ p + q + r \end{pmatrix}^2 = \frac{AA \quad Aa' \quad Aa \quad a'a' \quad a'a \quad aa}{p^2 + 2pq + 2pr + q^2 + 2qr + r^2}. \tag{1}$$

The direct extension of the Hardy-Weinberg Law to the case of multiple alleles was first made by Weinberg (1909; see Stern, 1943). That these genotypic proportions are actually in equilibrium status may be seen in various ways. One is to write out the twenty-one different types of mating and their corresponding offspring with the appropriate frequencies in the same manner as was done in Table 2. It will be found that the totals of the six kinds of offspring are the same as (1). This table of twenty-one matings is too long to be given in full here; but it is a fundamental table from which many corollaries may be drawn, just as many properties concerning two alleles were drawn from Table 2. The equilibrium condition (1) may, however, be much more easily verified by finding the total gametic output of the population and then using the principle that random mating of individuals is equivalent to random union of gametes (Chap. 1, § 5). The output of A-gamete of population (1) is $p^2 + pq + pr = p$, etc.

If an initial population is not in an equilibrium state, the condition (1) will be immediately established after one single generation of random mating, just as in the case with two alleles.

All the above properties would clearly still hold when there are more than three alleles. Generally speaking, if there are k alleles, there will be k types of homozygotes and

$$\binom{k}{2} = \frac{k\ (k-1)}{2}$$

types of heterozygotes, the total number of genotypes being

$$k + \binom{k}{2} = \binom{k+1}{2} = \frac{k\ (k+1)}{2}.$$

If we let q_i denote the frequency of A_i-gene ($\Sigma q_i = 1$, $i = 1, 2, \ldots, k$), the equilibrium proportions of the genotypes in a random-mating population are given by

$$\left(\sum_i q_i A_i\right)^2 = \sum_i q_i^2 A_i A_i + 2 \sum_{i<j} q_i q_j A_i A_j,$$

which is a general form of (1).

It should be remembered that one of the properties of Mendelism is that any group of alleles can be treated as one allele. Hence we can always treat k alleles as two alleles, distinguishing only A_1 (say) in contrast to all the remaining $k-1$ alleles. For instance, if we do not wish to distinguish the alleles a' and a in (1), we may regard $(q + r)$ as the frequency of one allele ($a' + a$). Thus, (1) will assume the ordinary form for two alleles:

$$AA \quad\quad Aa', Aa \quad\quad a'a', a'a, aa$$
$$p^2 + 2p(q + r) + (q + r)^2.$$

Conversely, some of the properties of multiple allelic inheritance may be derived from corresponding properties with two alleles by subdividing the frequencies.

If dominance is involved, there will be fewer than six distinguishable phenotypes for three alleles. Consider the example of coloring in rabbits, which was one of the earliest instances known to be due to three alleles. *Full color* (A) is dominant over both *Himalayan* (a', body white but with pigmented ears, nose, tips of feet, and tip of tail) and *Albino* (a); and *Himalayan* is dominant over *Albino*. If rabbits mate at random, we would expect the proportions of the three phenotypes in the population to be: ($p^2 + 2pq + 2pr$) full colors, ($q^2 + 2qr$) himalayans, and r^2 albinos.

§ 2. *Estimating Gene Frequencies from Samples*

When all the genotypes are distinguishable, the estimation of gene frequencies is very simple. The frequency of A_1, for example, is given by the proportion of $A_1 A_1$ individuals plus half the proportions of all heterozygotes involving A_1. The process of estimating gene frequencies from a random sample and testing the significance of its deviation from Weinberg equilibrium proportions (1) may best be illustrated by the following example.

In *Drosophila pseudoobscura* the III-chromosomes are very variable with respect to order of gene arrangements. More than seventeen different types of gene arrangements (related to each other as single or multiple inversions) are known. Dobzhansky and Queal (1938*a*, *b*) utilized this situation to make the first study of the genetics of natural populations of *D. pseudoobscura*. They collected random samples of flies from mountain forests in the Death Valley region of California and Nevada. Their findings in Grapevine, one of the several mountaintops they covered, are given in Table 17, in which ST = Standard,

TABLE 17

DISTRIBUTION OF 115 D. PSEUDOOBSCURA IN GRAPEVINE
(Dobzhansky and Queal, 1938*a*, *b*)

	"GENOTYPE"						TOTAL
	ST/ST	AR/AR	CH/CH	ST/AR	ST/CH	AR/CH	
Observed.......	12	27	3	36	10	27	115
Expected.......	10.65	29.76	4.02	35.60	13.10	21.87	115
Chromosome freq.: ST=0.3043, AR=0.5087, CH=0.1870							1.00

$\chi^2 = 2.63$ with 3 degrees of freedom, P between 0.3 and 0.5

AR = Arrowhead, and CH = Chiricahua denote the three types of chromosome-III of *D. pseudoobscura*. The estimation of the frequency of ST, for example, is $p = (2 \times 12 + 36 + 10)/2(115) = 70/230 = 0.3043$; the frequencies of AR and CH may be found in a similar way. The calculation of the expected numbers of flies in Table 17 is based upon distribution (1); thus, the expected number of ST/ST is $115(0.3043)^2 = 10.65$, etc. The observed and expected numbers agree very well, showing that the flies mate at random in nature.

In a case of dominance of the full-color–himalayan–albino type, there are only three phenotypes. The gene frequencies may also be estimated from the phenotypic proportions in a very simple manner. The algebra of the maximum likelihood estimates may be greatly simplified by the substitutions $R = r^2$ and $Q = (q + r)^2$, so that the theoretical frequencies of the three phenotypes may take the following form:

	PHENOTYPE			
	Full Color	Himalayan	Albino	TOTAL
Probabilities..........	$p^2+2pq+2pr$ $1-Q$	q^2+2qr $Q-R$	r^2 R	1.00
Observed numbers......	a	b	c	G

Since $p + q + r = 1$, we need to estimate only two of the three gene frequencies. The estimation of q and r will be obtained by estimating Q and R. Straightforward application of the method of maximum likelihood leads then to the following equations:

$$R = r^2 = \frac{c}{G}, \qquad Q = (q + r)^2 = \frac{b + c}{G},$$

and thus

$$r = \sqrt{R}, \qquad q = \sqrt{Q} - \sqrt{R}. \tag{2}$$

Table 18 provides a numerical example of the calculating process.

TABLE 18

ESTIMATION OF GENE FREQUENCIES FROM THREE PHENOTYPES

	PHENOTYPE			TOTAL
	A-Dominants	a'-Dominants	Recessives	
Observed.................	2527	1627	1846	6000
Preliminary estimates......		$Q = .5788$ $\sqrt{Q} = .7608$	$R = .3077$ $\sqrt{R} = .5547$	....
Gene freq................	$p = 0.2392$	$q = 0.2061$	$r = 0.5547$	1.00

§3. *Some Properties of Equilibrium*

With multiple alleles the total proportion of heterozygotes may exceed 50 per cent, unlike the case with two alleles. For example, with three alleles, the proportion of heterozygotes is $2(pq + pr + qr) = 2y$. It may be easily shown that the maximum value of y is $\frac{1}{3}$ when $p = q = r = \frac{1}{3}$, so that the maximum proportion of heterozygotes in a random-mating population is $\frac{2}{3}$, or nearly 67 per cent. Note that, in the example of Table 17, the proportion of "heterozygotes" is $(36 + 10 + 27)/115 = 63.5$ per cent.

By reasoning analogous with that of Section 7 and Exercise 15 of Chapter 1, the zygotic proportions of an equilibrium population with multiple alleles may also be related by one equation. Let q_i be the frequency of allele A_i $(i = 1, \ldots, k)$. Further, let the proportion of A_iA_i individuals be z_{ii}, and that of A_iA_j be $2z_{ij}$ $(i < j)$, so that $\Sigma z_{ii} + 2\Sigma z_{ij} = 1$. The gene frequencies are then $q_i = \sum_j z_{ij}$. For instance, $q_1 = z_{11} + z_{12} + \ldots + z_{1k}$. The fraction z_{ii}/q_i is the proportion of A_i-genes in homozygous condition among the total frequency of that allele. The sum of such proportions of all alleles in a random-mating population is unity (Li, 1953b). Hence we obtain the equation

$$\frac{z_{11}}{q_1} + \frac{z_{22}}{q_2} + \ldots + \frac{z_{kk}}{q_k} = 1. \tag{3}$$

With three alleles, a population consisting of six genotypes may be represented by a point in a five-dimensional space with homogeneous coordinates, so that the distances from the point to the six "sides" represent the genotypic proportions. The equation (in which $z_{11} + z_{12} + z_{13} = q_1$, etc.)

$$\frac{z_{11}}{z_{11} + z_{12} + z_{13}} + \frac{z_{22}}{z_{12} + z_{22} + z_{23}} + \frac{z_{33}}{z_{13} + z_{23} + z_{33}} = 1 \qquad (3')$$

defines the surface in that space representing all the equilibrium population points (analogous to the parabola in a triangle of Fig. 3). The equation (3) may, with slight modification, be extended to populations with inbreeding (Chap. 11).

§ 4. *The Human ABO Blood Groups*

The mechanism of the inheritance of ABO blood groups has been explained in almost all textbooks of genetics and need not be given here in detail. Briefly, Bernstein's (1930a, b) explanation was based upon three alleles: A (producing antigen-A) is dominant over a (not capable of producing any antigen); and another allele a' (producing antigen-B) is also dominant over a. But A and a' are not dominant over each other ("codominance") and produce their antigens independently, so that the heterozygote Aa' has both kinds of antigens. Consequently, there are four distinguishable phenotypes (blood groups) in human populations with the following proportions, where p, q, r are gene frequencies of A, a', a, respectively:

	GENOTYPE			
	Aa'	AA, Aa	$a'a'$, $a'a$	aa
Blood group.....	AB	A	B	O
Proportion......	$2pq$	$p^2 + 2pr$	$q^2 + 2qr$	r^2

$$(4)$$

Note that the proportions are symmetrical with respect to p and q. A diagrammatic method of showing the four phenotypic proportions as well as the three gene frequencies is given in Figure 5. A set of (p, q, r) values determines a point in an equilateral triangle; and the perpendicular distances from this point to the three sides represent the *gene frequencies*. The two lines parallel to the two sides divide the triangle into four portions whose *areas* are proportional to the four phenotypic proportions. If we draw another line through the point and parallel to the base of the triangle, it subdivides the areas of groups A and B into homozygous and heterozygous proportions. The figure is a complete representation of the six genotypic proportions of (1). If $p = q$, the proportions of groups A and B in the population will also be equal, and the point will be on the line from the vertex of the triangle and perpendicular to the base. It is also clear that, with the magnitudes of p, q, r as they are in most human populations ($p = 0.22$,

$q = 0.16$, $r = 0.62$, as shown in Fig. 5), most of the A and B individuals are heterozygotes:

	BLOOD GROUP			
	AB	A	B	O
Percentage.........	7.04	4.84+27.28	2.56+19.84	38.44
		32.12	22.40	

Now let us consider the problem of estimating gene frequencies from a random sample of G unrelated individuals. For the sake of brevity, we shall use the symbols O, A, B, and AB to denote both the blood groups and their corresponding proportions in the sample. An inspection of (4) shows that

$$A + O = (p + r)^2, \quad B + O = (q + r)^2, \quad O = r^2 ;$$

hence,

$$p = 1 - \sqrt{(B + O)}, \quad q = 1 - \sqrt{(A + O)}, \quad r = \sqrt{O}. \qquad (5)$$

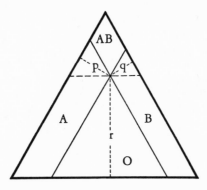

FIG. 5.—World blood groups. Perpendicular distances $p = 0.215$, $q = 0.162$, $r = 0.623$ represent gene frequencies; the four areas bounded by solid lines are proportional to phenotypic frequencies. If a horizontal (*dotted*) line is drawn through the population point, the three triangles represent homozygotes and the three parallelograms represent heterozygotes. (Modified from Penrose, 1951.)

The sum of the three quantities calculated by (5) should be close to unity if Bernstein's theory of triple allelic inheritance is correct. Table 19 gives a numerical example of the method of analysis. In actual cases the three estimated gene frequencies do not add up exactly to unity, although they are usually very close to it for large samples. The variance of the sum $p + q + r$, or of its deviation from unity, $d = 1 - (p + q + r)$, is

$$V(d) = \frac{pq}{2G(1 - p)(1 - q)},$$

where G is the number of individuals in the sample. With this formula the significance of the deviation from unity may be tested.

It is desirable, however, to adjust the three estimated gene frequencies so that they add up to unity. The following ingenious device for doing so is due to Bernstein (1930*b*):

$$p' = p(1 + \tfrac{1}{2}d), \qquad q' = q(1 + \tfrac{1}{2}d), \qquad r' = (r + \tfrac{1}{2}d)(1 + \tfrac{1}{2}d). \qquad (6)$$

Noting that $(p + q + r) + d = 1$ and hence $(p + q + r) + \tfrac{1}{2}d = 1 - \tfrac{1}{2}d$, we see that the sum of the three adjusted gene frequencies is

$$p' + q' + r' = (1 + \tfrac{1}{2}d)(1 - \tfrac{1}{2}d) = 1 - \tfrac{1}{4}d^2.$$

This will be very close to unity if d is small. Should the new sum still differ appreciably from unity, we may repeat the adjusting process, using the new devia-

TABLE 19

BLOOD-GROUP FREQUENCIES OF 6000 CHINESE
(Data Collected at the Blood Bank of Kunming, Yunnan, China.
[Courtesy of Dr. C. S. Fan, 1944, unpublished.])

	BLOOD GROUP				TOTAL
	AB	A	B	O	
No.............	607	1920	1627	1846	6000
Proportion.........	.10116	.32000	.27116	.30766	1.0000
$\sqrt{(A+O)} = \sqrt{.62766} = .79225, \quad \sqrt{(B+O)} = \sqrt{.57883} = .76081$					....
Gene freq. (5).......	$p=0.23919, \; q=0.20775, \; r=0.55468$				1.00162
Adjusted (6).......	$p'=0.23900, \; q'=0.20758, \; r'=0.55342$				1.00000

tion $d' = \tfrac{1}{4}d^2$. Usually one adjustment will be sufficiently accurate. In the example of Table 19, $d = -0.00162$, so that $p' = 0.23919(1 - 0.00081) = 0.23900$, etc., as shown in the bottom line of that table. This method of adjustment is highly practical because of its simplicity. Its only drawback is that it is difficult to assess the exact variances of the adjusted gene frequencies. The maximum likelihood method of estimation is admittedly tedious; but, since Stevens (1938) presented full details of its arithmetic procedure, it has come into more general use in recent years, and an account of the method is given in Exercise 8.

§5. *Types of Mating and Their Offspring*

If we write out the twenty-one different types of matings in regard to the six genotypes and their corresponding offspring, list the appropriate frequencies of mating, and then collect them into ten distinguishable phenotypic matings, and also collect the six genotypes of offspring into four blood groups, the results are those shown in Table 20. Dividing the proportions of offspring by the corresponding frequencies of parental mating, we obtain the percentages of the various types of offspring for any given type of mating. For instance, among the A $\times$ A matings, the percentage of Group O offspring is $r^2/(p + 2r)^2$, while the A $\times$ O matings produce $r/(p + 2r)$ recessives. As far as the two alleles A and a are concerned, these ratios are equivalent to Snyder's $S_2 = q^2/(p + 2q)^2$, $S_1 = q/(p + 2q)$ for two alleles with dominance (Chap. 2, § 3), except that here $p + r$ is not unity. These generalized Snyder's ratios are functions of

TABLE 20

FREQUENCIES OF TYPES OF MATING AND THEIR OFFSPRING

TYPE OF MATING	FREQUENCY OF MATING	OFFSPRING			
		O	A	B	AB
O×O......	r^4	r^4	....	....	....
O×A......	$2pr^2(p+2r)$	$2pr^3$	$2pr^2(p+r)$	....	....
O×B......	$2qr^2(q+2r)$	$2qr^3$	....	$2qr^2(q+r)$	....
O×AB.....	$4pqr^2$	.....	$2pqr^2$	$2pqr^2$	....
A×A......	$p^2(p+2r)^2$	p^2r^2	$p^2(p+r)(p+3r)$	....	....
A×B......	$2pq(p+2r)(q+2r)$	$2pqr^2$	$2pqr(p+r)$	$2pqr(q+r)$	$2pq(p+r)(q+r)$
B×B......	$q^2(q+2r)^2$	q^2r^2	....	$q^2(q+r)(q+3r)$	
A×AB....	$4p^2q(p+2r)$	.....	$2p^2q(p+2r)$	$2p^2qr$	$2p^2q(p+r)$
B×AB....	$4pq^2(q+2r)$	.....	$2pq^2r$	$2pq^2(q+2r)$	$2pq^2(q+r)$
AB×AB...	$4p^2q^2$	.....	p^2q^2	p^2q^2	$2p^2q^2$
Total..	1.00	r^2	p^2+2pr	q^2+2qr	$2pq$

gene frequencies except for the following three types of mating where the genotypes of both parents are completely known:

$$O \times O \to O ; \quad O \times AB \to \tfrac{1}{2}A + \tfrac{1}{2}B ; \quad AB \times AB \to \tfrac{1}{4}A + \tfrac{1}{2}AB + \tfrac{1}{4}B .$$

It may also be noted that, among all matings involving one Group O parent, there will be no AB offspring. Conversely, in all matings involving one AB parent, there will be no Group O offspring. If an antigen is lacking in both parents, their children could not possibly possess that antigen. Thus, among A $\times$ A and A $\times$ O matings, there could not be any B or AB child. Hence, A $\times$ B is the only type of mating which is capable of producing all four groups of children. As a matter of fact, this type of mating consists of four different types of genotypic mating of which there is only one, $Aa \times a'a$, capable of producing children of any group ($\tfrac{1}{4}O + \tfrac{1}{4}A + \tfrac{1}{4}B + \tfrac{1}{4}AB$).

If we distinguish the reciprocal crosses in Table 20, there will be sixteen phenotypic types of mating, of which four are of the type O $\times$ (O, A, B, AB); four of the type A $\times$ (O, A, B, AB); etc. Combining these sixteen types of mating into four groups according to the phenotype (blood group) of one parent, we obtain the frequencies of parent-child combinations with respect to the

ABO blood groups, as shown in Table 21. This is the classical way of deriving such frequencies. Table 21, however, may be obtained by the *ITO* method described in Chapter 3. The sib-sib combination frequencies with respect to blood groups may also be obtained very simply by that method (Exs. 6 and 7).

TABLE 21

PARENT-CHILD COMBINATION FREQUENCIES WITH
RESPECT TO ABO BLOOD GROUPS

MOTHER	CHILD			
	AB	A	B	O
AB.....	$pq(p+q)$	$pq(p+r)$	$pq(q+r)$	. . . .
A......	$pq(p+r)$	$p(p^2+3pr+r^2)$	pqr	pr^2
B......	$pq(q+r)$	pqr	$q(q^2+3qr+r^2)$	qr^2
O......	. . . .	pr^2	qr^2	r^3

§6. *Subgroups of A*

The allele A in the preceding sections is really an aggregate of several alleles, so that Group A may be subdivided into A_1, A_2, A_3, etc., subgroups. The alleles A_3, etc., are very rare in most human populations, and therefore in this section we shall only be concerned with A_1 and A_2. Here A_1 is dominant over A_2, so that the heterozygote A_1A_2 belongs to subgroup A_1. The AB group therefore also contains two subgroups, A_1B and A_2B. Let p_1 and p_2 be the frequencies of the alleles A_1 and A_2, respectively, so that $p_1 + p_2 = p$, the total frequency of A. The proportions of the six blood groups in the general population are thus as follows:

	GENOTYPE					
	A_1a'	A_2a'	A_1A_1, A_1A_2, A_1a	A_2A_2, A_2a	$a'a'$, $a'a$	aa
Blood group......	A_1B	A_2B	A_1	A_2	B	O
Proportion........	$2p_1q$	$2p_2q$	$p_1^2+2p_1p_2+2p_1r$	$p_2^2+2p_2r$	q^2+2qr	r^2
	$2pq$		p^2+2pr			

Therefore, $A_1 + A_2 + O = (p_1 + p_2 + r)^2$, $A_2 + O = (p_2 + r)^2$. The inefficient estimates are (Wellisch and Thomsen, 1930):

$$\left.\begin{array}{l} p_1 = \sqrt{(A_1 + A_2 + O)} - \sqrt{(A_2 + O)} \\ p_2 = \sqrt{(A_2 + O)} - \sqrt{O} \end{array}\right\} p = \sqrt{(A + O)} - \sqrt{O} \qquad (7)$$

$$q = \sqrt{(B + O)} - \sqrt{O}, \quad \text{and} \quad r = \sqrt{O}.$$

As an example, we may cite the data of Taylor and Prior (1938):

			Group				Total
	A_1B	A_2B	A_1	A_2	B	O	
No............	4	2	124	26	29	160	345
Proportion.....	0.0116	0.0058	0.3594	0.0754	0.0840	0.4638	1.00

$$p_1 = \sqrt{0.8986} - \sqrt{0.5392} = 0.2136 \Big\}$$
$$p_2 = \sqrt{0.5392} - \sqrt{0.4638} = 0.0533 \Big\} \quad p = 0.2669 ,$$
$$q = \sqrt{0.5478} - \sqrt{0.4638} = 0.0591 , \quad r = 0.6810 .$$

The sum of the four frequencies is 1.0070. We may take $r = 1 - p_1 - p_2 - q$ in order to make their sum unity. The estimates (7) are consistent but not fully efficient. They may be used as preliminary trial values for maximum likelihood estimates. Although it involves no new principle in the application of maximum likelihood method to estimate the three parameters, p_1, p_2, q, the arithmetic is very laborious, and the systematic procedure of Stevens (1938) should be followed.

The medicolegal and anthropological applications of the analysis of blood-group gene frequencies may be found in Snyder (1929, 1951), Wiener (1943, 1950), Boyd (1950), Neel and Schull (1954).

Notes and Exercises

1. Dobzhansky and Queal (1938a) examined 101 random individuals of *Drosophila pseudoobscura*, collected from Sheep Range in the Death Valley region, with the following results:

ST/ST	AR/AR	CH/CH	ST/AR	ST/CH	AR/CH	Total
0	77	0	20	0	4	101

Let g_1, g_2, g_3 be the number of ST, AR, CH chromosomes in a sample of G flies so that $g_1 + g_2 + g_3 = 2G$. The estimates of chromosome frequencies are $q_1 = g_1/2G$, etc. For the above observed data, we have:

$$g_1 = 20 \quad g_2 = 178 \quad g_3 = 4 \qquad 2G = 202$$
$$q_1 = .0990, \quad q_2 = .8812, \quad q_3 = .0198 \qquad \text{Sum} = 1.00$$

The expected numbers of flies may then be calculated from expression (1). However, since the frequencies of ST and CH are so low here that there are no individuals observed involving ST and CH chromosomes alone, Levene's formula may be applied to obtain the expected numbers:

$$E(z_{ii}) = \frac{g_i(g_i - 1)}{2(2G - 1)} , \qquad E(z_{ij}) = \frac{g_i g_j}{2G - 1} .$$

The results of these two methods are as follows:

	ST/ST	AR/AR	CH/CH	ST/AR	ST/CH	AR/CH	x^2
Expected (1).....	.99	78.43	.04	17.62	.40	3.52	1.84
Expected (Levene)	.95	78.37	.03	17.71	.40	3.54	1.76

Note that by both methods the observed numbers of homozygotes are slightly less than expected but that Levene's formula reduces the value of x^2 by a small amount.

2. Draw an equilateral triangle similar to Figure 5 for each of the following populations. What do you notice about the proportions of the four blood groups? What are the percentages of heterozygotes among the Group A and Group B individuals in these populations?

p	q	r	AB	A	B	O
0.30	0.10	0.60	0.060	0.450	0.130	0.360
.10	.30	.60	.060	.130	.450	.360
.20	.20	.60	.080	.280	.280	.360
.2265	.2265	.5470	.103	.299	.299	.299
.25	.25	.50	.125	.3125	.3125	.250
.2929	.2929	.4142	.172	.328	.328	.172
.33	.33	.33	.222	.333	.333	.111
0.40	0.40	0.20	0.320	0.320	0.320	0.040

3. Show that the minimum value of the total proportion of homozygotes with respect to three alleles is $\frac{1}{3}$ in a panmictic population.
   HINT: Let $h = p^2 + q^2 + r^2$ and solve the two equations, $\partial h/\partial p = 0$, $\partial h/\partial q = 0$, simultaneously.

4. The frequency of A $\times$ B mating in the general population is $2(p^2 + 2pr)$ $(q^2 + 2qr) = 2pq(p + 2r)(q + 2r)$. It consists of four different genotypic matings whose frequencies and offspring are as follows:

GENOTYPES	FREQUENCY	OFFSPRING			
		O	A	B	AB
$AA \times a'a'$.........	$2p^2q^2$	....	....	....	$2p^2q^2$
$AA \times a'a$.........	$4p^2qr$	....	$2p^2qr$	....	$2p^2q\imath$
$Aa \times a'a'$.........	$4pq^2r$	....	....	$2pq^2r$	$2pq^2r$
$Aa \times a'a$.........	$8pqr^2$	$2pqr^2$	$2pqr^2$	$2pqr^2$	$2pqr^2$

The sums of these four genotypic matings and their offspring are the values entered for the A $\times$ B mating in Table 20. Note that $Aa \times a'a$ is the only kind of family capable of producing all four kinds of children ($\frac{1}{4}$ of each kind).

5. Dividing the proportions of offspring by their corresponding parental combination frequencies in Table 20, we obtain the proportions of the various kinds of offspring for a certain given type of mating. Thus, among B × AB families, the proportion of their children are as follows:

$$(O): \text{none}; \quad (A): \frac{r}{2(q+2r)}; \quad (B): \tfrac{1}{2}; \quad (AB): \frac{q+r}{2(q+2r)}.$$

6. If we arrange the rows and columns in the order Aa', AA, Aa, $a'a'$, $a'a$, aa, then the parent-child transition matrix takes the form:

$$T = \begin{pmatrix} \tfrac{1}{2}p+\tfrac{1}{2}q & \tfrac{1}{2}p & \tfrac{1}{2}r & \tfrac{1}{2}q & \tfrac{1}{2}r & 0 \\ q & p & r & 0 & 0 & 0 \\ \tfrac{1}{2}q & \tfrac{1}{2}p & \tfrac{1}{2}r+\tfrac{1}{2}p & 0 & \tfrac{1}{2}q & \tfrac{1}{2}r \\ p & 0 & 0 & q & r & 0 \\ \tfrac{1}{2}p & 0 & \tfrac{1}{2}p & \tfrac{1}{2}q & \tfrac{1}{2}r+\tfrac{1}{2}q & \tfrac{1}{2}r \\ 0 & 0 & p & 0 & q & r \end{pmatrix}.$$

Multiplying the first, second, etc., rows by $2pq$, p^2, etc., we obtain the absolute frequencies of parent-child combinations in the population as follows:

MOTHER	CHILD					
	Aa'	AA	Aa	$a'a'$	$a'a$	aa
Aa'	$pq(p+q)$	p^2q	pqr	pq^2	pqr	....
AA	p^2q	p^3	p^2r	....	....	....
Aa	pqr	p^2r	$pr(p+r)$	....	pqr	pr^2
$a'a'$	pq^2	....	....	q^3	q^2r	....
$a'a$	pqr	....	pqr	q^2r	$qr(q+r)$	qr^2
aa	....	....	pr^2	....	qr^2	r^3

Collecting cells of the same phenotype, we obtain Table 21.

7. Direct multiplication shows that $T^2 = \tfrac{1}{2}T + \tfrac{1}{2}O$, where O consists of six rows of $2pq$, p^2, $2pr$, q^2, $2qr$, r^2, forming the independence matrix. In fact, all the relations described in Chapter 3 hold for the case of multiple alleles. The sibling transition matrix is $S = \tfrac{1}{4}I + \tfrac{1}{2}T + \tfrac{1}{4}O$. Writing out the thirty-six elements of this matrix and converting them into absolute frequencies, we obtain the sib-sib combination frequencies in the population as follows:

Full Sibs	Aa'	AA	Aa	$a'a'$	$a'a$	aa
Aa'	$\frac{1}{2}pq(1+p+q+2pq)$	$\frac{1}{2}p^2q(1+p)$	$\frac{1}{2}pqr(1+2p)$	$\frac{1}{2}pq^2(1+q)$	$\frac{1}{2}pqr(1+2q)$	$\frac{1}{2}pqr^2$
AA	$\frac{1}{2}p^2q(1+p)$	$\frac{1}{4}p^2(1+p)^2$	$\frac{1}{2}p^2r(1+p)$	$\frac{1}{4}p^2q^2$	$\frac{1}{2}p^2qr$	$\frac{1}{4}p^2r^2$
Aa	$\frac{1}{2}pqr(1+2p)$	$\frac{1}{2}p^2r(1+p)$	$\frac{1}{2}pr(1+p+r+2pr)$	$\frac{1}{2}pq^2r$	$\frac{1}{2}pqr(1+2r)$	$\frac{1}{2}pr^2(1+r)$
$a'a'$	$\frac{1}{2}pq^2(1+q)$	$\frac{1}{4}p^2q^2$	$\frac{1}{2}pq^2r$	$\frac{1}{4}q^2(1+q)^2$	$\frac{1}{2}q^2r(1+q)$	$\frac{1}{4}q^2r^2$
$a'a$	$\frac{1}{2}pqr(1+2q)$	$\frac{1}{2}p^2qr$	$\frac{1}{2}pqr(1+2r)$	$\frac{1}{2}q^2r(1+q)$	$\frac{1}{2}qr(1+q+r+2qr)$	$\frac{1}{2}qr^2(1+r)$
aa	$\frac{1}{2}pqr^2$	$\frac{1}{4}p^2r^2$	$\frac{1}{2}pr^2(1+r)$	$\frac{1}{4}q^2r^2$	$\frac{1}{2}qr^2(1+r)$	$\frac{1}{4}r^2(1+r)^2$

Collecting cells of the same phenotype, we obtain the blood-group combination frequencies for full sibs. The results given by Rife (1951a) for the case in which A is dominant over a' and a also follow from this table.

8. *Maximum likelihood estimates of ABO gene frequencies.*—Let (AB) be the observed *number* of individuals of Group AB and write (AB + A) for (AB) + (A). Probabilities (4) show that the logarithmic likelihood function is

$$L = (AB) \log pq + (A) \log (p^2 + 2pr) + (B) \log (q^2 + 2qr) + (O) \log r^2,$$

neglecting terms not involving gene frequencies. Since $\log (p^2 + 2pr) = \log p + \log (p + 2r)$, etc., the above expression may be simplified to some extent into the form:

$$L = (AB + A) \log p + (AB + B) \log q + (A) \log (p + 2r)$$
$$+ (B) \log (q + 2r) + 2(O) \log r.$$

We shall take p and q as the two independent parameters to be estimated and $r = 1 - p - q$. Then $\partial r/\partial p = -1$ and $\partial r/\partial q = -1$. The two partial derivatives with respect to p and q are then

$$\left.\begin{aligned}
\frac{\partial L}{\partial p} &= \frac{(AB+A)}{p} - \frac{(A)}{p+2r} - \frac{2(B)}{q+2r} - \frac{2(O)}{r} \\
\frac{\partial L}{\partial q} &= \frac{(AB+B)}{q} - \frac{2(A)}{p+2r} - \frac{(B)}{q+2r} - \frac{2(O)}{r}
\end{aligned}\right\} . \qquad (E1)$$

Our estimates of p and q should be the simultaneous solutions of the two equations: $\partial L/\partial p = 0$, $\partial L/\partial q = 0$. There seem to be no simple algebraic solutions of these two equations; so we have to adopt an iterative method beginning with some "trial" values p_0, q_0, r_0 such as those given by (5). If these trial values are close to true solutions, their substitution in (E1) would make the numerical values of $\partial L/\partial p$ and $\partial L/\partial q$ comparatively small. Let their numerical values be $\partial L/\partial p = c_p$ and $\partial L/\partial q = c_q$ on substitution of p_0, q_0, r_0 in (E1). The second step is to find the "information matrix":

$$\{I\} = \left\{\begin{matrix} I_{pp} & I_{pq} \\ I_{pq} & I_{qq} \end{matrix}\right\} .$$

where

$$I_{pp} = -\frac{\partial^2 L}{\partial p^2}, \qquad I_{pq} = -\frac{\partial^2 L}{\partial p \, \partial q}.$$

Thus,

$$
\left.
\begin{aligned}
I_{pp} &= \frac{(AB+A)}{p^2} + \frac{(A)}{(p+2r)^2} + \frac{4\,(B)}{(q+2r)^2} + \frac{2\,(O)}{r^2} \\[2mm]
I_{qq} &= \frac{(AB+B)}{q^2} + \frac{4\,(A)}{(p+2r)^2} + \frac{(B)}{(q+2r)^2} + \frac{2\,(O)}{r^2} \\[2mm]
I_{pq} &= \qquad\qquad \frac{2\,(A)}{(p+2r)^2} + \frac{2\,(B)}{(q+2r)^2} + \frac{2\,(O)}{r^2}
\end{aligned}
\right\} .
\qquad \text{(E2)}
$$

Substituting the trial values (p_0, q_0, r_0) in the above expressions, we obtain the numerical values of the elements of $\{I\}$. The third step is to invert the information matrix to obtain the variance-covariance matrix $\{V\} = \{I\}^{-1}$. The most straightforward arithmetic procedure for inverting $\{I\}$ is to solve the following two sets of equations:

$$
\left.
\begin{aligned}
I_{pp}x + I_{pq}y &= 1\,, \\
I_{pq}x + I_{qq}y &= 0\,,
\end{aligned}
\right\}
\qquad
\left.
\begin{aligned}
0 \\
1
\end{aligned}
\right\} .
\qquad \text{(E3)}
$$

Let x_1, y_1 and x_2, y_2 be the two sets of solutions of (E3). Then the variance-covariance matrix is

$$\{V\} = \begin{Bmatrix} x_1 & x_2 \\ y_1 & y_2 \end{Bmatrix} = \begin{Bmatrix} V_{pp} & V_{pq} \\ V_{pq} & V_{qq} \end{Bmatrix},$$

in which V_{pp} is the variance of p, and V_{qq} is the variance of q, while the sum of its four elements is the variance of r. The fourth and final step is to correct or improve our initial trial values on the basis of the numerical values of c_p and c_q together with the elements of $\{V\}$. Thus, the quantities to be *added* to p_0 and q_0 are, respectively,

$$\delta p = c_p V_{pp} + c_q V_{pq}\,, \qquad \delta q = c_p V_{pq} + c_q V_{qq}\,, \qquad \text{(E4)}$$

while δr is determined by the condition $\delta p + \delta q + \delta r = 0$, so that the improved estimates of gene frequencies still add up to unity. This completes one process of adjustment toward arriving at true maximum likelihood estimates. The whole process may be repeated for a second round of adjustments, but in most cases one adjustment is sufficiently accurate if the initial trial values are good.

As a numerical example of the procedure, let us use the same data in Table 19 and employ the ordinary inefficient estimates as our trial values except that we take $r_0 = 1 - p_0 - q_0$ (trial values must add up to unity themselves). The preliminary numerical calculations may be arranged in the following convenient form, where for simplicity the subscripts o of trial values have been dropped.

$(AB+A)=2527$	$(AB+B)=2234$	$(A)=1920$	$(B)=1627$	$2(O)=3692$
$p=0.23919$	$q=0.20775$	$p+2r=1.34531$	$q+2r=1.31387$	$r=0.55306$
$p^2=0.05721$	$q^2=0.04316$	$(p+2r)^2=1.80986$	$(q+2r)^2=1.72625$	$r^2=0.30588$

Substituting these values in (E1) and (E2), we obtain the numerical values of c_p, c_q and the matrix $\{I\}$. Note that some of the terms in (E1) and (E2) are either duplicated or are multiples of each other, so that the arithmetic is not so formidable as it may look. Substituting, we obtain

$$\{I\} = \begin{Bmatrix} 61071.57 & 16076.82 \\ 16076.82 & 69026.91 \end{Bmatrix}, \quad \begin{aligned} c_p &= -14.597, \\ c_q &= -14.965. \end{aligned}$$

Solving the following two sets of equations

$$\left. \begin{aligned} 61071.57x + 16076.82y &= 1 \\ 16076.82x + 69026.91y &= 0 \end{aligned} \right\} \quad \left. \begin{aligned} 0 \\ 1 \end{aligned} \right\},$$

we obtain the variance-covariance matrix

$$\{V\} = \begin{Bmatrix} 17.444 & -4.063 \\ -4.063 & 15.433 \end{Bmatrix} \times 10^{-6}, \quad V(r) = 24.75 \times 10^{-6}.$$

The corrections to be added to p_0 and q_0 are

$$\delta p = (-14.597 \times \quad 17.444 + 14.965 \times \quad 4.063)10^{-6} = -0.00019,$$

$$\delta q = (-14.597 \times - \quad 4.063 - 14.965 \times 15.433)10^{-6} = -0.00017.$$

The final results are as follows:

Trial	Correction	Improved	S.E.
$p=0.23919\ldots\ldots$	-0.00019	0.23900	0.00418
$q=\ \ .20775\ldots\ldots$	$-\ \ .00017$	$.20758$	$.00393$
$r=0.55306\ldots\ldots$	$+0.00036$	0.55342	0.00498
$1.00000\ldots\ldots$	0	1.00000	$\ldots\ldots\ldots$

Note that the maximum likelihood estimates obtained here are the same as those obtained by Bernstein's adjustment shown in the bottom line of Table 19. This is so because Bernstein's adjustment gives the maximum likelihood estimates for a set of p', q', r' which add up not to unity but to $1 - \frac{1}{4}d^2$. Since $d = -0.00162$, if we retain eight decimal places in calculating the bottom line of Table 19, it will be found that $p' + q' + r'$ will add up to $1 - 0.00000065$. Therefore the two sets of answers are the same up to the fifth significant figure.

9. Taylor and Prior (1938) reported the following results in England:

$$(AB): 6 ; \quad (A): 179 ; \quad (B): 35 ; \quad (O): 202 ; \quad \text{Total: } 422 .$$

Find the gene frequencies by the maximum likelihood method and check your results by Bernstein's adjustments to the initial trial values obtained by formula (5).
ANS.: Stevens (1938): $p = 0.2516 \pm 0.0157$, $q = 0.0500 \pm 0.0076$, $r = 0.6984 \pm 0.0167$.

10. Those who dislike the above method will welcome the good news that recent research enables us to distinguish the heterozygous A's and B's from the homozygotes, directly from their blood tests. When we say that the Group O individuals lack any antigen, or that the gene a is unable to produce any antigen, we really mean that we do not have the corresponding anti-O serum to detect its presence. Now that a potent anti-O serum may be obtained, so that the presence of antigen-O may be detected by blood tests, we have the following six blood groups, all distinguishable:

$$AA , \quad AB , \quad AO , \quad BB , \quad BO , \quad OO .$$

Hence, the estimation of gene frequencies reduces to the simple case described in Table 17. For example,

$$p = \frac{2 (AA) + (AB) + (AO)}{2G} , \qquad V (p) = \frac{p (1 - p)}{2G} ,$$

where G is the total number of individuals in the sample.

11. Boorman (1950) reported the following data:

MOTHER	CHILD				TOTAL
	O	A	B	AB	
O..........	622	227	43	....	892
A..........	223	596	28	19	866
B..........	56	29	58	22	165
AB.........	....	34	23	10	67
Total...	901	886	152	51	1990

He estimated the gene frequencies based upon the mothers alone. If we do the estimation based upon the 1990 mother-child pairs, using their combination probabilities of Table 21, the maximum likelihood estimates and their standard errors will be found as follows (the trial values are Boorman's estimates):

Trial Values	Correction	Improved	S.D.
$p = 0.27108\dots$	$+0.00069$	0.27177	0.00657
$q = .06008\dots$	$- .00465$	$.05543$	$.00380$
$r = 0.66884\dots$	$+0.00396$	0.67280	0.00708

Calculate the expected numbers of mother-child combinations, using the improved estimates of gene frequencies. The χ^2 will be found to be 17.25, with 11 degrees of freedom.

12. Wellisch and Thomsen (1930) reported the following results. Estimate the gene frequencies.

	Group						Total
	A_1B	A_2B	A_1	A_2	B	O	
No.	10	5	139	42	32	162	390
Proportion	0.0256	0.0128	0.3564	0.1077	0.0821	0.4154	1.00

ANS.: $p_1 = 0.2146$, $p_2 = 0.0787$, $q = 0.0608$, $r = 0.6445$, sum $= 1.0007$.

CHAPTER 5

Sex-linked Genes

SEX-LINKED genes are those located on sex chromosomes. We shall let the homogametic type XX be females and the heterogametic type XY (or XO) be males, where X denotes the sex chromosome. In the usual notation for gene frequencies it may be easily verified that the population

$$\begin{pmatrix} A & a \\ p & q \end{pmatrix} \male \quad \text{and} \quad \begin{pmatrix} A A & A a & a a \\ p^2 & 2pq & q^2 \end{pmatrix} \female \qquad (1)$$

is in equilibrium under panmixia. Note that for convenience we regard the males and females as two populations, for each of which the proportions of the genotypes add up to unity. Also note that the gene frequencies of males and females are equal in the equilibrium state. The student should write out the six types of matings with their appropriate frequencies and corresponding offspring (male and female offspring separately) in the same manner as in Table 2, because a number of properties regarding sex-linked traits may be derived from such a table.

§ 1. *Establishment of Equilibrium*

Because of the asymmetrical chromosomal complement of males and females, the equilibrium state is not established in one single generation of random mating from an arbitrary initial population but is approached rapidly in an oscillatory manner. Let the initial population be

$$Z' \equiv (p, q) \quad \text{and} \quad (r, 2s, t) \,,$$

where $p + q = r + 2s + t = 1$. In calculating the proportions of the various genotypes of the next generation, we make use of the principle that random mating between individuals is equivalent to random union of gametes (Chap. 1). Now, the females produce two kinds of eggs: $(r + s) A$ and $(s + t) a$. When these eggs unite with the Y-sperms, they form the male offspring and in that proportion. When they unite with the X-sperms $(p \cdot A + q \cdot a)$, they form the female offspring. Hence, the next generation is

$$Z \equiv (r + s, s + t) \quad \text{and} \quad [p(r + s), p(s + t) + q(r + s), q(s + t)] \,.$$

59

The expressions for Z and Z' (the prime indicating the preceding generation) are the fundamental relations between two successive generations. The numerical results of Table 22 may be obtained by repeated applications of that relation.

Several observations may be made, however, regarding the relations between Z and Z'. First, we note that the gene frequencies of the males in one generation are simply those of the females of the preceding generation. Second, since the female offspring are equally determined by sperms and eggs, their gene frequency is the mean of the gene frequencies of their male and female parents

TABLE 22

APPROACH TO EQUILIBRIUM FOR SEX-LINKED GENES

n	MALES		FEMALES			d
	A	a	AA	Aa	aa	
0.....	0.40	0.60	0.50	0.40	0.10	-0.30000
1.....	.70	.30	.28	.54	.18	$+$ .15000
2.....	.55	.45	.385	.480	.135	$-$ .07500
3.....	.625	.375	.34375	.48750	.16875	$+$ .03750
4.....	.5875	.4125	.3672	.4781	.1547	$-$ .01875
5.....	.60625	.39375	.3562	.4814	.1624	$+$ .009375
6.....	.596875	.403125	.3619	.4794	.1587	$-$ .00469
7.....	.60156	.39844	.3591	.4803	.1606	$+$ .00236
8.....	.5992	.4008	.3605	.4798	.1597	$-$ .0012
9.....	.6004	.3996	.3598	.4800	.1602	$+$ .0006
10.....	.5998	.4002	.3601	.4800	.1599	$-$ .0003
11.....	.6001	.3999	.35994	.48002	.16004	$+0.00015$
...	...	...	...	...	...	...
∞.....	0.6000	0.4000	0.3600	0.4800	0.1600	0

TABLE 23

RELATIONS BETWEEN MALE AND FEMALE GENE FREQUENCIES
OF SUCCESSIVE GENERATIONS OF RANDOM MATING
FOR SEX-LINKED LOCI

GENERATION	GENE FREQUENCIES	
	Male	Female
Grandparental, Z''.........	q''_x	q''_{xx}
Parental, Z'..............	q'_x	q'_{xx}
Offspring, Z.............	q_x	q_{xx}

(Ex. 2). These two preliminary observations may be stated as follows (Table 23):

$$q_x = q'_{xx}, \qquad q_{xx} = \tfrac{1}{2}(q'_x + q'_{xx}), \tag{2}$$

where q_x and q_{xx} are gene frequencies of males (haploids) and females (diploids), respectively, and the prime indicates the preceding generation. The reader may find this notation both easy to remember and helpful in understanding the subsequent relations.

Third, if the male and female gene frequencies are not equal, their difference is halved in each generation of random mating:

$$d = q_{xx} - q_x = -\tfrac{1}{2}(q'_{xx} - q'_x) = -\tfrac{1}{2}d'. \tag{3}$$

It also shows that the change in gene frequencies is oscillatory: if female q is greater than male q in one generation, the latter will be greater than the former in the next generation. Fourth, we observe that, although the male and female gene frequencies change from generation to generation when taken separately by sex, their combined gene frequency based on all X-chromosomes (ignoring sex) remains constant in all generations. The mere shuttling of genes from one sex to another does not affect the relative frequencies of A and a among the total number of X-chromosomes. Algebraically, it is seen that

$$\bar{q} = \tfrac{1}{3}(q_x + 2q_{xx}) = \tfrac{1}{3}(q'_x + 2q'_{xx}) = \text{const.} \tag{4}$$

After a number of generations of random mating, the gene frequency of both sexes will approach equality $(d \to 0)$, and $\bar{q}$ is their common equilibrium value. Finally, we may put (4) in the form

$$q_x - \bar{q} = -2(q_{xx} - \bar{q}), \tag{4'}$$

showing that in any generation the deviation from equilibrium of q_x is twice as great as that of q_{xx} but on the other side of the equilibrium value. This, together with (2), gives

$$q_{xx} - \bar{q} = -\tfrac{1}{2}(q'_{xx} - \bar{q}), \qquad q_x - \bar{q} = -\tfrac{1}{2}(q'_x - \bar{q}). \tag{5}$$

The deviation from equilibrium in either sex is halved in each generation of random mating, with sign reversed. All the above properties may be seen from Table 22 and are illustrated in Figure 6.

§ 2. Corollaries and Applications

It follows from the previous analysis that, if $s + t = q$, so that $d = 0$ for the initial females and males, equilibrium will be established after one single generation of random mating. For example:

$$(.70, .30) \times (.50, .40, .10) \to (.70, .30) \quad \text{and} \quad (.49, .42, .09).$$

Comparing this result with the first two generations of Table 22, we see that, if there is overlapping of generations, the rate of approaching equilibrium will be hastened, although its final value of q is not necessarily that given by (4) but depends upon the amount and manner of overlapping (also see Ex. 9).

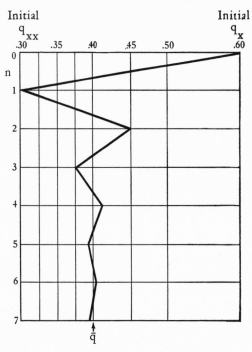

FIG. 6.—Oscillatory approach to equilibrium for sex-linked genes. The plotted values are male q's of Table 22. Female q's may be obtained by replacing n by $n - 1$ in the axis for the number of generations of random mating. Another form for the equilibrium value $\bar{q}$ is given in Exercise 4.

Recessive sex-linked traits.—The proportion of sex-linked recessive traits among males is always greater than among females. It is common experience that red-green color-blindness occurs much more often among men than among women. If the frequency of the recessive color-blind gene is q, which is also the proportion of color-blindness among men, the proportion of color-blindness among women will be only q^2. For example, when $q = \frac{1}{11}$, $q^2 = \frac{1}{121}$. The ratio of these two recessive phenotypes is $1\,\male : q\,\female$.

If q_0 is the estimate of the frequency of the recessive gene based upon a random sample of G_0 females, $V(q_0) = (1 - q_0^2)/4G_0$, according to (4) of Chapter 2. And if q_1 is the estimate of the frequency of the same gene based upon G_1 males, its variance is $V(q_1) = q_1(1 - q_1)/G_1$. These two estimates should be approximately equal for a random-mating population in equilibrium. The variance of the difference between these two estimates, if the two samples are completely independent, is

$$V(q_0 - q_1) = \frac{1 - q_0^2}{4G_0} + \frac{q_1(1 - q_1)}{G_1}.$$

Proportion of recessives in a given type of mating.—Snyder's method of calculating the proportion of recessives from a given type of mating may also be applied to the analysis of sex-linked genes. Some types of matings, however, produce all or no recessive children. In others the proportion varies with q. Furthermore, the proportions among male and female offspring are usually different and should be calculated separately. For instance, among the matings where both parents are dominants, $(AA + Aa) \times A$, all their female offspring will be dominants; but among their male offspring the proportion of recessives will be

$$\frac{1}{2}\left(\frac{2pq}{p^2 + 2pq}\right) = \frac{q}{1+q},$$

which is the same as S_1 for Dom $\times$ Rec matings with autosomal genes (Chap. 2, § 3).

Rare genes.—Since the proportion of male recessives to female recessives is $1:q$, if the recessive gene is rare, the number of male recessives is many times that of female recessives. Indeed, if q were very small, q^2 would be so small that there would be hardly any homozygous recessive females at all. The recessive genes of the females would practically all be hidden in the heterozygous condition. This is perhaps the case with hemophilia, one of the best known human sex-linked recessive traits. Hemophilia in women is extremely rare, if indeed it ever occurs. To account for this, we usually cite not only the low frequency of the recessive gene for hemophilia but also the possibility that the homozygous females are nonviable. This is strongly suggested by the fact that only 11 per cent of hemophilic men live to be twenty-two years old.

The female dominants are always more numerous than male dominants, whatever the gene frequency. The ratio of the former to the latter is $p^2 + 2pq:p$ $= 1 + q : 1$. When the dominant gene is rare ($q \to 1$), this ratio approaches $2:1$; that is to say, female dominants are twice as numerous as male dominants in the general population.

Frequencies of mating.—In the last paragraph of Section 7 of Chapter 1, it was pointed out that the mating $Aa \times Aa$ is twice as frequent as $AA \times aa$ in an equilibrium population. Similarly, for sex-linked genes, it may be shown that $Aa \times A$ is twice as frequent as $AA \times a$ and that $Aa \times a$ is also twice as frequent as $aa \times A$ in *any* equilibrium population, whatever the gene frequencies. In random-mating populations the frequencies of the above four types of matings are $2p^2q$, p^2q and $2pq^2$, pq^2, respectively.

§ 3. *Correlation between Relatives*

For autosomal genes the correlations between parent and offspring and between sibs are the same, all being $\frac{1}{2}$. For sex-linked genes, however, the asymmetrical chromosomal complement of males and females makes it necessary to distinguish the sexes of the relatives. There are four kinds of parent-offspring relationships: father-son, father-daughter, mother-son, and mother-daughter. Likewise, there are three kinds of sib-pairs: two brothers, two sisters, and brother-sister. The seven types of relatives must be considered separately.

The method of constructing their correlation tables is exactly the same as that we used in Chapter 2. As before, the six types of mating with appropriate frequencies are listed. The probabilities of the various combinations between their children are obtained for each type of mating. Then the same combinations are grouped together. Obviously, there is no correlation between father and son for sex-linked genes, since the son receives his father's Y-chromosome. The correlation for mother-daughter is the same as in the case of autosomal genes (Table 6), because the daughter also receives $p \cdot A$ and $q \cdot a$ from her father. The two correlations for father-daughter and mother-son are the same; their combination frequencies, together with those for the three kinds of sib-pairs, are given in Table 24. Their correlations are as follows:

Parent-Offspring		Sib-Pairs	
Father-son.............	$r=0$	Brothers..............	$r=\frac{1}{2}$
Father-daughter........	$r=\sqrt{\frac{1}{2}}$	Sisters................	$r=\frac{3}{4}$
Mother-son............	$r=\sqrt{\frac{1}{2}}$	Brother-sister.........	$r=\frac{1}{2\sqrt{2}}$
Mother-daughter.......	$r=\frac{1}{2}$		

TABLE 24

COMBINATION FREQUENCIES BETWEEN RELATIVES
FOR SEX-LINKED GENES

Father-Daughter or Mother-Son				Sisters		
	2	1	0	2	1	0
2				$\frac{1}{2}p^2(1+p)$	$\frac{1}{2}p^2q$	0
1	p^2	pq	0	$\frac{1}{2}p^2q$	$\frac{3}{4}pq$	$\frac{1}{2}pq^2$
0	0	pq	q^2	0	$\frac{1}{2}pq^2$	$\frac{1}{2}q^2(1+q)$

Brothers			Brother-Sister		
	1	0	2	1	0
1	$\frac{1}{2}p(1+p)$	$\frac{1}{2}pq$	$\frac{1}{2}p^2(1+p)$	$\frac{1}{2}pq(1+2p)$	$\frac{1}{2}pq^2$
0	$\frac{1}{2}pq$	$\frac{1}{2}q(1+q)$	$\frac{1}{2}p^2q$	$\frac{1}{2}pq(1+2q)$	$\frac{1}{2}q^2(1+q)$

The joint distributions and correlations for sex-linked traits between relatives outside the family circle may also be obtained by the *ITO* method, in a manner similar to that described in Chapter 3 for autosomal genes. The results are given by Li and Sacks (1954). Some of the correlation values are given at the end of Chapter 13, wherein the method of path coefficients is employed.

Notes and Exercises

1. Show that the population (1) is in equilibrium by writing out the six types of mating with appropriate frequencies and their corresponding offspring (males and females separately).

2. The gene frequency of the female offspring is the mean of the gene frequencies of their parents. From the expressions for Z and Z' show that

$$\tfrac{1}{2}[p(s + t) + q(r + s)] + q(s + t) = \tfrac{1}{2}(q + s + t) .$$

3. Show that q_{xx} of any generation is the arithmetic mean of those of its two preceding female generations, viz., from (2),

$$q_{xx} = \tfrac{1}{2}(q'_{xx} + q''_{xx}) .$$

Since q_{xx} will be q_x of the following generation, it follows that the q_x series in successive generations has the same property. Thus the successive values of q in either sex forms a "recurrent" series (see "Appendix on Recurrent Series," pp. 66–70). This property enables us to write down the value of q in any generation without ever calculating those of the intermediate generations.

4. Show that $\bar{q} = \tfrac{1}{3}q_x + \tfrac{2}{3}q_{xx} = q_{xx} - \tfrac{1}{3}d = q_x + \tfrac{2}{3}d$, where $d = q_{xx} - q_x$ is the initial difference in gene frequencies between the sexes. Hence, $\bar{q}$ is one-third the distance (d) from q_{xx} and two-thirds the distance from q_x (Fig. 6).

5. Given the initial population (.50, .50) and (.40, .50, .10), calculate the proportions of the various male and female genotypes for the next ten generations, assuming random mating. What are the equilibrium proportions? If the equilibrium state is the same as that shown in Table 22, do you know why?

6. Give the results of the next ten generations of the initial population (0, 1) and (1, 0, 0) and show that its limiting state is ($\tfrac{2}{3}$, $\tfrac{1}{3}$) and ($\tfrac{4}{9}$, $\tfrac{4}{9}$, $\tfrac{1}{9}$). This is the "general case" considered by Jennings (1916).

7. For a certain sex-linked trait the proportion of recessive individuals among females is 19.36 per cent. What percentage of males would you expect to show this trait?
   ANS.: 44 per cent.

8. If the frequency of a dominant sex-linked gene is $p = 0.003$, what will be the proportion of dominants among females? Calculate the ratio of the proportion of female dominants to that of males.

9. If we allow the individuals of the first two generations (Z_0 and Z_1, the first two lines in Table 22) to mate at random, show that their offspring genera-

tion would be the same as Z_3 (not Z_2). This shows that the overlapping of generations will hasten the attainment of equilibrium.

10. Assuming that A is dominant over a, show that the frequencies of the various types of sib-pairs for sex-linked traits are as given in the tabulation below. Verify some of the numerical values in the tabulation (Rife, 1938).

SIBS p	TWO BROTHERS			TWO SISTERS			ONE BROTHER, ONE SISTER		
	S_{11} $\frac{1}{2}p(1+p)$	S_{10} pq	S_{00} $\frac{1}{2}q(1+q)$	S_{11} $\frac{1}{2}p(3-p^2)$	S_{10} pq^2	S_{00} $\frac{1}{2}q^2(1+q)$	S_{11} $\frac{1}{2}p(2-q^2)$	S_{10} $pq(1+q)$	S_{00} $\frac{1}{2}q^2(1+q)$
0.20...	0.120	0.160	0.720	0.296	0.128	0.576	0.136	0.288	0.576
.40...	.280	.240	.480	.568	.144	.288	.328	.384	.288
0.80...	0.720	0.160	0.120	0.944	0.032	0.024	0.784	0.192	0.024

Appendix on Recurrent Series

A discussion of recurrent series is introduced here for two reasons. First, the frequencies of sex-linked genes form a recurrent series in successive generations of random mating. Second, and more important, we shall encounter various other series of a similar nature later in the book when we deal with inbreeding properties. A knowledge of the following section at this stage will greatly facilitate the reading of subsequent chapters. A series

$$u_0, u_1, u_2, u_3, \ldots, u_n, \ldots,$$

is called a *recurrent series* if each term is one and the same linear combination of some of its preceding terms. The simplest example is that

$$u_{n+2} = bu_{n+1} + cu_n,$$

where a term is a linear combination of the preceding two terms. The constants, b and c, are known as the *scales of relation*. For a series of this kind, when its first two terms and the scales of relation are known, all its subsequent terms may be written out. Conversely, if the first few terms are given, the scales may be found by solving the following two equations:

$$u_2 = bu_1 + cu_0 \quad \text{and} \quad u_3 = bu_2 + cu_1.$$

It is desirable to obtain an expression for the general term, u_n, because, in the first place, the value of any term may be obtained without calculating all its preceding terms and, second, the limiting value of u_n as $n \to \infty$ may be found from such a general expression. To obtain an expression for u_n, we need the following three propositions.

PROPOSITION I. The sums of corresponding terms of two recurrent series with the same scales of relation also form a recurrent series with the same scales.

Thus,

$$x_n = bx_{n-1} + cx_{n-2}, \qquad y_n = by_{n-1} + cy_{n-2}.$$

Adding,

$$u_n = x_n + y_n = b(x_{n-1} + y_{n-1}) + c(x_{n-2} + y_{n-2}) = bu_{n-1} + cu_{n-2}.$$

In fact, any linear combination of x_n and y_n will have the same scales.

PROPOSITION II. Any geometric series can be written in the form of a recurrent series with two (or more) scales. For example, the nth term of the geometric series, $x, x\lambda, x\lambda^2, x\lambda^3, \ldots$, where λ is a constant, the "common ratio," may also be written as

$$u_n = \lambda u_{n-1} = \lambda u_{n-1} - u_{n-1} + u_{n-1} = (\lambda - 1)u_{n-1} + \lambda u_{n-2},$$

showing a recurrence relation with scales $b = \lambda - 1$, $c = \lambda$. Alternatively, since $u_n = \lambda u_{n-1} = \lambda^2 u_{n-2}$, it may also be written as

$$u_n = \tfrac{1}{2}\lambda u_{n-1} + \tfrac{1}{2}\lambda^2 u_{n-2},$$

with scales $b = \tfrac{1}{2}\lambda$, $c = \tfrac{1}{2}\lambda^2$.

PROPOSITION III. Corresponding to any recurrent series with two scales, we can find two geometric series with the same scales of relation. Let the recurrence relation of the original series be $u_n = bu_{n-1} + cu_{n-2}$, as before. Now, any geometric series with the same scales b and c must have the recurrence relation

$$x\lambda^n = bx\lambda^{n-1} + cx\lambda^{n-2},$$

which yields the equation

$$\lambda^2 - b\lambda - c = 0.$$

Its two roots are

$$\lambda_1 = \frac{b + \sqrt{(b^2 + 4c)}}{2}, \qquad \lambda_2 = \frac{b - \sqrt{(b^2 + 4c)}}{2}.$$

Hence, the two geometric series with λ_1 and λ_2 as common ratios, when expressed in recurrent form, will have the same scales b and c as the original recurrent u-series, whatever their initial terms may be.

With these three propositions an expression for the general term of a recurrent series may be readily found. Suppose the first few terms of the recurrent series $u_0, u_1, u_2, u_3, \ldots$, are known, and thus the scales b and c are also known. The first step is to find the common ratios of two corresponding geometric series which have the same scales b and c. They are, say,

$$x, x\lambda_1, x\lambda_1^2, \ldots, x\lambda_1^n, \ldots,$$

$$y, y\lambda_2, y\lambda_2^2, \ldots, y\lambda_2^n, \ldots,$$

whatever their initial terms x and y. Adding the corresponding terms of these two series, we obtain another recurrent series, also with the scales b and c (by

Proposition I). Hence, the nth term of our original series may be written as

$$u_n = x\lambda_1^n + y\lambda_2^n .$$

Since the first few terms of u are known, the values of x and y may be found by solving the two equations involving u_0 and u_1 (i.e., putting $n = 0, 1$):

$$u_0 = x + y, \quad u_1 = x\lambda_1 + y\lambda_2 .$$

Now, the expression for u_n is completely determined. We have proved here the well-known theorem that *any recurrent series can be expressed as the sum of some corresponding geometric series*. The above proof can obviously be extended to recurrent series of higher order; for instance, if the recurrence relation is $u_{n+3} = bu_{n+2} + cu_{n+1} + du_n$, the general term may be expressed as the sum of corresponding terms of three geometric series with the same scales:

$$u_n = x\lambda_1^n + y\lambda_2^n + z\lambda_3^n ,$$

where $\lambda_1, \lambda_2, \lambda_3$ are the common ratios of the three geometric series. They are the roots of the equation:

$$\lambda^3 - b\lambda^2 - c\lambda - d = 0 .$$

The numerical values of x, y, z may be determined by the first few terms of u which are known.

EXAMPLE 1. Consider the male q series in Table 22. Its first few terms are known, and we have seen (Ex. 3) that its recurrence relation is $u_n = \frac{1}{2}u_{n-1} + \frac{1}{2}u_{n-2}$ with scales $b = \frac{1}{2}$ and $c = \frac{1}{2}$. The common ratios of the two corresponding geometric series with the same scales are then

$$\lambda_1 = \frac{\frac{1}{2} + \sqrt{(\frac{1}{4} + 2)}}{2} = 1 , \qquad \lambda_2 = \frac{\frac{1}{2} - \sqrt{(\frac{1}{4} + 2)}}{2} = -\frac{1}{2} .$$

Hence, the general expression for the male gene frequency is

$$u_n = x(1)^n + y(-\tfrac{1}{2})^n .$$

To determine the numerical values of x and y, we use the values of the first two generations (corresponding to $n = 0, 1$); thus

$$u_0 = 0.60 = x + y, \quad u_1 = 0.30 = x + y(-\tfrac{1}{2}) .$$

Solving, we obtain $x = 0.40$ and $y = 0.20$. The final explicit expression for u_n in this particular series is

$$u_n = 0.40 + 0.20(-\tfrac{1}{2})^n .$$

Thus, $u_8 = 0.4008$, $u_9 = 0.3996$, etc. Its limiting value is clearly 0.40. If it is greater than 0.40 in one generation, it will be less than 0.40 in the next generation (by half as much).

EXAMPLE 2. One of the frequently encountered series in genetics is the *Fibonacci series:*

$$1, \tfrac{1}{2}, \tfrac{2}{4}, \tfrac{3}{8}, \tfrac{5}{16}, \tfrac{8}{32}, \tfrac{13}{64}, \ldots .$$

The denominator doubles every term, while the numerator is the sum of its two preceding numerators. In other words, the recurrence relation is

$$u_{n+2} = \tfrac{1}{2}u_{n+1} + \tfrac{1}{4}u_n \quad (b = \tfrac{1}{2}, c = \tfrac{1}{4}).$$

The common ratios of its two corresponding geometric series may be found from the equation $\lambda^2 - \tfrac{1}{2}\lambda - \tfrac{1}{4} = 0$. Thus,

$$\lambda_1 = \frac{\tfrac{1}{2} + \sqrt{(\tfrac{1}{4}+1)}}{2} = \frac{1+\sqrt{5}}{4}, \qquad \lambda_2 = \frac{\tfrac{1}{2} - \sqrt{(\tfrac{1}{4}+1)}}{2} = \frac{1-\sqrt{5}}{4}.$$

Therefore, the nth term of the Fibonacci series is of the form

$$u_n = x\left(\frac{1+\sqrt{5}}{4}\right)^n + y\left(\frac{1-\sqrt{5}}{4}\right)^n.$$

Making use of the known first two terms of the Fibonacci series to determine the numerical values of x and y, we have

$$u_0 = 1 = x + y, \quad u_1 = \tfrac{1}{2} = \tfrac{1}{4}x(1 + \sqrt{5}) + \tfrac{1}{4}y(1 - \sqrt{5}).$$

Solving, we obtain

$$x = \frac{1+\sqrt{5}}{2\sqrt{5}} = \frac{2}{\sqrt{5}}\left(\frac{1+\sqrt{5}}{4}\right), \qquad y = \frac{-2}{\sqrt{5}}\left(\frac{1-\sqrt{5}}{4}\right).$$

The final explicit expression of the general term is

$$u_n = \frac{2}{\sqrt{5}}\left\{\left(\frac{1+\sqrt{5}}{4}\right)^{n+1} - \left(\frac{1-\sqrt{5}}{4}\right)^{n+1}\right\}.$$

Since $\lambda_1 = \tfrac{1}{4}(1 + \sqrt{5}) = 0.809$ and $\lambda_2 = \tfrac{1}{4}(1 - \sqrt{5}) = -0.309$, when n is sufficiently large, the quantity λ_2^n would be exceedingly small in comparison with λ_1^n. So after a sufficiently large number of terms, $u_{n+1} = 0.809u_n$, approximately; that is, each term of the Fibonacci series will be decreased by about 19.1 per cent. The limiting value of u_n is clearly zero.

EXAMPLE 3. Consider the series

$$1, \tfrac{17}{18}, \tfrac{29}{36}, \tfrac{437}{648}, \ldots .$$

The recurrence relation between its terms is not so obvious as those in the previous examples. However, it may be readily found by solving the equations $u_2 = bu_1 + cu_0$, etc., as we have pointed out before. Thus,

$$\left.\begin{aligned} \tfrac{29}{36} &= \tfrac{17}{18}b + c \\ \tfrac{437}{648} &= \tfrac{29}{36}b + \tfrac{17}{18}c \end{aligned}\right\} \begin{aligned} &\text{yielding } b = 1, \quad c = \tfrac{-5}{36}; \\ &\therefore\ u_{n+2} = u_{n+1} - \tfrac{5}{36}u_n. \end{aligned}$$

Having found the scales b and c, the common ratios of the two corresponding geometric series may be obtained as usual:

$$\lambda_1 = \frac{1 + \sqrt{(1 - \frac{20}{36})}}{2} = \frac{5}{6}, \quad \lambda_2 = \frac{1 - \sqrt{(1 - \frac{20}{36})}}{2} = \frac{1}{6}.$$

The numerical values of x and y in the general expression of u_n are found in the usual manner:

$$\left.\begin{array}{l} u_0 = \quad x + \quad y = 1 \\ u_1 = \frac{5}{6}x + \frac{1}{6}y = \frac{17}{18} \end{array}\right\} \text{ yielding } x = \frac{7}{6}, \quad y = \frac{-1}{6}.$$

Hence, the general expression of the nth term of the series is

$$u_n = \frac{7}{6}\left(\frac{5}{6}\right)^n - \frac{1}{6}\left(\frac{1}{6}\right)^n = \frac{7}{5}\left(\frac{5}{6}\right)^{n+1} - \left(\frac{1}{6}\right)^{n+1}$$

The limiting value of u_n as $n \to \infty$ is zero.

EXAMPLE 4. It should be clear that the scales merely specify the relations between successive terms of a recurrent series, while the general expression of the nth term depends upon both the scales of relation and the initial terms of the series. Two recurrent series with the same scales of relation may have different expressions for their general terms:

$$u_n = x_1 \lambda_1^n + y_1 \lambda_2^n, \quad v_n = x_2 \lambda_1^n + y_2 \lambda_2^n,$$

where u_n and v_n are the general expressions of two recurrent series with the same scales b and c. Note that values of λ_1 and λ_2 are the same in both cases but that x_1, y_1 are different from x_2, y_2, because they are determined by the values of the initial terms of the u and v series, respectively. To illustrate this point, let us consider the following series whose recurrence relation is the same as that of the Fibonacci series, viz., $u_{n+2} = \frac{1}{2}u_{n+1} + \frac{1}{4}u_n$:

$$1, \frac{2}{2}, \frac{3}{4}, \frac{5}{8}, \frac{8}{16}, \frac{13}{32}, \cdots .$$

The values of λ_1 and λ_2 will remain the same as before, because they are determined by values of b and c alone. Solving for x and y based on the first two terms of the present series, we have

$$1 = x + y, \quad 1 = \frac{1}{4}x(1 + \sqrt{5}) + \frac{1}{4}y(1 - \sqrt{5}) ;$$

$$\therefore x = \frac{5 + 3\sqrt{5}}{10}, \quad y = \frac{5 - 3\sqrt{5}}{10},$$

$$u_n = \frac{5 + 3\sqrt{5}}{10}\left(\frac{1 + \sqrt{5}}{4}\right)^n + \frac{5 - 3\sqrt{5}}{10}\left(\frac{1 - \sqrt{5}}{4}\right)^n.$$

EXAMPLE 5. The following two series have the same recurrence relation as that in Example 3, viz., $b = 1, c = \frac{-5}{36}$.

$$u: 0, \frac{8}{36}, \frac{16}{72}, \frac{248}{1296}, \frac{416}{2592}, \cdots ; \quad v: 1, \frac{18}{36}, \frac{26}{72}, \frac{378}{1296}, \frac{626}{2592}, \cdots .$$

Show that their general terms are, respectively,

$$u_n = \frac{1}{3}\left(\frac{5}{6}\right)^n - \frac{1}{3}\left(\frac{1}{6}\right)^n, \quad v_n = \cdot\frac{1}{2}\left(\frac{5}{6}\right)^n + \frac{1}{2}\left(\frac{1}{6}\right)^n.$$

CHAPTER 6

Autopolyploids

POLYPLOIDS are very common in plants, especially angiosperms. Many new species (and even new genera) have been produced in connection with tetraploids, amphidiploids, and higher polyploids. The polyploid forms are usually adapted to more extreme conditions than their diploid relatives and are thus of great practical value.

Polyploids may be roughly divided into two different kinds as to their origin. When two different varieties or species with n_1 and n_2 pairs of chromosomes are crossed, the hybrid usually contains $n_1 + n_2$ chromosomes. If these two sets of chromosomes are doubled so that the hybrid has $2(n_1 + n_2)$ chromosomes, forming $n_1 + n_2$ homologous pairs, the hybrid is an *amphidiploid;* it is fundamentally still of a diploid nature. More generally, the doubling of chromosomes of *different* sets is said to result in *allopolyploids.*

On the other hand, if the chromosomes of the *same set* are doubled so that an individual contains $4n$ chromosomes, forming n homologous quartets, it is said to be an *autotetraploid,* belonging to the more general category of *autopolyploids.* Polyploid forms may arise spontaneously in nature or may be artificially induced by high temperature, irradiation, and certain chemicals such as colchicine. The artificial doubling of chromosomes makes possible many new crosses involving species with different numbers of chromosomes.

Some organisms appear to be polyploids of a mixed kind; some of their chromosomes behave like diploids, others as tetraploids, etc. In this chapter we shall consider only autopolyploids with an even number of chromosome sets (Haldane, 1930).

§ 1. *Gametic Output of a Zygote*

Based upon Random Chromosomal Segregation

Consider first the simplest case: an autotetraploid. For brevity we write A^4 to denote the genotype $AAAA;$ A^3a for $AAAa$, etc. Since the four members (say, 1, 2, 3, 4) of the quartet are homologous to one another, the three segregation patterns, 1, 2 versus 3, 4; 1, 3 versus 2, 4; 1, 4 versus 2, 3, are equally likely. Hence, the gametic outputs of autotetraploids are as follows, assuming complete random chromosomal segregation:

$$
\begin{aligned}
&A^4 \rightarrow \text{all } (AA), \qquad A^3a \rightarrow \tfrac{1}{2}(AA) + \tfrac{1}{2}(Aa), \\
&a^4 \rightarrow \text{all } (aa), \qquad Aa^3 \rightarrow \tfrac{1}{2}(aa) + \tfrac{1}{2}(Aa), \\
&A^2a^2 \rightarrow \tfrac{1}{6}(AA) + \tfrac{4}{6}(Aa) + \tfrac{1}{6}(aa).
\end{aligned}
\tag{1}
$$

These gametic ratios are very nearly true for genes close to the centromere.

The enumeration method given above becomes cumbersome when dealing with higher polyploids. The following is a general method of deriving the gametic ratios, assuming that segregation is entirely at random. Consider a $2m$-ploid zygote of the constitution $A^T a^{2m-T}$. Its gametes will have m factors each. The total number of ways of forming gametes is the number of ways of taking m things at a time out of $2m$ things, viz., $\binom{2m}{m} = (2m)!/m!\,m!$. Now, the number of ways of choosing t things out of T is $\binom{T}{t}$, and that of choosing $m - t$ things out of $2m - T$ is $\binom{2m-T}{m-t}$. Therefore, the number of ways of forming an $(A^t a^{m-t})$ gamete from an $A^T a^{2m-T}$ zygote is $\binom{T}{t}\binom{2m-T}{m-t}$; and hence the probability is

$$
P(T, t) = \frac{\binom{T}{t}\binom{2m-T}{m-t}}{\binom{2m}{m}}.
\tag{2}
$$

If we let t take all possible values in the above expression, we obtain the proportions of the various kinds of gametes produced by a given type of zygote. For example, the octoploid zygote A^5a^3 (for which $2m = 8$, $T = 5$) will produce gametes in the proportions shown in Table 25. The sum of $P(T, t)$ for all possible

TABLE 25

GAMETIC OUTPUT OF A^5a^3, ASSUMING RANDOM
CHROMOSOMAL SEGREGATION

t	Gametes	Number of Ways	Total
4.......	A^4	$\binom{5}{4}\binom{3}{0} = 5$	
3.......	A^3a	$\binom{5}{3}\binom{3}{1} = 30$	$\binom{8}{4} = 70$
2.......	A^2a^2	$\binom{5}{2}\binom{3}{2} = 30$	
1.......	Aa^3	$\binom{5}{1}\binom{3}{3} = 5$	
0.......	a^4	None (impossible)*	

* Possible under random chromatid segregation (see Table 27).

values of t is unity; that is,

$$\sum_t \binom{T}{t}\binom{2m-T}{m-t} = \binom{2m}{m}.$$

Note that the gametic ratios are always symmetrical owing to the fact that $\binom{T}{t} = \binom{T}{T-t}$. Thus, in Table 25, they are 1:6:6:1. When the gametic output is known, the result of crossing between any two given zygotes may be obtained immediately by uniting their gametes at random.

§ 2. *Equilibrium Condition*

The equilibrium proportions of the five genotypes of an autotetraploid random-mating population are given by the terms of $(p+q)^4$. The population may thus be denoted by

$$Z \equiv \begin{pmatrix} A^4 & A^3a & A^2a^2 & Aa^3 & a^4 \\ p^4 + 4p^3q + 6p^2q^2 + 4pq^3 + q^4 \end{pmatrix}.$$

To see that Z is actually in equilibrium status, we note that its total gametic output is, with the aid of (1),

$$p^2(AA) + 2pq(Aa) + q^2(aa).$$

The random union of these gametes will give rise to Z again; thus, it is in equilibrium.

Now, let us prove the general theorem that the equilibrium zygotic proportions of an auto-$2m$-ploid random-mating population are given by the terms of $(p+q)^{2m}$, that is, the proportion of A^Ta^{2m-T} zygotes in the population is $\binom{2m}{T}p^Tq^{2m-T}$. As indicated in the simple example above, the proof is merely to show that the gametic output of such a population is given by the terms of $(p+q)^m$, because the random union of these gametes will give rise to the parental population again. Therefore, all we need to show is that the proportion of the (A^ta^{m-t}) gametes produced by the population is $\binom{m}{t}p^tq^{m-t}$.

The *total* proportion of (A^ta^{m-t}) gametes (i.e., t fixed) produced by the whole population (from various genotypes, i.e., T varies) is the following sum over all eligible values of T:

$$\sum_{T=t}^{m+t} \left\{ \binom{2m}{T} p^Tq^{2m-T} \times P(T,t) \right\}.$$

If we write out the full expression for $P(T,t)$ in terms of factorials, after some obvious canceling and simplification, it reduces to

$$\frac{m!}{t!\,(m-t)!} \sum_T \frac{m!}{(T-t)!\,(m-T+t)!}\, p^Tq^{2m-T}$$

$$= \frac{m!}{t!\,(m-t)!}\, p^tq^{m-t} \sum_T \binom{m}{T-t} p^{T-t}q^{m-T+t}$$

$$= \binom{m}{t}\, p^tq^{m-t}.$$

The sum in the expression at the right over all eligible values of T (which varies from t to $m + t$, or, in other words, $T - t$ varies from 0 to m) is simply $(q + p)^m = 1$. The theorem is proved.

§ 3. *Approach to Equilibrium*

If an initial population is not in equilibrium, such a state cannot be established in one single generation of random mating. The rate of approach to equilibrium differs with different degrees of polyploidy. The higher the degree of polyploidy, the slower the rate. In the following we shall consider the case of autotetraploids. Suppose that an arbitrary population produced the following gametes:

$$x(AA) + 2y(Aa) + z(aa) ,$$

where $x + 2y + z = 1$. The frequency of A is $p = x + y$ and that of a is $q = y + z$. On random mating the next generation will be

$$\begin{pmatrix} A^4 & A^3a & A^2a^2 & Aa^3 & a^4 \\ x^2, & 4xy, & 4y^2 + 2xz, & 4yz, & z^2 \end{pmatrix}. \tag{3}$$

From (1), the (AA) gametes produced by this population will be $x^2 + \frac{1}{2}(4xy) + \frac{1}{6}(4y^2 + 2xz)$. The proportions of (Aa) and (aa) gametes could be obtained in a similar way. On simplification, the gametic output of the above population will be

$$\begin{array}{ccc} (AA) & (Aa) & (aa) \\ x_1 = x + \frac{2}{3}(y^2 - xz), & 2y_1 = 2y - \frac{4}{3}(y^2 - xz), & z_1 = z + \frac{2}{3}(y^2 - xz). \end{array} \tag{4}$$

These are the recurrence relations between the gametic proportions of one generation and the next. Let the quantity $y^2 - xz = d$. Then the corresponding quantity in the next generation is, with the aid of (4),

$$d_1 = y_1^2 - x_1z_1 = (y - \tfrac{2}{3}d)^2 - (x + \tfrac{2}{3}d)(z + \tfrac{2}{3}d) = \tfrac{1}{3}d .$$

Hence, after n generations of random mating,

$$d_n = \tfrac{1}{3}d_{n-1} = (\tfrac{1}{3})^n d \to 0 \text{ as } n \to \infty ,$$

as equilibrium is reached. Note that, although gametic proportions change from generation to generation, the gene frequencies remain constant throughout; thus $x_1 + y_1 = x + y = p$, etc. This fact enables us to express the gametic proportions in terms of gene frequencies and the quantity d:

$$d = y^2 - xz = y^2 - (p - y)(q - y) = y - pq ;$$

$$\begin{aligned} \therefore \quad y_n &= pq + d_n = pq + (\tfrac{1}{3})^n d \to pq , \\ x_n &= p - y_n = p^2 - (\tfrac{1}{3})^n d \to p^2 , \\ z_n &= q - y_n = q^2 - (\tfrac{1}{3})^n d \to q^2 . \end{aligned} \right\} \tag{5}$$

The limiting values indicated above are the proportions of gametes in the equilibrium state. The quantity $d = y^2 - xz$ may be regarded as an index of divergence from the equilibrium condition. It diminishes by two-thirds in each generation of random mating, so that the population approaches equilibrium very rapidly. The final proportions of both zygotes and gametes of an equilibrium population are entirely determined by its original gene frequencies. Table 26 is a numerical representation of the process of establishing equi-

TABLE 26

APPROACH TO EQUILIBRIUM FOR AN AUTOTETRAPLOID
POPULATION IN WHICH $p = 0.30$, $q = 0.70$

n	ZYGOTES					GAMETES			d
	A^4	A^3a	A^2a^2	Aa^3	a^4	(AA)	(Aa)	(aa)	
0....	0.1300	0.1600	0.0600	0.0800	0.5700	0.2200	0.1600	0.6200	-0.1300
1....	.0484	.0704	.2984	.1984	.3844	.1333	.3333	.5333	$-$ .0433
2....	.0177	.0888	.2533	.3555	.2844	.1044	.3911	.5044	$-$ .0144
3....	.0109	.0817	.2583	.3946	.2545	.0948	.4104	.4948	$-$ .0048
4....	.0090	.0778	.2622	.4061	.2448	.0916	.4168	.4916	$-$ .0016
5....	.0084	.0764	.2638	.4098	.2417	.0905	.4190	.4905	$-$ .0005
6....	.0082	.0758	.2644	.4110	.2406	.0902	.4196	.4902	-0.0002
∞...	0.0081	0.0756	0.2646	0.4116	0.2401	0.0900	0.4200	0.4900	0

	Random Chromatid Segregation								
0....	0.130000	0.160000	0.060000	0.080000	0.570000	0.231428	0.137144	0.631428	....
1....	.053559	.063478	.311069	.173193	.398701	.160408	.279184	.560408	....
2....	.025731	.089567	.257731	.312914	.314057	.140116	.319768	.540116	....
3....	.019632	.089609	.253610	.345424	.291725	.134319	.331362	.534319	....
4....	.018042	.089016	.253339	.354106	.285497	.132662	.334676	.532662	....
5....	.017599	.088798	.253336	.356538	.283729	.132189	.335622	.532189	....
6....	.017474	.088731	.253341	.357229	.283225	.132054	.335892	.532054	....
∞...	0.017424	0.088704	0.253344	0.357504	0.283024	0.1320	0.3360	0.5320	....

librium. The gametic proportions of successive generations may be obtained by repeated application of (4) or more simply by (5) without calculating the proportions of previous generations.

COROLLARY: It follows from the above analysis that in any arbitrary auto-tetraploid population whose gametic output is such that $d = y^2 - xz = 0$, equilibrium will be reached immediately in the next generation on random mating. As an example, the population consisting of 50 per cent A^3a and 50 per cent Aa^3 (not in equilibrium) produces $\frac{1}{4}(AA) + \frac{1}{2}(Aa) + \frac{1}{4}(aa)$ gametes. The zygotic proportions in the next generation will be in the equilibrium state: $(1, 4, 6, 4, 1)/16$.

§ 4. *Random Chromatid Segregation*

For diploids, chromatid segregation, whether entirely at random or "equational," gives the same results as chromosome segregation for any number of loci. Each gamete formed after meiosis receives one of the four chromatids. But in autopolyploids the situation is different. In this section we shall investigate the case of random chromatid segregation for autotetraploids as an example of an essentially new type of equilibrium. Under this mechanism of segregation a gamete may receive two sister-chromatids of the eight present.

Adopting the general procedure used before, we shall first find the gametic output of each genotype. Now, the number of ways of choosing two out of eight chromatids is $\binom{8}{2} = 28$. Let us write the autotetraploid genotype $AAaa$ as

$$\begin{pmatrix} AA & aa \\ AA & aa \end{pmatrix} \quad \text{or} \quad \begin{pmatrix} AA & AA \\ aa & aa \end{pmatrix},$$

not only showing the eight chromatids but also indicating how this zygote was formed: the two chromosomes on the left represent maternal heritage, the two on the right paternal heritage. The origin and ratios of gametes produced by an individual are given in Table 27. It is not necessary for us to make the distinction in gametic origin to derive the subsequent formulas, but it helps to clarify the difference between chromosome and chromatid segregation mechanisms. Note that, of the twenty-eight possible gametes, four receive sister-chromatids, and the remaining twenty-four consist of nonsister-chromatids. If we ignore the four sister-chromatid-gametes, the segregation ratio becomes the same as that for chromosome segregation (1). The total (last column of Table 27) gametic

TABLE 27

GAMETIC OUTPUT OF AUTOTETRAPLOIDS BASED ON
RANDOM CHROMATID SEGREGATION

ZYGOTE→GAMETES	NONSISTER-CHROMATIDS			SUB-TOTAL	SISTER-CHROMATIDS		TOTAL
	Maternal Origin	Half-Half	Paternal Origin		Maternal Origin	Paternal Origin	
$\begin{pmatrix} AA & AA \\ AA & aa \end{pmatrix} \begin{matrix} \nearrow AA\ldots\ldots \\ \rightarrow Aa\ldots\ldots \\ \searrow aa\ldots\ldots \end{matrix}$	4 0 0	8 8 0	0 4 0	12 12 0	2 0 0	1 0 1	15 12 1
$\begin{pmatrix} AA & aa \\ AA & aa \end{pmatrix} \begin{matrix} \nearrow AA\ldots\ldots \\ \rightarrow Aa\ldots\ldots \\ \searrow aa\ldots\ldots \end{matrix}$	4 0 0	0 16 0	0 0 4	4 16 4	2 0 0	0 0 2	6 16 6
$\begin{pmatrix} AA & AA \\ aa & aa \end{pmatrix} \begin{matrix} \nearrow AA\ldots\ldots \\ \rightarrow Aa\ldots\ldots \\ \searrow aa\ldots\ldots \end{matrix}$	0 4 0	4 8 4	0 4 0	4 16 4	1 0 1	1 0 1	6 16 6
Each genotype.......	4	16	4	24	2	2	28

outputs of AA/aa and Aa/Aa are the same. Those of $Aaaa$ may be obtained from $AAAa$ by interchanging the letters A and a.

Let the initial gametic proportions be $x(AA) + 2y(Aa) + z(aa)$, as before. Then in the next generation the zygotic proportions will be those given by (3). Using the segregation ratios shown in the "Total" column of Table 27, we find that the gametic proportions produced by population (3) are

$$
\begin{aligned}
x_1 &= x^2 + \tfrac{15}{28}(4xy) + \tfrac{6}{28}(4y^2 + 2xz) + \tfrac{1}{28}(4yz), \\
2y_1 &= \tfrac{12}{28}(4xy) + \tfrac{16}{28}(4y^2 + 2xz) + \tfrac{12}{28}(4yz), \\
z_1 &= \tfrac{1}{28}(4xy) + \tfrac{6}{28}(4y^2 + 2xz) + \tfrac{15}{28}(4yz) + z^2.
\end{aligned}
\tag{6}
$$

Remembering that $x + 2y + z = 1$ and $x + y = p$, $y + z = q$, and that the gene frequencies of alleles A and a remain constant from generation to generation, we obtain, from (6), the following recurrence relations between the gametic proportions of two consecutive generations (see Exs. 5–7). For the sake of comparison, those for chromosome segregation (4) are also given below in the new form (Geiringer, 1949c).

	Chromosome Segregation, (4)	Chromatid Segregation, (6)
x_{n+1}	$= \tfrac{1}{3}x_n + \tfrac{2}{3}p^2$	$= \tfrac{2}{7}x_n + \tfrac{4}{7}p^2 + \tfrac{1}{7}p$
$2y_{n+1}$	$= \tfrac{1}{3}(2y_n) + \tfrac{2}{3}(2pq)$	$= \tfrac{2}{7}(2y_n) + \tfrac{4}{7}(2pq)$
z_{n+1}	$= \tfrac{1}{3}z_n + \tfrac{2}{3}q^2$	$= \tfrac{2}{7}z_n + \tfrac{4}{7}q^2 + \tfrac{1}{7}q$

Thus, the rate of approach to equilibrium is two-sevenths per generation for random chromatid segregation in contrast to one-third for random chromosome segregation. As $n \to \infty$, the x_n, $2y_n$, z_n components vanish, so that the limiting (equilibrium) gametic proportions will be:

$$
\hat{x} = \tfrac{4}{5}p^2 + \tfrac{1}{5}p, \qquad 2\hat{y} = \tfrac{4}{5}(2pq), \qquad \hat{z} = \tfrac{4}{5}q^2 + \tfrac{1}{5}q,
\tag{7}
$$

and the equilibrium proportions of zygotes are given by the terms of $(\hat{x} + 2\hat{y} + \hat{z})^2$. This is an entirely new type of equilibrium in contrast to the old $(p + q)^4$. The lower half of Table 26 is a numerical example based on the same initial population as in the upper half.

A similar analysis, based on the assumption that chromatid segregation is always equational (Fisher and Mather, 1943), has also been given by Geiringer (1949c). For hexaploids the equilibrium gametic proportions are cubic polynomials of gene frequencies. In actual cases, however, genes near the spindle-attachment regions usually segregate on a chromosomal basis, while those near the ends usually segregate on a chromatid basis; thus, most segregations are somewhere in between.

Notes and Exercises

1. Winge (1929; cf. Haldane, 1930) reported that in the Japanese hop, *Humulus japonicus*, the female plant is of the type XX, while the male plant is XXX, where X denotes the sex-chromosome. As far as sex-linked genes are concerned, the female is an ordinary diploid, but the male is an autotriploid, producing two kinds of pollen, XX and X. When an ovule is fertilized by an X pollen, it develops into a female plant; if fertilized by XX, a male.

   The heterozygous male plants AAa and Aaa have the following gametic output, assuming chromosome segregation:

$$\boxed{AAa}\nearrow \tfrac{1}{6}(AA) + \tfrac{2}{6}(Aa) = \tfrac{1}{2}(XX)\,, \text{ male-producing gametes}\,,$$
$$\searrow \tfrac{2}{6}(A)\ \ + \tfrac{1}{6}(a)\ \ = \tfrac{1}{2}(X)\,,\ \ \text{ female-producing gametes}\,.$$

$$\boxed{Aaa}\nearrow \tfrac{2}{6}(Aa) + \tfrac{1}{6}(aa) = \tfrac{1}{2}(XX)\,, \text{ male-producing gametes}\,,$$
$$\searrow \tfrac{1}{6}(A)\ \ + \tfrac{2}{6}(a)\ \ = \tfrac{1}{2}(X)\,,\ \ \text{ female-producing gametes}\,.$$

Among the offspring of any mating, the numbers of males and females are equal because the numbers of (X) and (XX) pollen grains are equal. The segregation properties of the twelve types of mating are given in Table 28,

TABLE 28

SEGREGATION RATIOS OF HUMULUS JAPONICUS
(Based on Chromosome Segregation)

Mating $♀ \times ♂$	♀ Offspring					♂ Offspring						
	AA	:	Aa	:	aa	AAA	:	AAa	:	Aaa	:	aaa
$AA \times AAA$	1					1						
$AA \times AAa$	2	:	1			1	:	2				
$AA \times Aaa$	1	:	2					2	:	1		
$AA \times aaa$			1							1		
$Aa \times AAA$	1	:	1			1	:	1				
$Aa \times AAa$	2	:	3	:	1	1	:	3	:	2		
$Aa \times Aaa$	1	:	3	:	2			2	:	3	:	1
$Aa \times aaa$			1	:	1					1	:	1
$aa \times AAA$			1					1				
$aa \times AAa$			2	:	1			1	:	2		
$aa \times Aaa$			1	:	2					2	:	1
$aa \times aaa$					1							1

with the aid of which it may be readily shown that the population

$$(p^2,\ 2pq,\ q^2)XX \quad \text{and} \quad (p^3,\ 3p^2q,\ 3pq^2,\ q^3)XXX$$

is in equilibrium with random mating. The ratio of the recessive proportions in the two sexes is $q^2:q^3 = 1:q$. Starting with an arbitrary population, equilibrium is not reached by one generation of random mating; but the rate of approach is very rapid.

2. If there are 36 per cent dominants for a certain sex-linked trait among the females in *Humulus japonicus*, what proportion of dominants among the males do you expect?

   ANS.: 48.8 per cent.

3. Given an initial population consisting of all A^2a^2 individuals, calculate the gametic and zygotic proportions of the next few generations, assuming random mating. Tabulate your results separately for chromosome and chromatid segregations. What are the equilibrium proportions?

n	A^4	A^3a	A^2a^2	Aa^3	a^4	(AA)	(Aa)	(aa)
0	0	0	1	0	0	$\frac{1}{6}$	$\frac{4}{6}$	$\frac{1}{6}$
1	$\frac{1}{36}$	$\frac{8}{36}$	$\frac{18}{36}$	$\frac{8}{36}$	$\frac{1}{36}$	$\frac{2}{9}$	$\frac{5}{9}$	$\frac{2}{9}$
2	$\frac{4}{81}$	$\frac{20}{81}$	$\frac{33}{81}$	$\frac{20}{81}$	$\frac{4}{81}$	$\frac{6.5}{27}$	$\frac{14}{27}$	$\frac{6.5}{27}$
...	...	...	...	...	...			
∞	$\frac{1}{16}$	$\frac{4}{16}$	$\frac{6}{16}$	$\frac{4}{16}$	$\frac{1}{16}$	$\frac{1}{4}$	$\frac{2}{4}$	$\frac{1}{4}$

			Random Chromatid Segregation					
0	0	0	1	0	0	$\frac{3}{14}$	$\frac{8}{14}$	$\frac{3}{14}$
1	$\frac{9}{196}$	$\frac{48}{196}$	$\frac{82}{196}$	$\frac{48}{196}$	$\frac{9}{196}$	$\frac{27}{98}$	$\frac{44}{98}$	$\frac{27}{98}$
2	...	...	...	...	...	...	...	...
∞	$\frac{9}{100}$	$\frac{24}{100}$	$\frac{34}{100}$	$\frac{24}{100}$	$\frac{9}{100}$	$\frac{3}{10}$	$\frac{4}{10}$	$\frac{3}{10}$

4. The yellow ground color of the flower of *Dahlia variabilis* is inherited as a tetrasomic trait (Lawrence, 1931). Being self-incompatible, *D. variabilis* probably mates at random in nature. One dominant gene is sufficient to produce flavone, the yellow pigment, so that only a^4 genotypes are white. If there are 25 per cent white-flowered plants in a natural population, what is the frequency of the recessive gene and what are the proportions of the yellow genotypes? Give answers for both chromosome (I) and chromatid (II) segregations.

	A^4	A^3a	A^2a^2	Aa^3	a^4	(AA)	(Aa)	(aa)	q
I	0.00736	0.07107	0.25736	0.41421	0.25000	0.0858	0.4142	0.5000	0.7071
II	0.02226	0.10468	0.27226	0.35080	0.25000	0.1492	0.3508	0.5000	0.6754

5. If $x + 2y + z = 1$, and $x + y = p, y + z = q$, then

$$p^2 = x^2 + 2xy + y^2 = x(x + 2y + z) - xz + y^2 = x - xz + y^2 \,.$$

Find the corresponding expressions for q^2 and for pq.

6. The gametic recurrence relation based on chromosome segregation, as given

by (4), may be written as

$$x_1 = x + \tfrac{2}{3}(y^2 - xz) = \tfrac{1}{3}x + \tfrac{2}{3}(x + y^2 - xz) = \tfrac{1}{3}x + \tfrac{2}{3}p^2 \,.$$

Find the corresponding recurrence relations for y_1 and z_1.

7. The gametic recurrence relation based on chromatid segregation, as given by (6), may be rewritten as

$$x_1 = \tfrac{1}{7}\{7x^2 + 15xy + 6y^2 + 3xz + yz\}$$

$$= \tfrac{1}{7}\left\{ \begin{array}{lll} 2x^2 + 4xy & + 2xz & \\ + 4x^2 + 8xy + 4y^2 & & \\ + \ x^2 + 2xy & + \ xz & \\ + \ xy + 2y^2 & + yz & \end{array} \right\}$$

$$= \tfrac{1}{7}\{2x + 4p^2 + p\} \,.$$

Find the corresponding expressions for $2y_1$ and z_1 .

8. Further references on the subject of separation of chromosomes in auto-polyploids may be found in Mather (1935, 1936).

CHAPTER 7

Self-sterility Alleles

SELF-STERILITY is a very common phenomenon among higher plants. In most cases it is due to a series of multiple alleles, $S_1, S_2, S_3, \ldots$, such that the pollen containing the gene S_1 will not function in a style which contains the same gene. Thus S_1S_2 plants cannot be fertilized by S_1 or S_2 pollen but can be fertilized by $S_3, S_4, \ldots$, pollen. This mechanism was first discovered by East and Mangelsdorf (1925) in *Nicotiana*. Selfing or crossing between individuals of the same genotype is sterile, while outcrosses with plants of other genotypes are fertile. Such plants are said to be "intragroup sterile, intergroup fertile." The physiological basis of this sterility mechanism has been found to be an inhibition of the growth of the pollen tube. In styles containing the same allele, the pollen tube is so inhibited that it does not reach the embryo sac. Under this mechanism all plants must necessarily be heterozygous with respect to the S alleles, because no two like genes can ever unite to produce an embryo.

§ 1. *The Simplest Case: Three Alleles*

The minimum number of self-sterility alleles is, of course, three, which is indeed the case first discovered. With three alleles, S_1, S_2, S_3, there are three groups (genotypes) of plants: S_1S_2, S_1S_3, S_2S_3. Individuals of each group are sterile on crossing with those in the same group but fertile with the other two groups. The results of crosses between them are as follows:

$$S_1S_2 \, \text{♀} \; \times \; (S_1S_3 \text{ or } S_2S_3)\text{♂} \rightarrow \qquad \tfrac{1}{2}S_1S_3 + \tfrac{1}{2}S_2S_3 \, ,$$

$$S_1S_3 \, \text{♀} \; \times \; (S_1S_2 \text{ or } S_2S_3)\text{♂} \rightarrow \tfrac{1}{2}S_1S_2 \qquad + \tfrac{1}{2}S_2S_3 \, ,$$

$$S_2S_3 \, \text{♀} \; \times \; (S_1S_2 \text{ or } S_1S_3)\text{♂} \rightarrow \tfrac{1}{2}S_1S_2 + \tfrac{1}{2}S_1S_3 \, .$$

Note that in any particular cross the female parental genotype never appears in the offspring and that reciprocal crosses never give the same results. Among the offspring there are 50 per cent like the male parent, while the other 50 per cent belong to the third group (other than the two groups to which the parents belong). The two crosses, $S_1S_2 \, \text{♀} \times S_1S_3\text{♂}$ and $S_1S_2 \, \text{♀} \times S_2S_3\text{♂}$, give the same results, because, in both cases, only the S_3 pollen of the male parents can function on a style of the S_1S_2 constitution.

Let us consider an arbitrary population consisting of various proportions of S_1S_2, S_1S_3, S_2S_3 individuals. Assume that S_1S_2 is the most numerous genotype in one generation. Then, since the mother genotype never appears in the offspring, it follows that this genotype will be least numerous in the next generation. Conversely, if S_1S_2 is less numerous than others in one generation, it will become more numerous in the next generation. Thus, under random mating there will not be any equilibrium state unless none of the genotypes is more numerous than others. The equilibrium condition is reached when the population consists of one-third of each genotype, and hence the gene frequency of each allele is also one-third.

The algebraic relations under random mating may be deduced most easily in the following manner. Let the initial population be $(x_0\ S_1S_2,\ y_0\ S_1S_3,\ z_0\ S_2S_3)$, where $x_0 + y_0 + z_0 = 1$. Under panmixia the frequencies of various fertile

TABLE 29

RANDOM MATING OF THREE GROUPS OF INTRASTERILE,
INTERFERTILE PLANTS

FEMALE PARENT	FREQUENCY	OFFSPRING		
		S_1S_2	S_1S_3	S_2S_3
S_1S_2...........	x_0	0	$\frac{1}{2}x_0$	$\frac{1}{2}x_0$
S_1S_3...........	y_0	$\frac{1}{2}y_0$	0	$\frac{1}{2}y_0$
S_2S_3...........	z_0	$\frac{1}{2}z_0$	$\frac{1}{2}z_0$	0
Total.......	1.00	$\frac{1}{2}(1-x_0)$	$\frac{1}{2}(1-y_0)$	$\frac{1}{2}(1-z_0)$

crosses and their corresponding offspring are shown in Table 29. It is seen that the proportion of S_1S_2 individuals in the offspring generation is

$$x_1 = \tfrac{1}{2}(1 - x_0) . \tag{1}$$

The expressions for y_1 and z_1 are similar. So we need only to investigate the changes of x in successive generations. By repeated substitution of (1), we obtain

$$x_2 = \tfrac{1}{2}(1 - x_1) = \tfrac{1}{4}(1 + x_0) , \qquad x_3 = \tfrac{1}{2}(1 - x_2) = \tfrac{1}{8}(3 - x_0) ,$$

$$x_4 = \tfrac{1}{2}(1 - x_3) = \tfrac{1}{16}(5 + x_0) , \qquad x_5 = \tfrac{1}{32}(11 - x_0) , \text{ etc.}$$

Now, the series $\tfrac{1}{2}, \tfrac{1}{4}, \tfrac{3}{8}, \tfrac{5}{16}, \tfrac{11}{32}, \ldots$, approaches one-third as the limit (Chap. 5, Appendix), so we have

$$x_n \to \tfrac{1}{3} \quad \text{as} \quad n \to \infty ,$$

because the term $x_0/2^n \to 0$. The successive values of x are oscillatory about its limiting value $\tfrac{1}{3}$. The difference between two consecutive x's is

$$\Delta x_n = x_{n+1} - x_n = \tfrac{1}{2}(1 - x_n) - x_n = \tfrac{1}{2}(1 - 3x_n) . \tag{2}$$

At equilibrium $\Delta x = 0$; hence $x = \frac{1}{3}$. This is perhaps a simpler way of obtaining the limiting value of x_n. The properties of y_n and z_n are identical.

We have so far investigated only the zygotic proportions of a population. The values of gene frequencies may be easily found for each generation. Let q_1 be the frequency of S_1, etc. Its value in the nth generation of random mating is then

$$q_{1(n)} = \tfrac{1}{2}x_n + \tfrac{1}{2}y_n = \tfrac{1}{2}(1 - z_n) = z_{n+1},$$

which is the proportion of S_2S_3 zygotes in the next generation. Similarly, q_3 (frequency of S_3) in one generation will be the proportion of S_1S_2 individuals in the next generation. Therefore, the properties of the gene frequencies are the same

TABLE 30

APPROACH TO EQUILIBRIUM OF THREE SELF-STERILITY
ALLELES UNDER RANDOM MATING

n	ZYGOTIC PROPORTIONS			GENE FREQUENCIES		
	S_1S_2	S_1S_3	S_2S_3	S_1	S_2	S_3
0.........	0.8000	0.1600	0.0400	0.480	0.420	0.100
1.........	.1000	.4200	.4800	.260	.290	.450
2.........	.4500	.2900	.260	.370	.355	.275
3.........	.2750	.3550	.3700	.3150	.3225	.3625
4.........	.3625	.3225	.3150	....	....	....
5.........	.31875	.33875	.3425	....	....	....
6.........	.340625	.330625	.32875	....	....	....
7.........	.3297	.3347	.3356	....	....	....
8.........	.3351	.3327	.3322	....	....	....
9.........	.3325	.3336	.3339	....	....	....
10.........	.3337	.3332	.3331	....	....	....
...	...	...	...	...	...	...
∞.........	0.3333	0.3333	0.3333	0.333	0.333	0.333

as those of zygotic properties, (1) and (2). Table 30 is a numerical example illustrating the various points we have discussed in the foregoing paragraphs.

One important feature of the equilibrium condition of self-sterility alleles is that the final values of zygotic proportions and gene frequencies are all absolute constants, being entirely independent of the initial values x_0, y_0, z_0. It follows that, even if a considerable proportion of one genotype, or even if all of one genotype, is wiped out of a population, a new equilibrium will be established at the same point, $q_i = \frac{1}{3}$, in a few generations. Therefore, no selection could be effective with regard to these alleles. A population cannot exist with only two such alleles. If a population practices inbreeding, all but three alleles will disappear ultimately. Moreover, a population consisting of equal numbers of the three genotypes will be in stable equilibrium under any mating system. Further, no gene frequency could have a value greater than 0.50, whatever the zygotic proportions might be.

§ 2. *The General Case:* k *Alleles*

Let q_i be the frequency of the allele S_i $(i = 1, 2, \ldots, k)$, where $\Sigma q_i = 1$. Further, let s_{ij} be the proportion of $S_i S_j$ individuals in the population. Since all individuals are heterozygotes with respect to the self-sterility alleles, we have $q_i = \frac{1}{2} \Sigma_j s_{ij}$ $(i \neq j)$. In other words, the total proportion of zygotes containing S_i in a population must be $2q_i$, and that of non-S_i zygotes $1 - 2q_i$. For the sake of concreteness let us concentrate on one of the alleles, say, S_1, with frequency q_1. The total frequency of functioning S_1 ovules among all female gametes in the population is q_1, but the frequency of functional S_1 pollen grains among male gametes is not equal to q_1, because S_1 pollen grains do not function on $S_1 S_j$ styles, which comprise $2q_1$ of the population. On non-S_1 styles, however, the chance for the S_1 pollen grains to function is better than the average chance for other $k - 1$ kinds of pollen. This is so because each of the non-S_1 styles $(S_2 S_3, S_2 S_4, S_3 S_4, \ldots)$ inhibits the function of two of the $k - 1$ kinds of pollen, while the S_1 pollen can function on all of them.

The frequency of functional S_1 pollen is determined by its relative success on the $1 - 2q_1$ non-S_1 styles. Among the other $k - 1$ kinds of pollen (with a total frequency $1 - q_1$), only $k - 3$ kinds are able to function on any particular type of non-S_1 style. If we assume that $k - 1$ kinds of non-S_1 pollen are approximately equally numerous, then, as far as the non-S_1 styles are concerned, the ratio of successful S_1 pollen to all other successful pollen would be

$$q_1 : \frac{k-3}{k-1} (1 - q_1) .$$

Since there are $1 - 2q_1$ non-S_1 styles in the population, the total frequency of functioning S_1 pollen is

$$\frac{q_1 \times (1 - 2 q_1)}{q_1 + \dfrac{k-3}{k-1} (1 - q_1)} = \frac{(k-1) \, q_1 \, (1 - 2 q_1)}{k - 3 + 2 q_1} .$$

As the frequency of functioning S_1 ovules is simply q_1, the *average* frequency of functioning S_1 gametes (ovules and pollen) is thus

$$q_1' = \frac{1}{2} \left\{ q_1 + \frac{(k-1) \, q_1 \, (1 - 2 q_1)}{k - 3 + 2 q_1} \right\} = \frac{(k-2) \, q_1 \, (1 - q_1)}{k - 3 + 2 q_1} ,$$

which is the gene frequency of S_1 in the next generation. The amount of change from the previous generation is

$$\Delta q = q' - q = \frac{q \, (1 - k q)}{k - 3 + 2 q} .$$

We dropped the subscript of q in the last expression because the foregoing discussions and expressions apply equally well to any one of the k alleles. At equilibrium there is no change in gene frequency (or in zygotic proportions) from generation to generation (i.e., $\Delta q = 0$). Hence, the equilibrium value of q is $1/k$.

The only arbitrary assumption in the above discussions is that, on non-S_1 styles, $(k - 3)/(k - 1)$ of the $1 - q_1$ non-S_1 pollen is successful. More generally, however, we may assume that R_1 (a fraction) of the $1 - q_1$ non-S_1 pollen is able to function on non-S_1 styles. Then the ratio of successful S_1 pollen to all other types of successful pollen on non-S_1 styles is $q_1 : R_1(1 - q_1)$; and the frequency of functioning S_1 pollen is $q_1(1 - 2q_1)/[q_1 + R_1(1 - q_1)]$. The average frequency of functional S_1 gametes (ovules and pollen) is (dropping the subscript)

$$q' = \frac{1}{2}\left\{ q + \frac{q\,(1 - 2q)}{q + R\,(1 - q)} \right\} = \frac{q\,(1 - q)\,(1 + R)}{2\,[q + R\,(1 - q)]}\,;$$

$$\Delta q = q' - q = \frac{q\,[\,(1 - R) - q\,(3 - R)\,]}{2\,[R + q\,(1 - R)]}\,.$$

At equilibrium (Wright, 1939)

$$\Delta q = 0\,; \qquad \hat{q} = \frac{1 - R}{3 - R}\,.$$

In the simplest case of $k = 3$, $R = 0$, as on non-S_1 styles $(S_2 S_3)$ none of the S_2 and S_3 (with total frequency $1 - q_1$) pollen can function, and thus S_1 is the only kind of pollen that functions. Hence the equilibrium value is $\hat{q} = \frac{1}{3}$.

Notes and Exercises

1. For the case of three self-sterility alleles show that

$$\Delta q_i = \tfrac{1}{2}(1 - 3q_i) \quad \text{and} \quad \Delta q_1 + \Delta q_2 + \Delta q_3 = 0\,.$$

2. Let q, q', q'' be the frequencies of a certain self-sterility allele in three successive generations so that $\Delta q = q' - q$ and $\Delta' q = q'' - q'$. Assuming that there are only three alleles, show that the "increment" of q per generation is halved (with sign changed) in each generation of random mating, viz.: $\Delta' q = -\tfrac{1}{2}\Delta q$.

3. Calculate the zygotic proportions, and the gene frequencies and their increments, of the next ten generations, assuming random mating, for the initial population $(0\ S_1 S_2,\ 0.60\ S_1 S_3,\ 0.40\ S_2 S_3)$.

n	ZYGOTES			GENES			INCREMENTS		
	$S_1 S_2$	$S_1 S_3$	$S_2 S_3$	S_1	S_2	S_3	Δq_1	Δq_2	Δq_3
0........	0	0.60	0.40	0.30	0.20	0.50	....	....	....
1........	0.50	.20	.30	.35	.40	.25	+0.05	+0.20	−0.25
2........	.25	.40	.35	0.325	0.300	0.375	−0.025	− .10	+0.125
3........	0.375	0.300	0.325	....	0.350	....	....	+0.05	....
...	...	...	...	...	...	...	...	...	...

4. Show that a population consisting of one-sixth each of the genotypes $S_1 S_2$, $S_1 S_3$, $S_1 S_4$, $S_2 S_3$, $S_2 S_4$, and $S_3 S_4$ is in equilibrium condition.

CHAPTER 8

Two Pairs of Genes

IN THIS final chapter on panmictic populations the equilibrium theorems will be extended to cases where more than one locus is involved.

§ 1. *Zygotic Proportions and Gametic Output*

In regard to two pairs of genes, for instance, there are nine genotypes in a population. For convenience of notation they may be arranged in a systematic pattern, and their proportions in a population may be represented by the elements of a 3×3 matrix as shown in the following:

$$
\begin{matrix} AABB & AABb & AAbb \\ AaBB & AaBb & Aabb, \\ aaBB & aaBb & aabb \end{matrix} \qquad Z \equiv \begin{pmatrix} z_{11} & z_{12} & z_{13} \\ z_{21} & z_{22} & z_{23} \\ z_{31} & z_{32} & z_{33} \end{pmatrix},
$$

where the sum of the nine z's is unity. Further, the sums of the three rows give us the proportions of AA, Aa, aa, while the sums of the columns give us the proportions of BB, Bb, bb, respectively.

The four kinds of gametes may be arranged into a similar pattern, and their proportions may be represented by a 2×2 matrix:

$$
\begin{matrix} AB & Ab \\ aB & ab \end{matrix}, \qquad g \equiv \begin{pmatrix} g_{11} & g_{13} \\ g_{31} & g_{33} \end{pmatrix},
$$

where the sum of the four g's is unity. Further, the sums of the two rows give us the gene frequencies of the A-a pair, while the sums of the columns give us the gene frequencies of the B-b pair.

When the zygotic proportions (z_{ij}) in a population are given, it is easy to calculate the total gametic output of the population. Since $AABB$ zygotes produce only (AB) gametes, $AABb$ and $AaBB$ zygotes produce 50 per cent (AB) gametes, and $AaBb$ zygotes produce 25 per cent (AB) gametes, etc., we have (Fig. 7)

$$
\left. \begin{aligned} g_{11} &= z_{11} + \tfrac{1}{2}(z_{12} + z_{21}) + \tfrac{1}{4}z_{22}, & g_{13} &= z_{13} + \tfrac{1}{2}(z_{12} + z_{23}) + \tfrac{1}{4}z_{22}, \\ g_{31} &= z_{31} + \tfrac{1}{2}(z_{21} + z_{32}) + \tfrac{1}{4}z_{22}, & g_{33} &= z_{33} + \tfrac{1}{2}(z_{23} + z_{32}) + \tfrac{1}{4}z_{22}. \end{aligned} \right\} \quad (1)
$$

Let p, q be the frequencies of A, a and u, v be those of B, b. These values may be obtained directly from the given zygotic proportions or from their gametic outputs; thus (Fig. 7)

$$p = g_{11} + g_{13} = z_{1.} + \tfrac{1}{2}z_{2.} \quad\} \qquad u = g_{11} + g_{31} = z_{.1} + \tfrac{1}{2}z_{.2} \quad\}$$
$$q = g_{31} + g_{33} = z_{3.} + \tfrac{1}{2}z_{2.} \quad\} , \qquad v = g_{13} + g_{33} = z_{.3} + \tfrac{1}{2}z_{.2} \quad\} , \qquad (2)$$

where $z_{1.} = z_{11} + z_{12} + z_{13}$ = the sum of the first row of the zygotic matrix; $z_{.3} = z_{13} + z_{23} + z_{33}$ = the sum of the third column of the same matrix, etc.

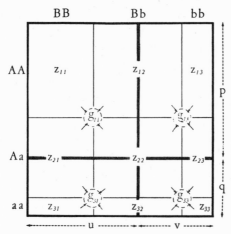

FIG. 7.—Relations between zygotic proportions (Z), gametic proportions (g), and gene frequencies. See formulas (1) and (2) and also $\hat{Z}$ of Table 31.

§ 2. *Equilibrium Condition under Panmixia*

It may be readily verified that the following population is in equilibrium under random mating:

$$\hat{Z} \equiv \begin{pmatrix} p^2u^2 & 2p^2uv & p^2v^2 \\ 2pqu^2 & 4pquv & 2pqv^2 \\ q^2u^2 & 2q^2uv & q^2v^2 \end{pmatrix} . \qquad (3)$$

If a population is in equilibrium with respect to two pairs of genes simultaneously, it must necessarily also be in equilibrium with respect to the two pairs of genes separately. It is seen that the row totals of $\hat{Z}$ are p^2, $2pq$, q^2, and its column totals are u^2, $2uv$, v^2.

There are $(9 \times 10)/2 = 45$ different crosses without distinguishing the reciprocals. It is not necessary to enumerate them in order to verify that (3) is in equilibrium. Since the results of random mating of individuals are the same as random union of gametes (Chap. 1, § 5), we need only to find the gametic output of $\hat{Z}$. From (1), we have

$$\hat{g}_{11} = p^2u^2 + p^2uv + pqu^2 + pquv = pu(pu + pv + qu + qv) = pu .$$

The proportions of the other three kinds of gametes may be found in a similar manner. Thus, the gametic output of $\hat{Z}$ is

$$\hat{g} = \begin{pmatrix} \hat{g}_{11} & \hat{g}_{13} \\ \hat{g}_{31} & \hat{g}_{33} \end{pmatrix} = \begin{pmatrix} pu & pv \\ qu & qv \end{pmatrix} ,$$

the random union of which will give

$$\begin{pmatrix} AB & Ab & aB & ab \\ pu + pv + qu + qv \end{pmatrix}^2 = \begin{pmatrix} A & a \\ p + q \end{pmatrix}^2 \begin{pmatrix} B & b \\ u + v \end{pmatrix}^2 ,$$

which is the same as $\hat{Z}$. Therefore, it is in equilibrium.

§ 3. *Establishment of Equilibrium*

With an arbitrary population, equilibrium is not established in one generation of random mating with respect to the nine genotypes; but the approach to equilibrium is very rapid. Suppose the initial population is $Z_0 = [z_{ij}]$, whose gametic output is $(g_{11}, g_{13}, g_{31}, g_{33})$. Combining these gametes at random (which can be most easily done by the usual checkerboard method) and collecting the terms of the same genotype, we find that the zygotic proportions in the next generation are the elements of

$$Z_1 = [z'_{ij}] = \begin{pmatrix} g_{11}^2 & 2g_{11}g_{13} & g_{13}^2 \\ 2g_{11}g_{31} & 2(g_{11}g_{33} + g_{13}g_{31}) & 2g_{13}g_{33} \\ g_{31}^2 & 2g_{31}g_{33} & g_{33}^2 \end{pmatrix} . \tag{4}$$

After one generation of random mating, each of the two pairs of genes should be in equilibrium when taken separately. That this is actually the case may be seen from the row and column totals of the zygotic proportions of (4). For instance, the sums of its three rows are

$$(g_{11} + g_{13})^2 , \quad 2(g_{11} + g_{13})(g_{31} + g_{33}) , \quad (g_{31} + g_{33})^2 ;$$

that is (from [2]),

$$p^2 , \quad 2pq , \quad q^2 ,$$

corresponding to proportions of AA, Aa, aa, respectively. Similarly, its column totals are u^2, $2uv$, v^2, giving the proportions of BB, Bb, bb, respectively. But when we consider both pairs of genes simultaneously (that is to say, consider the proportions of the nine genotypes in the population), Z_1 is not in equilibrium at all. Its gametic output may be calculated from (1); thus

$$g'_{11} = g_{11}^2 + g_{11}g_{13} + g_{11}g_{31} + \tfrac{1}{2}(g_{11}g_{33} + g_{13}g_{31})$$
$$= g_{11}(g_{11} + g_{13} + g_{31} + g_{33}) - \tfrac{1}{2}(g_{11}g_{33} - g_{13}g_{31}) .$$

The proportions of the other three kinds of gametes may be calculated in a similar way. If we let d denote the determinant of a gametic matrix so that

$$d_0 = \begin{vmatrix} g_{11} & g_{13} \\ g_{31} & g_{33} \end{vmatrix} = g_{11}g_{33} - g_{13}g_{31} ,$$

the gametic output of Z_1 will then be (remembering that the sum of the four g's is unity):

$$\left. \begin{array}{ll} g'_{11} = g_{11} - \tfrac{1}{2}d_0 , & g'_{13} = g_{13} + \tfrac{1}{2}d_0 , \\ g'_{31} = g_{31} + \tfrac{1}{2}d_0 , & g'_{33} = g_{33} - \tfrac{1}{2}d_0 . \end{array} \right\} \tag{5}$$

It should be noted that the gene frequencies remain unchanged from generation to generation; for example, $g'_{11} + g'_{13} = g_{11} + g_{13} = p$, etc. The gametic determinant obtained from Z_1 is therefore

$$d_1 = \begin{vmatrix} g'_{11} & g'_{13} \\ g'_{31} & g'_{33} \end{vmatrix} = \begin{vmatrix} g_{11} - \tfrac{1}{2}d_0 & g_{13} + \tfrac{1}{2}d_0 \\ g_{31} + \tfrac{1}{2}d_0 & g_{33} - \tfrac{1}{2}d_0 \end{vmatrix}$$

$$= \begin{vmatrix} g_{11} & g_{13} \\ g_{31} & g_{33} \end{vmatrix} + \begin{vmatrix} g_{11} & \tfrac{1}{2}d_0 \\ g_{31} & -\tfrac{1}{2}d_0 \end{vmatrix} + \begin{vmatrix} -\tfrac{1}{2}d_0 & g_{13} \\ \tfrac{1}{2}d_0 & g_{33} \end{vmatrix} + \begin{vmatrix} -\tfrac{1}{2}d_0 & \tfrac{1}{2}d_0 \\ \tfrac{1}{2}d_0 & -\tfrac{1}{2}d_0 \end{vmatrix}$$

$$= d_0 - \tfrac{1}{2}d_0(g_{11} + g_{31}) - \tfrac{1}{2}d_0(g_{13} + g_{33}) + 0$$

$$= d_0 - \tfrac{1}{2}d_0 = \tfrac{1}{2}d_0 . \tag{6}$$

Thus we see that the gametic proportions change in such a way that the quantity $d = g_{11}g_{33} - g_{13}g_{31}$ is diminished by one-half in each generation of random mating. Hence, after n generations of random mating,

$$d_n = \tfrac{1}{2}d_{n-1} = (\tfrac{1}{2})^n d_0 \to 0 \quad \text{as} \quad n \to \infty .$$

When the final equilibrium condition is reached, the gametic proportions will be

$$\hat{g}_{11} = pu = (g_{11} + g_{13})(g_{11} + g_{31}) = g_{11} - d_0 , \text{ etc. },$$

so that its gametic determinant is zero, as expected,

$$\hat{d} = \begin{vmatrix} g_{11} - d_0 & g_{13} + d_0 \\ g_{31} + d_0 & g_{33} - d_0 \end{vmatrix} = 0 .$$

In other words, in an equilibrium population, $\hat{g}_{11}\hat{g}_{33} = \hat{g}_{13}\hat{g}_{31}$. The initial gametic proportions differ from those in the equilibrium condition by the amount d_0, which thus may be regarded as an index of divergence of an arbitrary population from equilibrium. Since the maximum numerical value of d cannot exceed $\tfrac{1}{4}$, and, since it is halved in each generation, the approach to equilibrium is very rapid. Table 31 is a numerical example of the various points we have just covered.

§ 4. *Some Particular Cases*

1. If the frequencies of the two pairs of genes are equal, the zygotic proportions of a random-mating population are symmetrical with respect to the prin-

cipal diagonal of the zygotic matrix; that is, $z_{ij} = z_{ji}$ (owing to the fact that $p = u$ and $q = v$) whether the population is in equilibrium or not. Since

$$p = g_{11} + g_{13} = g_{11} + g_{31} = u ,$$

we have $g_{13} = g_{31}$ in all generations. Substituting in the zygotic matrix (4), we see that its elements are symmetrical with respect to its principal diagonal. That is to say, the proportions of $AaBB$ and $AABb$ are equal, and so are those of $AAbb$ and $aaBB;$ etc. On the other hand, if $p = v$ and $q = u$, the zygotic proportions will be symmetrical with respect to its other diagonal.

2. In any arbitrary population whose gametic output is such that $d = g_{11}g_{33} - g_{13}g_{31} = 0$, equilibrium will be established in one generation of random mating. For example:

$$\begin{pmatrix} .14 & .26 & .07 \\ .20 & .20 & .06 \\ .01 & .04 & .02 \end{pmatrix} \rightarrow \begin{pmatrix} .42 & .28 \\ .18 & .12 \end{pmatrix} \rightarrow \begin{pmatrix} .1764 & .2352 & .0784 \\ .1512 & .2016 & .0672 \\ .0324 & .0432 & .0144 \end{pmatrix} .$$

TABLE 31

APPROACH TO EQUILIBRIUM FOR TWO PAIRS OF GENES UNDER PANMIXIA
(In initial population, $p = 0.70$, $q = 0.30$; and $u = 0.60$, $v = 0.40$)

$Z_0 = \begin{pmatrix} .25 & .16 & .14 \\ .02 & .24 & .04 \\ .12 & .02 & .01 \end{pmatrix}$			$g_0 = \begin{pmatrix} .40 & .30 \\ .20 & .10 \end{pmatrix}$		$d_0 = -0.02$
$Z_1 = \begin{pmatrix} .16 & .24 & .09 \\ .16 & .20 & .06 \\ .04 & .04 & .01 \end{pmatrix}$			$g_1 = \begin{pmatrix} .41 & .29 \\ .19 & .11 \end{pmatrix}$		$d_1 = -0.01$
$Z_2 = \begin{pmatrix} .1681 & .2378 & .0841 \\ .1558 & .2004 & .0638 \\ .0361 & .0418 & .0121 \end{pmatrix}$			$g_2 = \begin{pmatrix} .415 & .285 \\ .185 & .115 \end{pmatrix}$		$d_2 = -0.005$
$Z_3 = \begin{pmatrix} .172225 & .236550 & .081225 \\ .153550 & .200900 & .065550 \\ .034225 & .042550 & .013225 \end{pmatrix}$			$g_3 = \begin{pmatrix} .4175 & .2825 \\ .1825 & .1175 \end{pmatrix}$		$d_3 = -0.0025$
$Z_4 = \begin{pmatrix} .1743 & .2359 & .0798 \\ .1524 & .2012 & .0664 \\ .0333 & .0429 & .0138 \end{pmatrix}$			$g_4 = \begin{pmatrix} .41875 & .28125 \\ .18125 & .11875 \end{pmatrix}$		$d_4 = -0.00125$
$Z_5 = \begin{pmatrix} .17535 & .23555 & .07910 \\ .15180 & .20140 & .06680 \\ .03285 & .04305 & .01410 \end{pmatrix}$			$g_5 = \begin{pmatrix} .4194 & .2806 \\ .1806 & .1194 \end{pmatrix}$		$d_5 = -0.0006$
. . .	. . .	. . .	. . .		. . .
$\hat{Z} = \begin{pmatrix} .1764 & .2352 & .0784 \\ .1512 & .2016 & .0672 \\ .0324 & .0432 & .0144 \end{pmatrix}$			$\hat{g} = \begin{pmatrix} .420 & .280 \\ .180 & .120 \end{pmatrix}$		$\hat{d} = 0$

NOTE.—From Z_1 on, row totals are .49, .42, .09; column totals are .36, .48, .16.

3. A very special case is the population that consists wholly of double hetero-zygotes, $AaBb$ (such as the F_1 individuals from cross $AABB \times aabb$ or $AAbb \times aaBB$). Here, $p = u = \frac{1}{2}$. Equilibrium is established in one generation, and the zygotic proportions are symmetrical with respect to both diagonals. Thus

$$\begin{pmatrix} 0 & 0 & 0 \\ 0 & 1 & 0 \\ 0 & 0 & 0 \end{pmatrix} \rightarrow \begin{pmatrix} \frac{1}{4} & \frac{1}{4} \\ \frac{1}{4} & \frac{1}{4} \end{pmatrix} \rightarrow \begin{pmatrix} \frac{1}{16} & \frac{2}{16} & \frac{1}{16} \\ \frac{2}{16} & \frac{4}{16} & \frac{2}{16} \\ \frac{1}{16} & \frac{2}{16} & \frac{1}{16} \end{pmatrix} .$$

This is the composition of the F_2 population. Under random mating it will re-main the same in all subsequent generations. Several other special cases have been given by Jennings (1917).

§ 5. *The Effect of Linkage*

If the two pairs of genes are located on the same homologous pair of chromo-somes, the approach to equilibrium will be slower than if they are independent. The higher the intensity of linkage, the slower the rate of approach.

Obviously, linkage does not affect the gametic output of genotypes with one or two pairs of genes in the homozygous condition. For instance, the zygote $aaBb$ will produce 50 per cent (aB) and 50 per cent (ab) gametes whether the two loci are linked or not. The only effect that linkage has is to modify the gametic output of the double heterozygotes, depending upon whether they are in the "coupling" or "repulsion" phase. Let their gametic output be as follows:

	PROPORTION OF GAMETES						
TYPE OF ZYGOTE	(AB)		(Ab)		(aB)		(ab)
Coupling: AB/ab.....	r	:	1	:	1	:	r
Repulsion: Ab/aB....	1	:	r	:	r	:	1

where $r > 1$, and r is known as the "linkage ratio"; $c = 1/(1 + r)$ is the frac-tion of "crossovers"; and $C = 1 - c = r/(1 + r)$ is the proportion of non-crossovers (parental combinations).

The proportion of double heterozygotes in (4) is the sum of two different com-binations of gametes

$$z'_{22} = 2g_{11}g_{33} \text{ (coupling)} + 2g_{13}g_{31} \text{ (repulsion)} ,$$

and their gametic output should be calculated separately. Proceeding as before, we find that the proportion of (AB) gametes produced by Z_1 is

$$g'_{11} = g_{11}^2 + g_{11}g_{13} + g_{11}g_{31} + \left(\frac{r}{1+r}\right) g_{11}g_{33} + \left(\frac{1}{1+r}\right) g_{13}g_{31} .$$

The expressions are similar for the other three kinds of gametes. Simplifying, we obtain (Robbins, 1918a, b, c)

$$g'_{11} = g_{11} - cd_0\,, \qquad g'_{13} = g_{13} + cd_0\,,$$
$$g'_{31} = g_{31} + cd_0\,, \qquad g'_{33} = g_{33} - cd_0\,.$$

Since $r > 1$, the fraction $c = 1/(1 + r)$ is always less than $\frac{1}{2}$, so that the change in gametic proportions per generation is always less than in the case of independent genes. The gametic determinant of Z_1 may be found easily by replacing $\frac{1}{2}$ by c in (6); thus

$$d_1 = \begin{vmatrix} g'_{11} & g'_{13} \\ g'_{31} & g'_{33} \end{vmatrix} = d_0 - cd_0 = Cd_0\,, \tag{6L}$$

where the fraction $C = 1 - c = r/(1 + r)$ is always greater than $\frac{1}{2}$, so that the quantity d is diminished at a slower rate per generation. Its limiting value is, however, also zero, because $d_n = Cd_{n-1} = C^n d_0 \to 0$ as $n \to \infty$. When equilibrium is reached, $\hat{d} = 0$, which means that

$$\hat{g}_{11}\hat{g}_{33} = \hat{g}_{13}\hat{g}_{31}\,,$$

just as in the case of independent genes. It follows that the coupling zygote AB/ab and the repulsion zygote Ab/aB are equally numerous (each with a proportion $2pquv$) in an equilibrium population, so that the combined gametic output of these two phases of double heterozygotes are the same as those from $4pquv\ AaBb$ with independent genes. The final gametic proportions are also the same as those for independent genes, viz., $\hat{g}_{11} = pu = g_{11} - d_0$, etc. As a numerical example, let us start with the same gametic proportions (g_0), as in Table 31, but assume that $r = 4$, so that the fraction of crossovers is $c = 20$ per cent. The gametic proportions of the next few generations under panmixia would be as follows (compare with Table 31):

$g_0 = \begin{pmatrix} .40 & .30 \\ .20 & .10 \end{pmatrix}$ $d_0 = -0.0200$	$g_1 = \begin{pmatrix} .404 & 0.296 \\ .196 & 0.104 \end{pmatrix}$ $d_1 = -0.0160$	$g_2 = \begin{pmatrix} .4072 & .2928 \\ .1928 & .1072 \end{pmatrix}$ $d_2 = -0.0128$
$g_3 = \begin{pmatrix} .40976 & .29024 \\ .19024 & .10976 \end{pmatrix}$ $d_3 = -0.01024$	$g_4 = \begin{pmatrix} .4118 & .2882 \\ .1882 & .1118 \end{pmatrix}$ $d_4 = -0.0082$	$g_5 = \begin{pmatrix} .41344 & .28656 \\ .18656 & .11344 \end{pmatrix}$ $d_5 = -0.00656$
$g_6 = \begin{pmatrix} .41475 & .28525 \\ .18525 & .11475 \end{pmatrix}$ $d_6 = -0.00524$	$\ldots \to$	$\hat{g} = \begin{pmatrix} .420 & .280 \\ .180 & .120 \end{pmatrix}$ $\hat{d} = 0$

In the example above, where the fraction of crossovers is $c = 0.20$, the approach to equilibrium is still fairly rapid. Thus we see that in six generations of random mating the d value has been reduced to $(1 - 0.20)^6 = 0.262$ of its original value: i.e., $0.00524 = 0.262(0.02)$. But, when the linkage is very strong, the attainment of equilibrium condition may take a considerable number of generations. For example, when $c = 0.01$, it will take sixty-nine generations to halve the value of d according to (6L): $(1 - 0.01)^{69} = 0.50$, very nearly.

The most important conclusion to be derived from the previous analysis is that the zygotic proportions with respect to two pairs of linked genes are identical with those for independent genes in a random-mating equilibrium population. In other words, the zygotic proportions are entirely determined by gene frequencies, whether or not these genes are located on the same chromosome. Consequently, linkage of genes cannot be detected by examining genotypic or phenotypic proportions in the general population. Two traits caused by two pairs of linked genes are still independently distributed, as shown in population (3). This is one of the chief difficulties in detecting linkage in human inheritance. The usual assertion that the association or correlation between two traits in man may be due to linked genes is clearly erroneous. Any observed association of traits in the general population may be due to a variety of causes: common environmental influences, multiple effects of the same gene or genes (pleiotropy), subdivision of a population into heterogeneous groups, differential inbreeding, physiological consequences of development, or simply *bias in sampling procedure*. But it is never an evidence for genetic linkage (Li, 1954, Part IV).

Any systematic account of the available methods of detecting and measuring linkage in man would require many pages of explanation and is beyond the scope of this book. But it is important for all students of genetics to have a clear conception of where the effects of linkage may be found in an equilibrium population. As was pointed out before, linkage does not affect the gametic output of genotypes, except of those of double heterozygotes. Consequently, the effects of linkage will be revealed in segregation ratios among those children who have at least one parent who is a double heterozygote. If dominance is involved, only a few types of families are useful in studying linkage: $AaBb \times aabb$; $AaBb \times Aabb$ or $aaBb$; $AaBb \times AaBb$. Remembering that AB/ab and Ab/aB are equally numerous in the general population, we see that in some sibships the two traits will be positively correlated, while in an equal number of other sibships the two traits will be negatively correlated; so that in the total population the two traits are independent. One strong evidence for the existence of linkage, therefore, is the presence of both positive and negative correlations in approximately equal numbers of sibships. Another method of detecting linkage is to examine the concordance and discordance of sib-pairs with respect to both traits. Many methods and their modifications have been given by Bernstein, Fisher, Haldane, Hogben, Penrose, and Finney; perhaps the briefest account is that of Mather (1951). All methods require a fairly large number of sibships in order to obtain significant results, because of the small size of human sibships.

§ 6. *Phenotypic Proportions and Applications*

The phenotypic proportions in the general population depend on the scheme of the interactions between the two pairs of genes. First, consider the case in which A is dominant over a and B over b without any interaction between the two loci. Collecting the elements of the same phenotype in matrix (3), we obtain the following four phenotypic proportions:

	B-	bb	Total	
A-	$(1-q^2)(1-v^2)$	$(1-q^2)v^2$	$1-q^2$	(3P)
aa	$q^2(1-v^2)$	q^2v^2	q^2	
Total	$1-v^2$	v^2	1	

If we let $[A\text{-}B\text{-}]$ denote the proportion of double dominants, etc., we note that the following relation holds, whatever the gene frequencies:

$$[A\text{-}B\text{-}][aabb] = [A\text{-}bb][aaB\text{-}] .$$

The gene frequencies may be calculated from the marginal totals of (3P). Thus,

$$q^2 = [aaB\text{-}] + [aabb] , \qquad v^2 = [A\text{-}bb] + [aabb] .$$

As a numerical example, we may cite the findings of Philip (1938), who collected and examined a random sample of a polyphagous beetle (*Dermestes vulpinus*) taken from the sheepskins stored on London docks. By various crosses it has been shown that dark wing color (A) is dominant over light wing color (a) and that black body color (B) is dominant over brown body color (b). The results of classifying 152 beetles with respect to these two traits are shown in Table 32. It is seen that the fit between observed and expected numbers of beetles is very close.

TABLE 32

ANALYSIS OF FOUR PHENOTYPIC PROPORTIONS OF DERMESTES VULPINUS
(Philip, 1938)

	PHENOTYPE				TOTAL
	Dark Wing		Light Wing		
	Black Body A-B-	Brown Body A-bb	Black Body aaB-	Brown Body $aabb$	
Observed number.....	35	24	61	32	152
Observed proportion...	0.2303	0.1579	0.4013	0.2105	1.00
	$v^2 = 0.3684$, $q^2 = 0.6118$				
Expected proportion...	0.2452	0.1430	0.3864	0.2254	1.00
Expected number.....	37.3	21.7	58.7	34.3	152

$$\chi^2 = 0.60, \quad df = 4-2-1 = 1, \quad 0.30 < P < 0.50$$

§ 7. *Duplicate and Complementary Genes*

Next let us consider the case of "duplicate" genes, in which only *aabb* manifests the recessive trait, and the other eight genotypes are dominants with a combined proportion, $1 - q^2v^2$, in the general population. Then there will be only three distinguishable types of mating (just as in the case of one pair of genes with dominance). The values of q and v cannot be estimated separately from a random sample of the general population. All we can know is the value of qv as $(qv)^2 = [aabb]$.

Among the 45 different genotypic matings, $(8 \times 9)/2 = 36$ of them are of the type Dom $\times$ Dom, 8 of the type Dom $\times$ Rec, and one Rec $\times$ Rec. The frequencies of mating and their corresponding offspring are given in Table 33.

TABLE 33

TYPES OF MATING AND THEIR OFFSPRING FOR TWO PAIRS
OF DUPLICATE GENES WITH DOMINANCE

TYPE OF MATING AND FREQUENCY	RECESSIVE OFFSPRING, *aabb*	
	Proportion in General Population	Proportion in This Type of Mating
36 Dom$\times$Dom $(1-q^2v^2)^2$	$q^2v^2(1-qv)^2$	$\left(\dfrac{qv}{1+qv}\right)^2 = S_2$
8 Dom$\times$Rec $2q^2v^2(1-q^2v^2)$	$2q^3v^3(1-qv)$	$\dfrac{qv}{1+qv} = S_1$
1 Rec$\times$Rec $(q^2v^2)^2$	q^4v^4	1
45 matings, total	q^2v^2	. . . .

Among the 36 crosses between dominants, only 6 of them are able to produce double recessives (see Ex. 9), while 3 of the 8 crosses between dominants and recessives are able to do so. Note that the proportions of recessives among the offspring of a given type of mating are the same as Snyder's ratios (Chap. 2 eq. [5]), except that q is replaced by qv. Therefore, the method described in Section 3 of Chapter 2 does not differentiate the case of duplicate genes from that of one pair of genes (Li, 1953*d*). This is self-evident when we consider that only (*ab*) gametes are "recessive" ones with a frequency qv, while the other three kinds of gametes are all "dominants" with a frequency $1 - qv$. (The same situation holds with three or more pairs of duplicate genes.) The two cases may be distinguished from the segregation ratios of those families which are able to produce recessive offspring. In the case of one pair of genes the only kind of mating of the type Dom $\times$ Dom which produces recessives is $Aa \times Aa$. Among the offspring $\frac{1}{4}$ are recessives, whatever the gene frequencies in the general population. In the case of duplicate genes, as mentioned before, there are six matings capable of producing recessives. The proportions of these recessives may be $\frac{1}{4}$, $\frac{1}{8}$, or $\frac{1}{16}$, the average proportion being dependent upon the frequencies of matings (and thus gene frequencies) but always less than $\frac{1}{4}$. In practice, however, owing to the small size of human sibships, the distinction is not always clear.

Finally, we may consider the case of complementary genes, where a trait requires the presence of both dominant genes. Let us call the phenotype A-B-"Dom," whose proportion in the general population is $(1 - q^2)(1 - v^2)$, and the other phenotype (A-bb, aaB-, $aabb$, all alike) "Rec," with a proportion $q^2 + v^2 - q^2v^2$. There are also only three distinguishable types of mating: ten crosses of the type Dom $\times$ Dom, twenty of Dom $\times$ Rec and fifteen of Rec $\times$ Rec. The most important characteristic of this type of gene interaction is that all three types of mating are capable of producing both Dom and Rec offspring, thus distinguishing it from the cases of duplicate and of one pair of genes. It may be shown that the proportion of Rec offspring among all the ten Dom $\times$ Dom matings is

$$\left(\frac{q}{1+q}\right)^2 + \left(\frac{v}{1+v}\right)^2 - \left(\frac{q}{1+q}\right)^2 \left(\frac{v}{1+v}\right)^2 < \frac{7}{16}.$$

It is tedious to give all the results. Suffice it to say that, among Dom $\times$ Dom matings, there will be more than $\frac{9}{16}$ Dom and thus less than $\frac{7}{16}$ Rec offspring; among the Dom $\times$ Rec matings the proportion of Dom offspring is usually much higher than $\frac{1}{4}$ because only $AaBb \times aabb \to \frac{1}{4}$ $AaBb;$ while the other nineteen matings may give $\frac{3}{8}$, $\frac{1}{2}$, $\frac{3}{4}$ or all Dom's; among the Rec $\times$ Rec matings there may be any proportions of Dom and Rec offspring.

§ 8. *Metrical Characters and Genetic Variance*

Let the variable Z_1 take the values $2a_1$, a_1, 0 when a zygote contains AA, Aa, $aa;$ and Z_2 be $2a_2$, a_2, 0 when a zygote contains BB, Bb, bb, respectively, so that there is no dominance in either locus. Further, let us assume no epistasis between the different loci so that the zygote $AaBB$, say, takes the value $a_1 + 2a_2$. In other words, if we let Z be the value of a two-factor genotype, then $Z = Z_1 + Z_2$. The nine possible values of Z are as follows:

$AABB$	$2a_1+2a_2$	$AABb$	$2a_1+a_2$	$AAbb$	$2a_1$
$AaBB$	a_1+2a_2	$AaBb$	a_1+a_2	$Aabb$	a_1
$aaBB$	$2a_2$	$aaBb$	a_2	$aabb$	0

The corresponding frequencies of these values of Z are given by the corresponding elements of matrix (3). It is easy to show that the mean and variance of Z are

$$\bar{Z} = 2pa_1 + 2ua_2, \qquad \sigma_Z^2 = 2pqa_1^2 + 2uva_2^2.$$

They are the sum of the means and variances of single pairs of genes taken separately: that is, $\bar{Z} = \bar{Z}_1 + \bar{Z}_2$ and $\sigma_Z^2 = \sigma_{Z_1}^2 + \sigma_{Z_2}^2$. Generally speaking, if there are k pairs of genes and we let q_i be the frequency of the "positive" allele of a locus and we let Z be the value of a k-factor genotype, it may be shown that

$$\bar{Z} = 2 \sum_i q_i a_i, \qquad \sigma_Z^2 = 2 \sum_i q_i (1 - q_i) a_i^2.$$

If Z be thought of as the value of measurement of a metrical character, and a_i as the effect of substitution of one gene with respect to that character, then we have the theorem that the mean and variance of the character are all *additive*, being the sum of those contributed by each pair of genes. A special application of the above theorem to F_2 populations is given in Exercise 7.

The above are but the first theorems in the genetics of quantitative characters. A further analysis that would include the effects of dominance and epistasis, as well as environmental influences, is well beyond the scope of this book. The important applications of quantitative genetics in plant and animal breeding must be left to experts in their respective fields. Valuable references to this subject, however, may be found in Lush (1943), Mather (1949), Lerner (1950), and Wright (1952b).

Notes and Exercises

1. Show that the determinant of the zygotic matrix (4) is

$$z_1 = 2 \begin{vmatrix} g_{11}^2 & 2g_{11}g_{13} & g_{13}^2 \\ g_{11}g_{31} & (g_{11}g_{33} + g_{13}g_{31}) & g_{13}g_{33} \\ g_{31}^2 & 2g_{31}g_{33} & g_{33}^2 \end{vmatrix} = 2 \begin{vmatrix} g_{11} & g_{13} \\ g_{31} & g_{33} \end{vmatrix}^3$$

HINT: Expand the determinant z_1 by the elements of its second row and note that

$$\begin{vmatrix} g_{11}^2 & g_{13}^2 \\ g_{31}^2 & g_{33}^2 \end{vmatrix} = (g_{11}g_{33} + g_{13}g_{31})d_0 .$$

Hence, $z_{n+1} = \frac{1}{8}z_n$, since $d_{n+1} = \frac{1}{2}d_n$. As $n \to \infty$, both d_n and z_n vanish. Also, the determinant of (3) is zero.

2. Calculate the zygotic and gametic proportions of the next few generations, assuming random mating, for the following initial populations:

$$\begin{pmatrix} .02 & .14 & .05 \\ .04 & .08 & .06 \\ .07 & .12 & .42 \end{pmatrix} ; \qquad \begin{pmatrix} .01 & .04 & .16 \\ .04 & .20 & .14 \\ .03 & .10 & .28 \end{pmatrix} .$$

Note the symmetrical property of the first population. What do you notice about the second?

3. There are two populations, one consisting of equal proportions of the four homozygous genotypes and the other of four single-heterozygous types:

$$\begin{pmatrix} \frac{1}{4} & 0 & \frac{1}{4} \\ 0 & 0 & 0 \\ \frac{1}{4} & 0 & \frac{1}{4} \end{pmatrix}, \quad \begin{pmatrix} 0 & \frac{1}{4} & 0 \\ \frac{1}{4} & 0 & \frac{1}{4} \\ 0 & \frac{1}{4} & 0 \end{pmatrix}.$$

Calculate the gametic output of each of them. What will be the constitution of their next generation on random mating? If we cross the individuals of these two populations at random, what will be the constitution of the hybrid population?

4. Show that

$$\begin{pmatrix} 0 & 0 & p^2 \\ 0 & 0 & 2pq \\ 0 & 0 & q^2 \end{pmatrix} \times \begin{pmatrix} 0 & 0 & 0 \\ 0 & 0 & 0 \\ u^2 & 2uv & v^2 \end{pmatrix} \rightarrow \begin{pmatrix} 0 & 0 & 0 \\ 0 & pu & pv \\ 0 & qu & qv \end{pmatrix}.$$

The meaning of the $\times$ symbol above is biological; it refers to the *crossing* of two populations, not to the multiplication of two matrices. The hybrid population is obtained from the random union of gametes produced by the two parental populations. Show that the gametic output and gene frequencies of this "F_1" population are as follows:

	B	b	Total
A	$\frac{1}{4}pu$	$\frac{1}{2}pv+\frac{1}{4}pu$	$\frac{1}{2}p$
a	$\frac{1}{2}qu+\frac{1}{4}pu$	$qv+\frac{1}{2}(pv+qu)+\frac{1}{4}pu$	$\frac{1}{2}(1+q)$
Total . .	$\frac{1}{2}u$	$\frac{1}{2}(1+v)$	1.00

Note that the gametic determinant $d_1 = 0$. Then, what will be the composition of the next generation on random mating? For an alternative algebraic form see Bunak (1936). Will the next generation be in equilibrium status?

5. If two pairs of genes are additive *and* equal in their effects with respect to a metrical trait, there will be five distinguishable phenotypes with the following equilibrium proportions:

Genotypes	Grade of Character	Proportion in Population
AABB	4	p^2u^2
AaBB, AABb	3	$2pu(qu+pv)$
AAbb, AaBb, aaBB	2	$p^2v^2+4pquv+q^2u^2$
Aabb, aaBb	1	$2qv(pv+qu)$
aabb	0	q^2v^2

Let [4] denote the proportion of Grade 4 individuals in the population, etc. Show that the ratio (Rife, 1951)

$$\frac{[4]}{[0]} \text{ is the square of } \frac{[3]}{[1]}.$$

This relation may provide a simple test for two-factor inheritance if the gene effects are cumulative and equal.

6. In the previous problem we have actually assumed that $a_1 = a_2 = 1$. Show that the mean and variance of the metrical character are, respectively, $\bar{Z} = 2p + 2u$ and $\sigma_Z^2 = 2pq + 2uv$.

7. The F_2 population derived from an original cross between two pure lines is always in equilibrium condition. Further, its gene frequencies are $q_i = \frac{1}{2}$ for all genes involved in the cross. Show that the variance of a metrical character in F_2 is $\frac{1}{2}\Sigma a_i^2$, assuming cumulative effects of genes (no dominance or epistasis).

8. The proportion of recessives (*aabb*) among all the eight Dom × Rec crosses is S_1 (Table 33) for two pairs of duplicate genes, but the proportion among the three matings capable of producing *aabb* is as follows:

Mating	Frequency, f	Segregation ratio, r
$AaBb \times aabb$......	$2q^2v^2 \times 2pq \cdot 2uv$	$\frac{1}{4}$
$Aabb \times aabb$......	$2q^2v^2 \times 2pq \cdot v^2$	$\frac{1}{2}$
$aaBb \times aabb$......	$2q^2v^2 \times q^2 \cdot 2uv$	$\frac{1}{2}$

Total mating frequency $= \Sigma f = 2q^3v^3\{(2p + q)(2u + v) - qv\}$.

Total recessive offspring $= \Sigma fr = 2q^3v^3\{(p + q)(u + v) - qv\}$.

Therefore the proportion of recessives among these segregating families with one dominant parent is (Li, 1953*d*)

$$R_1 = \frac{\Sigma fr}{\Sigma f} = \frac{1 - qv}{2(p + u)} = \frac{1 - qv}{(2 - q)(2 - v) - qv}.$$

This value lies between $\frac{1}{2}$ and $\frac{1}{4}$. The last form admits immediate generalization to k pairs of duplicate genes.

9. The six segregating matings among the thirty-six Dom × Dom crosses are shown in the following table. The value at the bottom of the third column is that entered in Table 33. The proportion of recessives among all the thirty-six Dom × Dom matings is S_2, as pointed out in the text, but that among these six segregating families is

$$R_2 = \frac{(1 - qv)^2}{4(p + u)^2} = R_1^2.$$

Its value lies between $\frac{1}{4}$ and $\frac{1}{16}$. It may be shown (Li, 1953d) that the relations $R_2 = R_1^2$ and $S_2 = S_1^2$ hold for any number of duplicate genes.

Mating	Frequency, f	Proportion of $aabb$, r
$AaBb \times AaBb$	$(2pq \cdot 2uv) \times (2pq \cdot 2uv)$	$\frac{1}{16}$
$AaBb \times aaBb$	$2(2pq \cdot 2uv) \times (q^2 \cdot 2uv)$	$\frac{1}{8}$
$AaBb \times Aabb$	$2(2pq \cdot 2uv) \times (2pq \cdot v^2)$	$\frac{1}{8}$
$aaBb \times aaBb$	$(q^2 \cdot 2uv) \times (q^2 \cdot 2uv)$	$\frac{1}{4}$
$aaBb \times Aabb$	$2(q^2 \cdot 2uv) \times (2pq \cdot v^2)$	$\frac{1}{4}$
$Aabb \times Aabb$	$(2pq \cdot v^2) \times (2pq \cdot v^2)$	$\frac{1}{4}$
	$\Sigma f = 4q^2v^2(p+u)^2$	$\Sigma fr = q^2v^2(1-qv)^2$

10. For complementary genes, as has been pointed out in the text, all three types of mating are capable of producing both phenotypes. There are fifteen crosses of the type "Rec" $\times$ "Rec," of which the following four are capable of producing "Dom" offspring:

"Rec" $\times$ "Rec"	Frequency	Proportion of "Dom" Offspring
$aaBB \times AAbb$	$2p^2q^2 \cdot u^2v^2$	1
$aaBB \times Aabb$	$4pq^3 \cdot u^2v^2$	$\frac{1}{2}$
$AAbb \times aaBb$	$4p^2q^2 \cdot uv^3$	$\frac{1}{2}$
$Aabb \times aaBb$	$8pq^3 \cdot uv^3$	$\frac{1}{4}$

Show that the proportion of "Dom" offspring among these four crosses is $1/(1 + q)(1 + v)$.

11. For any 2×2 contingency table with proportional frequencies, as shown in the following, where $a + b = 1$ and $x + y = 1$, the difference between the sums of diagonal cells is equal to the product of marginal differences; that is,

ax	ay	a
bx	by	b
x	y	1

$$ax + by - ay - bx = (a - b)(x - y).$$

12. In Chapter 2 it was shown that for one pair of genes with dominance the concordant sib-pairs (both dominant or both recessive) are always in excess of discordant pairs. If we now consider two traits simultaneously, there will

be four kinds of sib-pairs according to their concordance and discordance.
Let the first trait be shape and the second color. The four kinds of sib-pairs
are: (i) both shape and color alike; (ii) shape unlike but color alike; (iii)
shape alike but color unlike; and (iv) both shape and color unlike (Fig. 8).
If we take the traits separately, the frequency of shape-unlike pairs is
$S_{10} = \frac{1}{2}pq^2(3 + q)$, and the frequency of color-unlike pairs is $S'_{10} =
\frac{1}{2}uv^2(3 + v)$, whether the genes are linked or independent. Let X_1, X_2, X_3, X_4
be the frequencies of the four classes of pairs (Fig. 8) in the general population. If the two traits are due to independently assorted genes, the four
frequencies will be in simple proportion (as shown in the previous problem).

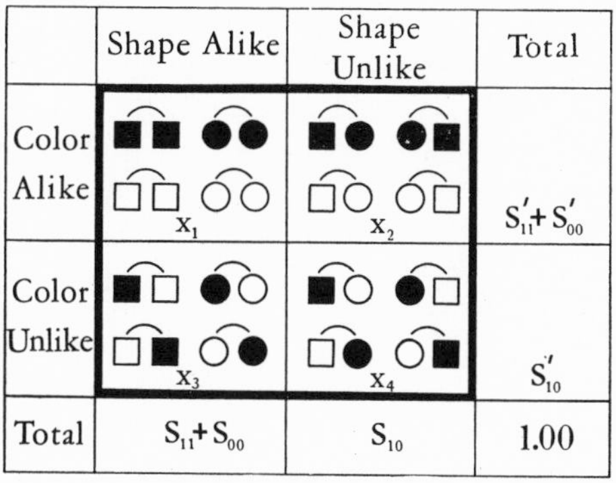

	Shape Alike	Shape Unlike	Total
Color Alike	X_1	X_2	$S'_{11}+S'_{00}$
Color Unlike	X_3	X_4	S'_{10}
Total	$S_{11}+S_{00}$	S_{10}	1.00

Fig. 8.—Four classes of sib-pairs according to their concordance and discordance with
respect to two traits. There are four possible phenotypes to each individual.

Let us call the classes (1) and (4) "even" pairs, since they are either all
alike or all unlike with respect to both traits, and call the classes (2) and (3)
"odd" pairs, since they are alike in one trait but unlike in the other. Then
in the case of independent genes, the excess of even pairs over odd pairs is,
from Exercise 11,

$$L_0 = X_1 + X_4 - X_2 - X_4 \qquad = (S_{11} + S_{00} - S_{10})(S'_{11} + S'_{00} - S'_{10})$$
$$= (1 - 2S_{10})(1 - 2S'_{10}) \qquad = [1 - pq^2(3 + q)][1 - uv^2(3 + v)].$$

If, however, the two pairs of genes are linked, the two traits will be positively correlated in some sibships and negatively correlated in others, as has
been pointed out earlier. For genes with dominance, this type of association
will show up in sibships of four matings: $AaBb \times aabb$, $AaBb \times Aabb$,
$AaBb \times aaBb$, $AaBb \times AaBb$. Therefore, for linked genes, the frequencies
of even pairs will be relatively increased (marginal frequencies remain unchanged, of course), so that the excess of even pairs over odd pairs will be
greater than L_0. The principle of Penrose's method (1935) of detecting autosomal linkage is to compare the observed value of the excess L with its theoretical value L_0. This method requires, in addition to a large number of

sib-pairs, that the traits are fairly common in the general population. More recently, Penrose has proposed (1946) a substantially better method of detecting linkage in sib-pair data. It is based on a new (3 $\times$ 3) classification of sib-pairs with respect to the two traits.

13. The cases for three or more pairs of genes, linked or independent, with two or multiple alleles, for diploids or autopolyploids, have been investigated in a series of papers by Geiringer (1944 and later); and the references, together with those to related works of other authors, may be found in her review (1949d). For diploids the equilibrium zygotic proportions under panmixia are given by terms of $(p_1 + q_1)^2 (p_2 + q_2)^2 \ldots (p_k + q_k)^2$, where p_i and q_i are the gene frequencies of the various pairs. The greater the number of loci involved, the slower the approach to equilibrium with respect to all genes simultaneously.

CHAPTER 9

Selfing

IN CHAPTERS 1–8 we have dealt only with random-mating populations; in this and in the next few chapters we shall consider some inbreeding populations. The problem of inbreeding is more involved than that of random mating. To study only the frequencies of certain kinds of gametes in a population would not be adequate. We must study separately each type of mating which is determined by the pattern of the inbreeding system. We shall begin with the simplest and most extreme inbreeding system: self-fertilization, or mating between individuals of identical genotypes.

§ 1. *Selfing of Diploids*

With respect to one pair of genes there are only three kinds of mating ($AA \times AA$, $Aa \times Aa$, $aa \times aa$) for selfing in contrast to six for random mating. When homozygotes are selfed or crossed with identical homozygotes, their offspring will all be homozygotes of the parental type. When a heterozygote is selfed or crossed with other heterozygotes, the offspring will be, as is well known, $\frac{1}{4}AA + \frac{1}{2}Aa + \frac{1}{4}aa$. In other words, heterozygotes on selfing produce $\frac{1}{2}$ heterozygotes and $\frac{1}{2}$ homozygotes, among which AA and aa are equally numerous. It follows, therefore, that if H_0 is the proportion of heterozygotes in an initial population, and H_n is the proportion after n generations of continued selfing,

$$H_n = \tfrac{1}{2}H_{n-1} = (\tfrac{1}{2})^n H_0 \to 0 \quad \text{as} \quad n \to \infty . \tag{1}$$

Since the heterozygotes produce an equal number of AA and aa in each generation of selfing, an initial population (D, H, R) will eventually become $(D + \frac{1}{2}H, 0, \frac{1}{2}H + R) = (p, 0, q)$, where p, q are frequencies of A, a in the population. Note that the gene frequencies remain constant from generation to generation. The mating system per se does not change the gene frequencies but does affect the zygotic proportions in a population. In selfing populations the heterozygotes disappear rapidly, and the final proportions of the homozygotes are equal to their corresponding gene frequencies.

The properties of continued selfing described above apply equally well to multiple alleles. Let H_0 be the total proportion of heterozygotes (A_1A_2, A_1A_3, A_2A_3) in an initial population. Since each heterozygote on selfing produces 50 per cent heterozygotes like itself, while the other 50 per cent are the two corresponding homozygotes, H will be reduced by one-half in each generation. Eventually the population will consist of $q_1(A_1A_1) + q_2(A_2A_2) + q_3(A_3A_3)$, where q_i is the frequency of allele A_i and $\Sigma q = 1$.

The recurrence relation $H_{n+1} = \frac{1}{2}H_n$ is an intrinsic property of the mating system—in this case, self-fertilization. It shows how the proportion of heterozygotes diminishes in each generation. But the absolute proportions of the various genotypes in a population depend upon the composition of the initial population as well as the number of generations it has been subjected to a particular pattern of inbreeding. For example, if the initial population is (.54, .32, .14), on selfing it becomes in subsequent generations: (.62, .16, .22), (.66, .08, .26), (.68, .04, .28), (.69, .02, .29), etc., and eventually (.70, 0, .30). A particular but important case is that in which the initial population consists wholly of hetero-

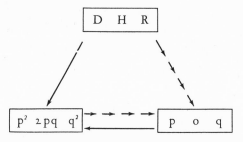

Fig. 9.—Results of random mating (*one long arrow*) and close inbreeding (*a series of short arrows*) in a population.

zygotes (0, 1, 0). In such a case the proportions of homozygotes ($AA + aa$) and heterozygotes after n generations of selfing are, respectively, $(2^n - 1)/2^n$ and $(\frac{1}{2})^n$.

If, however, during the process of inbreeding, the population is allowed to practice random mating at any time, it will become (p^2, $2pq$, q^2) in the very next generation, whatever the proportions of homozygotes and heterozygotes before the random mating occurred. Thus, one generation of random mating wipes out the effects of generations of inbreeding as far as homozygosis (or heterozygosis) is concerned. This is illustrated in Figure 9.

§ 2. *Several Pairs of Genes*

We shall consider first the two-factor genotypes. Assuming two independent loci, $AaBb$ on selfing will produce $\frac{1}{16}$ of each of the four homozygous types, $\frac{2}{16}$ of each of the four "mixed" types (one pair homozygous, the other heterozygous), and $\frac{4}{16}$ double heterozygotes like itself. Therefore, $[AaBb]_{n+1} = \frac{1}{4}[AaBb]_n$. The "mixed" types (e.g., $AABb$) on selfing will be reduced by one-half in the next generation but will be increased by $\frac{1}{8}[AaBb]$. Eventually, all heterozygotes will disappear, and the population will consist of $\frac{1}{4}$ each of the four homozygous types. Adopting the notations of the last chapter, the effect of continued selfing may be represented thus:

$$
\begin{pmatrix} 0 & 0 & 0 \\ \\ 0 \leftarrow 1 \rightarrow 0 \\ \\ 0 & 0 & 0 \end{pmatrix}
\longrightarrow
\begin{pmatrix} \frac{1}{16} & \frac{2}{16} & \frac{1}{16} \\ \\ \frac{2}{16} & \frac{4}{16} & \frac{2}{16} \\ \\ \frac{1}{16} & \frac{2}{16} & \frac{1}{16} \end{pmatrix}
\rightarrow \cdots \rightarrow
\begin{pmatrix} \frac{1}{4} & 0 & \frac{1}{4} \\ \\ 0 & 0 & 0 \\ \\ \frac{1}{4} & 0 & \frac{1}{4} \end{pmatrix}
$$

Similarly, continued selfing of $AABb$ will eventually yield $\frac{1}{2}AABB$ and $\frac{1}{2}AAbb$, and so on. Therefore, the eventual composition resulting from the selfing of any given population is

$$
\begin{pmatrix} z_{11} & z_{12} & z_{13} \\ \\ z_{21} & z_{22} & z_{23} \\ \\ z_{31} & z_{32} & z_{33} \end{pmatrix}
\longrightarrow \cdots \cdots \longrightarrow
\begin{pmatrix} \hat{z}_{11} & 0 & \hat{z}_{13} \\ \\ 0 & 0 & 0 \\ \\ \hat{z}_{31} & 0 & \hat{z}_{33} \end{pmatrix}
\tag{2}
$$

where $\hat{z}_{11} = z_{11} + \frac{1}{2}(z_{12} + z_{21}) + \frac{1}{4}z_{22} = g_{11}$, etc. (Chap. 8, eq. [1]). In other words, the final proportions of the four homozygous types are equal to the frequencies of the four corresponding kinds of gametes produced by the population. Note that there is no change in gene frequencies and that the proportion of A is still $p = \hat{z}_{11} + \hat{z}_{13}$, etc.

This result can be extended to cases involving any number of pairs of genes. Linkage slows down the rate of approach to complete homozygosis but does not affect the final results.

When there are several pairs of genes involved, it is convenient to classify the genotypes according to the number of pairs of genes for which they are homozygous or heterozygous. For k pairs of independent genes the proportions of the various classes of genotypes from selfing $AaBbCc \ldots$ will be given by the terms of

$$
\frac{1}{2^{nk}}[(2^n - 1) + 1]^k,
$$

where n is the number of generations of selfing. The approach to complete homozygosis is very rapid. Even if there are fifteen or twenty heterozygous pairs of genes in the initial individuals, complete homozygosis will be reached, for all practical purposes, within ten or a dozen generations of continued selfing. The calculations for one, five, ten, and fifteen pairs of independent genes have been given by East and Jones (1919). The left half of Table 34 gives the results for three pairs of genes as an illustration.

Now let us consider the problem of heterozygosis from a different point of view. If we disregard the genotype as an entity and merely consider it as k pairs of genes, then the total number of heterozygous pairs in any generation will be halved in each generation of selfing, because each pair A_ia_i produces $\frac{1}{2}A_ia_i + \frac{1}{4}A_iA_i + \frac{1}{4}a_ia_i$. Thus, as shown in the right half of Table 34, the proportion of heterozygous pairs is $1, \frac{1}{2}, \frac{1}{4}, \frac{1}{8}, \frac{1}{16}, \ldots$, in successive generations.

Finally, it is seen that the proportions of heterozygous pairs, as calculated from the right half of Table 34, may also be regarded as the *average* proportion

TABLE 34

PROPORTIONS OF VARIOUS CLASSES OF GENOTYPES FROM
SELFING $A_1a_1A_2a_2A_3a_3$ INDIVIDUALS

GENER- ATIONS OF SELF- ING n	NO. OF HETEROZYGOUS PAIRS IN A GENOTYPE				TOTAL No. OF INDI- VIDUALS 2^{3n}	TOTAL PAIRS	
	0	1	2	3		Hetero- zygous	All
0......	0	0	0	1	1	3	3
1......	1	3	3	1	$8 = 2^3$	12	24
2......	27	27	9	1	$64 = 2^6$	48	192
3......	343	147	21	1	$512 = 2^9$	192	1536
4......	3375	675	45	1	$4096 = 2^{12}$	768	12,288
$\cdots$	$\cdots$	$\cdots$	$\cdots$	$\cdots$	$\cdots$	$\cdots$	$\cdots$
∞.....	1	0	0	0	1	0	1

of heterozygous pairs per *individual*. This leads us to another point of view on heterozygosis. If an initial individual (or a group of identical individuals) is heterozygous for a large number (k) of loci, the average individual in the next generation produced by self-fertilization will have $\frac{1}{2}k$ pairs of loci in heterozygous condition, and so on. Eventually, all loci will be homozygous for all individuals (which consist of 2^k different "lines").

In summary, it may be said that the recurrence relation $H_{n+1} = \frac{1}{2}H_n$ can be interpreted in three ways. The simplest interpretation is with respect to the proportion of Aa in the general population for one pair of genes. The second is with respect to heterozygous pairs (of all loci) in a population. But for most practical breeding purposes the third interpretation is the most important—it measures the degree of genetic uniformity of individuals subjected to selfing or crosses among themselves. The same interpretations apply to all recurrence relations of H to be derived in subsequent chapters. This fact justifies the limitation of our analysis to one locus; and the recurrence relation applies to the degree of genotypic heterozygosis of individuals, regardless of the number of loci involved.

§ 3. *Selfing of Autotetraploids*

For the sake of simplicity we shall assume random chromosome segregation in the following analysis. The recurrence relation of heterozygosis is purely a property of the mating system and independent of the initial composition of a population to begin with. Suppose the initial group of individuals is all A^2a^2, as would be the case for the F_1 from the cross $A^4 \times a^4$. The gametes produced by each kind of zygote are given in Chapter 6, equation (1). On selfing each genotype, the offspring will be formed by the random union of the parental gametes. For in-

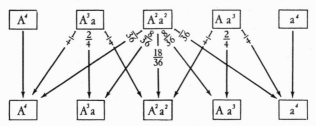

FIG. 10.—Relations between the zygotic proportions of two consecutive generations on selfing.

TABLE 35

RESULTS OF SELFING AUTOTETRAPLOIDS, ASSUM-
ING CHROMOSOME SEGREGATION

n	A^4	A^3a	A^2a^2	Aa^3	a^4	H
0.....	0	0	1	0	0	1
1.....	$\frac{1}{36}$	$\frac{8}{36}$	$\frac{18}{36}$	$\frac{8}{36}$	$\frac{1}{36}$	$\frac{17}{18}$
2.....	$\frac{7}{72}$	$\frac{16}{72}$	$\frac{26}{72}$	$\frac{16}{72}$	$\frac{7}{72}$	$\frac{29}{36}$
3.....	$\frac{211}{1296}$	$\frac{248}{1296}$	$\frac{378}{1296}$	$\frac{248}{1296}$	$\frac{211}{1296}$	$\frac{437}{648}$
4.....	$\frac{567}{2592}$	$\frac{416}{2592}$	$\frac{626}{2592}$	$\frac{416}{2592}$	$\frac{567}{2592}$	$\frac{729}{1296}$
. . .	. . .	. . .	. . .	. . .	. . .	. . .
∞....	$\frac{1}{2}$	0	0	0	$\frac{1}{2}$	0

stance, the results of selfing A^2a^2 are given in the second line of the table in Exercise 3 of Chapter 6. The selfing of A^3a will produce $\frac{1}{4}A^4 + \frac{1}{2}A^3a + \frac{1}{4}A^2a^2$, etc. The relations between the zygotic proportions of two consecutive generations are illustrated in Figure 10. The absolute values of zygotic proportions in successive generations are given in Table 35, assuming the initial population to be all A^2a^2.

Let H denote the combined proportion of all types of heterozygotes ($A^3a + A^2a^2 + Aa^3$). Now we see that the successive values of H (Table 35) form a recurrent series whose recurrence relation and general term are, respectively (Chap. 5, Appendix, Example 3),

$$H_{n+2} = H_{n+1} - \tfrac{5}{36}H_n ; \qquad H_n = \tfrac{7}{5}(\tfrac{5}{6})^{n+1} - (\tfrac{1}{6})^{n+1} . \tag{3}$$

The limiting value of H is clearly zero, but the rate of approach to complete homozygosis is much slower than for diploids. After four generations of selfing, for instance, $H = 729/1296 = 56.25$ per cent, a figure still higher than the one that would represent what diploids would accomplish in one generation. After a sufficient number of generations of selfing (n moderately large), the heterozygosis will decrease by $\frac{1}{6}$ per generation, approximately; that is, $H_{n+1} = \frac{5}{6}H_n$.

If we consider the heterozygous types separately, we see that each of the series of values for A^3a, A^2a^2, Aa^3 (Table 35) is also a recurrent series with the same scales of relation as H. But the expressions for their general terms are different (see Chap. 5, Appendix, Example 5), because their two initial terms are different. After a sufficient number of generations they all decrease by $\frac{1}{6}$ per generation.

If we start with any arbitrary population (z_4, z_3, z_2, z_1, z_0), where z_4 is the proportion of A^4, etc., continued selfing will lead eventually to complete homozygosis consisting only of A^4 and a^4 in the proportions of $p:q$, the frequencies of the alleles A and a. These frequencies are determined by the initial population. Thus,

$$p = z_4 + \tfrac{3}{4}z_3 + \tfrac{1}{2}z_2 + \tfrac{1}{4}z_1 .$$

§ 4. *A More General Method*

A simple method of finding the recurrence relation of a series with known initial terms was given in the appendix to Chapter 5. There it was shown also that the general term can be expressed as the sum of the corresponding terms of two or more geometric series. The problem of selfing autotetraploids was solved quite successfully by that method in the preceding section. However, another somewhat more general method may be applied to the same problem. This method has been applied extensively by Haldane, by Bartlett, and by Fisher in solving various problems of inbreeding; and it will be applied to the case of sib mating in our next chapter. In this section our chief purpose is to expose the algebra of this method.

1. Consider the set of homogeneous linear equations:

$$\left.\begin{aligned}
x' &= c_{11}x + c_{12}y + c_{13}z \\
y' &= c_{21}x + c_{22}y + c_{23}z \\
z' &= c_{31}x + c_{32}y + c_{33}z
\end{aligned}\right\} , \tag{4}$$

where the c's are constants. It is called a *linear transformation* set. With given values of x, y, z we can thus calculate the corresponding values of x', y', z'. In terms of geometry, we say that the point (x, y, z) is transformed to the point (x', y', z').

2. If a function of the original variables, $f(x, y, z)$, is such that it is identically equal to the same function of the transformed variables, that is, $f(x', y', z') \equiv f(x, y, z)$, it is called an *invariant* of the transformation (4). If they are propor-

tional, viz., $f(x', y', z') \equiv \lambda f(x, y, z)$, where the value of λ is independent of x, y, z, the function is called a *relative invariant* of the substitution (4). In particular, if the relative invariant function f is a linear function of x, y, z, such that

$$(l_1x' + l_2y' + l_3z') \equiv \lambda(l_1x + l_2y + l_3z), \qquad (5)$$

where the l's are constants, it is called a *linear relative invariant* of the transformation (4). For this kind of function it is obvious that only the proportional values $l_1:l_2:l_3$ are relevant, because any other three numbers with the same proportions will also satisfy the identity (5).

3. Suppose that we want to find a linear relative invariant function with respect to the given transformation (4). This merely amounts to finding some sets of three numbers, l_1, l_2, l_3, which will satisfy the identity (5). For each specified value of λ there will be a set of l_1, l_2, l_3. To solve for λ and the l's, we substitute (4) in (5); thus,

$$\left.\begin{array}{l} l_1(c_{11}x + c_{12}y + c_{13}z) \\ + l_2(c_{21}x + c_{22}y + c_{23}z) \\ + l_3(c_{31}x + c_{32}y + c_{33}z) \end{array}\right\} \equiv \lambda(l_1x + l_2y + l_3z).$$

Since it is an identity, the coefficients of x, y, z of both sides of the identity must be equal. Hence we obtain the following three equations:

$$\left.\begin{array}{lll} \text{coeff. of } x: & \lambda l_1 = c_{11}l_1 + c_{21}l_2 + c_{31}l_3 \\ \text{coeff. of } y: & \lambda l_2 = c_{12}l_1 + c_{22}l_2 + c_{32}l_3 \\ \text{coeff. of } z: & \lambda l_3 = c_{13}l_1 + c_{23}l_2 + c_{33}l_3 \end{array}\right\}, \qquad (6)$$

from which the values of λ and the l's may be solved (the latter in proportional values only). Note that the c's here are those of (4), except that the rows and columns are interchanged (transposed).

If we regard (6) as a linear transformation set, the three numbers l_1, l_2, l_3 must be such that their transformed values $\lambda l_1, \lambda l_2, \lambda l_3$ are in the same proportions as the numbers themselves. The numbers l_1, l_2, l_3 are then said to define a "pole" of (6).

4. If we rewrite the set of homogeneous equations (6) in the form $(c_{11} - \lambda)l_1 + c_{21}l_2 + c_{31}l_3 = 0$, etc., we see that there are solutions for l_1, l_2, l_3 only when the determinant of their coefficients vanishes:

$$\begin{vmatrix} c_{11} - \lambda & c_{21} & c_{31} \\ c_{12} & c_{22} - \lambda & c_{32} \\ c_{13} & c_{23} & c_{33} - \lambda \end{vmatrix} = f(\lambda) = 0. \qquad (7)$$

This is called the *characteristic equation* of (6), from which the values of λ may be determined. This equation has three roots; let them be $\lambda_1, \lambda_2, \lambda_3$. Only when λ takes one of these three root values can we have a solution for l_1, l_2, l_3. For example, when $\lambda = \lambda_1$, a "pole" (l_1, l_2, l_3) may be found from the equations (6). Hence, there are three poles, corresponding to the three cases: $\lambda = \lambda_1, \lambda_2, \lambda_3$. No pole is possible for values of λ other than $\lambda_1, \lambda_2, \lambda_3$. With λ and l_1, l_2, l_3 all determined, the linear relative invariant function (5) is completely solved; and we will have three solutions for it too.

5. Now let us consider the original transformation (4) once more. Let $x_0, y_0,$ z_0 be the first set of numbers we substitute in the right side of (4), and x_1, y_1, z_1 be the transformed values on the left side. These values will satisfy the identity (5) in which the values of λ and l's have all been properly determined by the procedure just given. If we repeat the operation of transformation by substituting x_1, y_1, z_1 in the right side of (4), we obtain the transformed values x_2, y_2, z_2 on the left side, and so on. After n such successive transformations, we obtain the values x_n, y_n, z_n. Of course, this is a laborious procedure. Now, since the values of x, y, z in any two successive transformations satisfy the relation (5), we see that, for each eligible value of λ,

$$(l_1 x_n + l_2 y_n + l_3 z_n) = \lambda(l_1 x_{n-1} + l_2 y_{n-1} + l_3 z_{n-1}) = \lambda^n (l_1 x_0 + l_2 y_0 + l_3 z_0) .$$

The above expression simply says that the quantity $(l_1 x + l_2 y + l_3 z)$ forms a geometric series with common ratio λ and the first term $(l_1 x_0 + l_2 y_0 + l_3 z_0)$. It is this property that enables us to find the values of x_n, y_n, z_n from their initial values x_0, y_0, z_0 without actually going through the n successive transformations. To solve for x_n, y_n, z_n, we set up the following three equations corresponding to the three cases $\lambda = \lambda_1, \lambda_2, \lambda_3$:

$$\left. \begin{array}{l} l_1 x_n + l_2 y_n + l_3 z_n = (l_1 x_0 + l_2 y_0 + l_3 z_0)\lambda_1^n \quad = C_1 \lambda_1^n \\ l_1' x_n + l_2' y_n + l_3' z_n = (l_1' x_0 + l_2' y_0 + l_3' z_0)\lambda_2^n \quad = C_2 \lambda_2^n \\ l_1'' x_n + l_2'' y_n + l_3'' z_n = (l_1'' x_0 + l_2'' y_0 + l_3'' z_0)\lambda_3^n = C_3 \lambda_3^n \end{array} \right\} , \qquad (8)$$

where we write C_1 for $(l_1 x_0 + l_2 y_0 + l_3 z_0)$, etc. These are constants determined by the initial values x_0, y_0, z_0, with which we started the transformation process.

6. Solving for three unknowns from three equations should present no difficulty. Note that (8) is a set of linear equations, because the l's, C's, and λ's are all known numbers. Solving (8), we will find that x_n, y_n, z_n may all be expressed in the form

$$k_1 \lambda_1^n + k_2 \lambda_2^n + k_3 \lambda_3^n , \qquad (9)$$

where the k's are constants. Since λ is the common ratio of a geometric series, it means that each of the variables x, y, z may be expressed as the sum of the corresponding terms of three geometric series. Recalling the contents of the appendix to Chapter 5, we see that this implies that the variable x (or y or z) in successive transformations will form a recurrent series in which each term is formed by a linear combination of its preceding three terms: $u_{n+3} = b u_{n+2} + c u_{n+1} + d u_n$. It is important to see the analogy between these two methods. For instance, the characteristic equation, $f(\lambda) = 0$, is the same equation, $\lambda^3 - b\lambda^2 - c\lambda - d = 0$, as was given in the appendix to Chapter 5. Thus, our characteristic equation will give us the recurrence relation of the series. The only difference between these two methods is that in the appendix we started out with a recurrence series with known scales of relation, while here we started out with a transformation set. The latter method also reveals that the three recurrence series, x, y, z, all have the same scales of relation. Furthermore, any linear combination of x, y, and z may also be expressed in the form (9) and thus has the same scales of relation.

§ 5. *Application to Selfing Autotetraploids*

Now let us illustrate the above procedure by the case of selfing autotetraploids. Let $2x_n = [A^4 + a^4]$, $2y_n = [A^3a + Aa^3]$, $z_n = [A^2a^2]$ in the nth generation of continued selfing, where $2x_n + 2y_n + z_n = 1$. In the particular population shown in Table 35, $[A^4] = [a^4] = x_n$ and $[A^3a] = [Aa^3] = y_n$ in all generations. In the general case, x_n may be thought of as the average proportion of A^4 and a^4, etc. On selfing, the zygotic proportions in the next generation will be, according to Figure 10,

$$\left.\begin{array}{l} x_{n+1} = x_n + \tfrac{1}{4}y_n + \tfrac{1}{36}z_n \\ y_{n+1} = \qquad \tfrac{1}{2}y_n + \tfrac{2}{9}z_n \\ z_{n+1} = \qquad \tfrac{1}{2}y_n + \tfrac{1}{2}z_n \end{array}\right\}, \tag{4'}$$

where $2x_{n+1} + 2y_{n+1} + z_{n+1} = 1$. The last two equations form an independent set for the variables y and z. The first equation concerning the proportion of homozygotes may be left out of consideration. The properties of selfing autotetraploids in regard to changes in proportions of heterozygotes are all embodied in (4'). The next step is to find a relative linear invariant function with respect to (4'); that is, to find a function to satisfy

$$l_1y_{n+1} + l_2z_{n+1} \equiv \lambda(l_1y_n + l_2z_n). \tag{5'}$$

Substituting (4') in (5'), and equating the coefficients of y_n and z_n on both sides of the identity, we obtain

$$\left.\begin{array}{l} \tfrac{1}{2}l_1 + \tfrac{1}{2}l_2 = \lambda l_1 , \\ \tfrac{2}{9}l_1 + \tfrac{1}{2}l_2 = \lambda l_2 . \end{array}\right\} \tag{6'}$$

This set of equations has solutions only for certain values of λ. The characteristic equation is then

$$\begin{vmatrix} \tfrac{1}{2} - \lambda & \tfrac{1}{2} \\ \tfrac{2}{9} & \tfrac{1}{2} - \lambda \end{vmatrix} = \lambda^2 - \lambda + \tfrac{5}{36} = 0 , \tag{7'}$$

with roots

$$\lambda_1 = \tfrac{5}{6} \quad \text{and} \quad \lambda_2 = \tfrac{1}{6} .$$

Note that the characteristic equation also gives us the recurrence relation of the y or z series or the $2y + z = H$ series. Hence,

$$H_{n+2} - H_{n+1} + \tfrac{5}{36}H_n = 0,$$

because λ_1 and λ_2 are the common ratios of two corresponding geometric series. Now, since we have found the values of λ, the corresponding two sets of (l_1, l_2) may be found from equations (6'). Thus,

$$\lambda_1 = \tfrac{5}{6}, \qquad l_1 : l_2 = 3 : 2 ;$$
$$\lambda_2 = \tfrac{1}{6}, \qquad l_1 : l_2 = 3 : -2 .$$

The identity (5') is now completely solved. We proceed to find the general terms of y and z. After n generations of continued selfing, we have

$$\left.\begin{array}{l} 3y_n + 2z_n = \tfrac{5}{6}(3y_{n-1} + 2z_{n-1}) = (\tfrac{5}{6})^n(3y_0 + 2z_0), \\ 3y_n - 2z_n = \tfrac{1}{6}(3y_{n-1} - 2z_{n-1}) = (\tfrac{1}{6})^n(3y_0 - 2z_0), \end{array}\right\} \qquad (8')$$

from which, with any given initial values y_0 and z_0, their corresponding values after n generations may be obtained easily. It is seen that the expressions for y_n, z_n, and H_n will all be of the form $\text{Const.}_1 (5/6)^n + \text{Const.}_2 (1/6)^n$. For example, in Table 35, $z_0 = 1$, $y_0 = 0$. Substituting in (8') and solving, we find

$$y_n = \tfrac{1}{3}(\tfrac{5}{6})^n - \tfrac{1}{3}(\tfrac{1}{6})^n ; \quad z_n = \tfrac{1}{2}(\tfrac{5}{6})^n + \tfrac{1}{2}(\tfrac{1}{6})^n . \qquad (9')$$

These results are identical with those of Example 5 in the appendix to Chapter 5. Furthermore, $H_n = 2y_n + z_n$ will be of the form given in (3). As was mentioned earlier, it is unnecessary to employ this method for the case of selfing autotetraploids, since all its properties may be obtained by the simpler procedure in Section 3. But it is helpful to be familiar with this more general method, as we shall use it for more complicated cases in the next chapter.

Notes and Exercises

1. Calculate the zygotic proportions of the next four generations and the limiting proportions, assuming continued selfing, for the following populations:

$$\begin{pmatrix} AA & Aa & aa \\ p^2, & 2pq, & q^2 \end{pmatrix} ; \quad \begin{pmatrix} AA & Aa' & Aa & a'a' & a'a & aa \\ .05, & .20, & .10, & .06, & .28, & .31 \end{pmatrix} ;$$

$$\begin{pmatrix} AA & Aa' & Aa & a'a' & a'a & aa \\ .04, & .12, & .20, & .09, & .30, & .25 \end{pmatrix} .$$

2. Given the following four initial populations with respect to two pairs of independent genes:

$$\begin{pmatrix} \tfrac{1}{4} & 0 & 0 \\ 0 & \tfrac{1}{2} & 0 \\ 0 & 0 & \tfrac{1}{4} \end{pmatrix}, \quad \begin{pmatrix} 0 & 0 & \tfrac{1}{4} \\ 0 & \tfrac{1}{2} & 0 \\ \tfrac{1}{4} & 0 & 0 \end{pmatrix}, \quad \begin{pmatrix} 0 & \tfrac{1}{4} & 0 \\ 0 & \tfrac{1}{2} & 0 \\ 0 & \tfrac{1}{4} & 0 \end{pmatrix}, \quad \begin{pmatrix} 0 & 0 & 0 \\ \tfrac{1}{4} & \tfrac{1}{2} & \tfrac{1}{4} \\ 0 & 0 & 0 \end{pmatrix},$$

show that under random mating they will all have the same final equilibrium state and that under continued selfing they will all be different except for the last two populations.

3. If the initial population consists entirely of A^3a zygotes and practices selfing, the zygotic proportions will be as shown in the table that follows. Investigate the recurrence relations and general expressions for H.

n	A^4	A^3a	A^2a^2	Aa^3	a^4	H
0.....	0	1	0	0	0	1
1.....	$\frac{1}{4}$	$\frac{2}{4}$	$\frac{1}{4}$	0	0	$\frac{3}{4}$
2.....	$\frac{55}{144}$	$\frac{44}{144}$	$\frac{36}{144}$	$\frac{8}{144}$	$\frac{1}{144}$	$\frac{11}{18}$
3.....	$\frac{67}{144}$	$\frac{30}{144}$	$\frac{31}{144}$	$\frac{12}{144}$	$\frac{4}{144}$	$\frac{73}{144}$
4.....	$\frac{2713}{5184}$	$\frac{788}{5184}$	$\frac{936}{5184}$	$\frac{464}{5184}$	$\frac{283}{5184}$	$\frac{547}{1296}$
...	...	...	...	...	...	...
∞....	$\frac{3}{4}$	0	0	0	$\frac{1}{4}$	0

4. The following table illustrates a general case. Show that the proportions of A^2a^2 and the combined proportions of A^3a and Aa^3 in successive generations all have the same recurrence relation as that of H.

n	A^4	A^3a	A^2a^2	Aa^3	a^4	H
0.....	0.100	0.160	0.360	0.200	0.180	0.720
1.....	.150	.160	.270	.180	.240	.610
2.....	.1975	.140	.220	.150	.2225	.510
3.....	.2386$\dot{1}$	.1188$\dot{8}$	.18250	.1238$\dot{8}$	.3361$\dot{1}$	.4252$\dot{7}$
4.....	.2734	0.1000	0.1519	0.1025	.3722	0.3544
...	...	...	...	...	...	...
∞....	0.450	0	0	0	0.550	0

5. If an initial population consists of 40 per cent A^3a and 60 per cent Aa^3 individuals and practices selfing, what will be the zygotic proportions in the next few generations? What will be its ultimate status? If it is the same as that in the previous problem, why is this so?

6. The recurrence relation of H may be derived directly from the transformation set (4′). Thus,

$$H_{n+2} = 2y_{n+2} + z_{n+2} = 2(\tfrac{1}{2}y_{n+1} + \tfrac{2}{9}z_{n+1}) + \tfrac{1}{2}(y_{n+1} + \tfrac{1}{2}z_{n+1})$$

$$= 2y_{n+1} + z_{n+1} - \tfrac{1}{2}y_{n+1} - \tfrac{1}{18}z_{n+1}$$

$$= H_{n+1} - \tfrac{1}{2}(\tfrac{1}{2}y_n + \tfrac{2}{9}z_n) - \tfrac{1}{18}(\tfrac{1}{2}y_n + \tfrac{1}{2}z_n)$$

$$= H_{n+1} - \tfrac{5}{36}(2y_n + z_n) = H_{n+1} - \tfrac{5}{36}H_n .$$

Show that both y_n and z_n have the same recurrence relation as H_n.

7. The genetic variance (Chap. 3) of a population with inbreeding is higher than that of a panmictic population:

n	Z			GENETIC VARIANCE
	2	1	0	
0............	p^2	$2pq$	q^2	$2pq=\sigma_0^2$
1............	$p^2+\frac{1}{2}pq$	pq	$q^2+\frac{1}{2}pq$	$3pq=(1+\frac{1}{2})\sigma_0^2$
2............	$p^2+\frac{3}{4}pq$	$pq/2$	$q^2+\frac{3}{4}pq$	$3.5pq=(1+\frac{3}{4})\sigma_0^2$
General......	p^2+Fpq	$2pq(1-F)$	q^2+Fpq	$2(1+F)pq=(1+F)\sigma_0^2$
Limit........	p	0	q	$4pq=2\sigma_0^2$

This problem will be treated in greater detail later.

8. It follows from (2) that, if the initial population is a random-mating one (in equilibrium), continued selfing will lead to complete homozygosis with the following proportions.

	GENOTYPE			
	$AABB$	$AAbb$	$aaBB$	$aabb$
Frequency.......	pu	pv	qu	qv
Z value........	$2a_1+2a_2$	$2a_1$	$2a_2$	0

Show that the mean of Z is the same as that of the original random-mating population but that the variance of Z is twice as large (see Chap. 8, § 8). Therefore, if we let σ_0^2, σ_F^2, σ_1^2 be the genetic variances of a random-mating population, of a population with a certain extent of inbreeding as measured by the fraction F, and of a population with complete homozygosis, respectively, the relations

$$\sigma_F^2 = (1 + F)\sigma_0^2, \qquad \sigma_1^2 = 2\sigma_0^2$$

hold, regardless of the number of loci involved, as long as the gene effects are additive. A more precise definition of F will be given in Chapter 11.

CHAPTER 10

Sib Mating

FOR dioecious organisms the most intensive system of inbreeding is the mating between full sibs, usually known as brother-sister mating. The properties of this system of inbreeding have been carefully studied by a number of geneticists (Fish, Haldane, Jennings, Pearl, Robbins, Schäfer, Wright, and others) and are of importance in both theoretical and applied genetics, especially in animal breeding.

§ 1. *Types of Parental Combinations and Sibships*

As noted in the previous chapter, a study of inbreeding problems must do more than consider the proportions of various kinds of gametes produced by a population. The zygotic proportions of one generation of a sib-mating population do not help us to calculate the zygotic proportions of the next generation, because, all matings being between sibs, it is the frequencies of the types of sibships that determine the composition of the next generation (see Ex. 1). The type of a sibship, in turn, depends upon its parental combination. Therefore we must study the changes in frequencies of the various types of mating, from generation to generation, in a sib-mating population.

Assume that brothers and sisters are always equally numerous in a sibship. Assume also that members of a sibship mate at random among themselves, so that each sibship may be regarded as a small random-mating unit. The entire population then may be thought of as an assemblage of numerous small "isolates," each isolate a sibship.

There are six types of mating with respect to one pair of autosomal genes. For each type of mating there will be a certain type of sibship, which in turn will produce various types of mating in the next generation in fixed proportions. The two types of mating, $(AA \times AA)$ and $(aa \times aa)$, need no comment. All matings between their offspring will be of the same type as that of the parents. The mating $(AA \times aa)$ produces a sibship $\{Aa\}$, which yields only $(Aa \times Aa)$ matings in the next generation. The mating $(AA \times Aa)$ produces a sibship $\{\frac{1}{2}AA + \frac{1}{2}Aa\}$, which in turn yields $\frac{1}{4}(AA \times AA) + \frac{1}{2}(AA \times Aa) + \frac{1}{4}(Aa \times Aa)$ matings in the next generation. The same is true for $(aa \times Aa)$ except that

A and a are interchanged. Finally, the mating $(Aa \times Aa)$ produces a sibship $\{\frac{1}{4}AA + \frac{1}{2}Aa + \frac{1}{4}aa\}$, which is capable of yielding all six types of mating in the next generation in the proportions $\frac{1}{16}(AA \times AA)$, $\frac{1}{16}(aa \times aa)$, $\frac{1}{8}(AA \times aa)$, $\frac{1}{4}(AA \times Aa)$, $\frac{1}{4}(aa \times Aa)$, $\frac{1}{4}(Aa \times Aa)$. These relations have been summarized and illustrated in Figure 11, wherein $(AA \times AA)$ and $(aa \times aa)$ are combined as are $(AA \times Aa)$ and $(aa \times Aa)$. The frequencies of the four groups of matings are denoted by w, x, y, z, whose sum is unity.

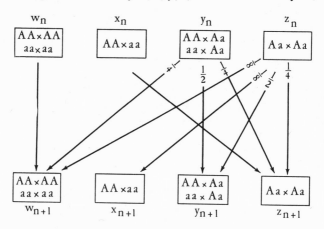

FIG. 11.—Relations between frequencies of various types of matings in two successive generations under the system of sib mating.

§ 2. *Decrease of Heterozygosis*

We learned in the preceding chapter that selfing makes heterozygosis of diploids decrease by one-half in each generation. In this section we shall see how heterozygosis decreases with continued sib mating. Reciprocal crosses are not distinguished, since we are dealing with autosomal genes. The relations between frequencies of the four types of matings in two successive generations of sib mating, as illustrated in Figure 11, may be restated in the form of the following equations (Haldane, 1937a):

$$
\begin{aligned}
w_{n+1} &= w_n + \tfrac{1}{4}y_n + \tfrac{1}{8}z_n \,, \\
x_{n+1} &= \phantom{w_n + \tfrac{1}{4}y_n +} \tfrac{1}{8}z_n \,, \\
y_{n+1} &= \tfrac{1}{2}y_n + \tfrac{1}{2}z_n \,, \\
z_{n+1} &= x_n + \tfrac{1}{4}y_n + \tfrac{1}{4}z_n \,.
\end{aligned}
\qquad (1)
$$

The last *three* equations form an independent set for the variables x, y, z. To find the values of x_n, y_n, z_n of any generation, as well as their recurrence relations between successive generations, we employ the method of relative linear invariant functions described in the last chapter. Now, we have to find an identity

such that
$$l_1 x_{n+1} + l_2 y_{n+1} + l_3 z_{n+1} \equiv \lambda (l_1 x_n + l_2 y_n + l_3 z_n) . \tag{2}$$

Substituting (1) in (2) and equating the coefficients of x, y, z on both sides of the identity, we obtain the following set of equations:

$$\left. \begin{aligned} l_3 &= \lambda l_1 , \\ \tfrac{1}{2} l_2 + \tfrac{1}{4} l_3 &= \lambda l_2 , \\ \tfrac{1}{8} l_1 + \tfrac{1}{2} l_2 + \tfrac{1}{4} l_3 &= \lambda l_3 . \end{aligned} \right\} \tag{3}$$

The characteristic equation is then

$$f(\lambda) = \begin{vmatrix} -\lambda & 0 & 1 \\ 0 & \tfrac{1}{2} - \lambda & \tfrac{1}{4} \\ \tfrac{1}{8} & \tfrac{1}{2} & \tfrac{1}{4} - \lambda \end{vmatrix} = \lambda^3 - \tfrac{3}{4}\lambda^2 - \tfrac{1}{8}\lambda + \tfrac{1}{16} = 0 ; \tag{4}$$

or

$$(4\lambda - 1)(4\lambda^2 - 2\lambda - 1) = 0 , \tag{4'}$$

with roots:
$$\lambda_1 = \tfrac{1}{4} , \qquad \lambda_2 = \tfrac{1}{4}(1 + \sqrt{5}) , \qquad \lambda_3 = \tfrac{1}{4}(1 - \sqrt{5}) .$$

For each eligible value of λ we may find a set of $l_1 : l_2 : l_3$ from equations (3) so that the identity (2) may be satisfied. Thus:

	l_1	l_2	l_3
$\lambda_1 = \tfrac{1}{4}$	4	-1	1
$\lambda_2 = \tfrac{1}{4}(1 + \sqrt{5})$	4	$\tfrac{1}{2}(3 + \sqrt{5})$	$1 + \sqrt{5}$
$\lambda_3 = \tfrac{1}{4}(1 - \sqrt{5})$	4	$\tfrac{1}{2}(3 - \sqrt{5})$	$1 - \sqrt{5}$

(5)

Now the identity (2) has been completely solved. The recurrence relations for x, y, z, or any linear combination of them, according to (4), are all of the form

$$z_{n+3} = \tfrac{3}{4} z_{n+2} + \tfrac{1}{8} z_{n+1} - \tfrac{1}{16} z_n . \tag{6}$$

Since the proportion of heterozygotes Aa in the population is $H_n = \tfrac{1}{2} y_n + z_n$, the recurrence relation of H is of the same form (6). But for this particular linear combination of y and z the recurrence relation of H may take a simpler form which is more familiar to geneticists. To show this, let us proceed to find the general expressions for x_n, y_n, z_n, assuming some convenient given initial values x_0, y_0, z_0. For instance, let the initial population be all Aa so that $z_0 = 1$, $x_0 = y_0 = 0$ (Table 36). From (2) and (5), we have

$$\left. \begin{aligned} 4x_n \quad\quad\quad - y_n \quad\quad\quad + z_n &= \quad\quad\quad \lambda_1^n , \\ 4x_n + \tfrac{1}{2}(3 + \sqrt{5})y_n + (1 + \sqrt{5})z_n &= (1 + \sqrt{5})\lambda_2^n , \\ 4x_n + \tfrac{1}{2}(3 + \sqrt{5})y_n + (1 - \sqrt{5})z_n &= (1 - \sqrt{5})\lambda_3^n . \end{aligned} \right\} \tag{7}$$

Solving (after first eliminating x_n), we obtain the explicit expressions for the general terms of y and z:

$$y_n = -\tfrac{2}{5}\lambda_1^n + \frac{1+\sqrt{5}}{5}\lambda_2^n + \frac{1-\sqrt{5}}{5}\lambda_3^n,$$
$$z_n = \tfrac{1}{5}\lambda_1^n + \qquad \tfrac{2}{5}\lambda_2^n + \qquad \tfrac{2}{5}\lambda_3^n, \qquad (8)$$

where λ_1, etc., take the values shown in (5). The general expression for x_n need not concern us here, as it does not involve heterozygotes. Now, the proportion

TABLE 36

RESULTS OF SIB MATING FROM AN INITIAL HETEROZYGOUS POPULATION

No. of Generations n	Types and Frequencies of Mating in Population				Zygotic Proportions in Population			Segregating Crosses
	$AA \times AA$ $aa \times aa$ w	$AA \times aa$ x	$AA \times Aa$ $aa \times Aa$ y	$Aa \times Aa$ z	AA	Aa H	aa	$x+y+z$ S
0.........	0	0	0	1	0	1	0	1
1.........	$\frac{1}{8}$	$\frac{1}{8}$	$\frac{4}{8}$	$\frac{2}{8}$	$\frac{1}{4}$	$\frac{1}{2}$	$\frac{1}{4}$	$\frac{7}{8}$
2.........	$\frac{9}{32}$	$\frac{1}{32}$	$\frac{12}{32}$	$\frac{10}{32}$	$\frac{2}{8}$	$\frac{2}{4}$	$\frac{2}{8}$	$\frac{23}{32}$
3.........	$\frac{53}{128}$	$\frac{5}{128}$	$\frac{44}{128}$	$\frac{26}{128}$	$\frac{5}{16}$	$\frac{3}{8}$	$\frac{5}{16}$	$\frac{75}{128}$
4.........	$\frac{269}{512}$	$\frac{13}{512}$	$\frac{140}{512}$	$\frac{90}{512}$	$\frac{11}{32}$	$\frac{5}{16}$	$\frac{11}{32}$	$\frac{243}{512}$
5.........	$\frac{1261}{2048}$	$\frac{45}{2048}$	$\frac{460}{2048}$	$\frac{282}{2048}$	$\frac{24}{64}$	$\frac{8}{32}$	$\frac{24}{64}$	$\frac{787}{2048}$
6.........	$\frac{5645}{8192}$	$\frac{141}{8192}$	$\frac{1484}{8192}$	$\frac{922}{8192}$	$\frac{51}{128}$	$\frac{13}{64}$	$\frac{51}{128}$	$\frac{2547}{8192}$
...	...	...	...	...	...	...	...	...
∞.........	1	0	0	0	$\frac{1}{2}$	0	$\frac{1}{2}$	0

of heterozygotes in the nth generation is

$$H_n = \tfrac{1}{2}y_n + z_n = \frac{5+\sqrt{5}}{10}\lambda_2^n + \frac{5-\sqrt{5}}{10}\lambda_3^n, \qquad (9)$$

the term involving λ_1 being canceled out. Substituting the numerical values of λ_2 and λ_3, we have the familiar expression H_n for the special case $H_0 = 1$,

$$H_n = \frac{2}{\sqrt{5}}\left\{\left(\frac{1+\sqrt{5}}{4}\right)^{n+1} - \left(\frac{1-\sqrt{5}}{4}\right)^{n+1}\right\} \qquad (10)$$

(see Chap. 5, Appendix, Example 2). Now we see that the value of H is independent of $\lambda_1 = \tfrac{1}{4}$. Therefore, as far as the value of H is concerned, its characteristic equation becomes $4\lambda^2 - 2\lambda - 1 = 0$ (see [4′]). Hence the recurrence relation of H is $4H_{n+2} - 2H_{n+1} - H_n = 0$, or

$$H_{n+2} = \tfrac{1}{2}H_{n+1} + \tfrac{1}{4}H_n, \qquad (11)$$

forming the well-known Fibonacci series. As pointed out in Section 2 of Chapter 9, the value of H may be interpreted in three different ways. Thus, for a group of mice subjected to sib mating for six generations, we expect (Table 36) $\frac{13}{64} = 20.3$ per cent of their original heterozygous loci to remain heterozygous and 79.7 per cent to become homozygous. The "pure" strains of mice used in laboratories are those which have been subjected to continuous inbreeding for many generations, so that all their loci may be assumed to be in homozygous condition.

§ 3. *Correlations between Mates and between Uniting Gametes*

If in Table 36 we were to break the values of w, x, y, z into their nine components, with reciprocal crosses distinguished, we would obtain a correlation table between mating genotypes. For instance, in the second generation of sib mating $(n = 2)$, there are $\frac{9}{64}(AA \times AA) + \frac{9}{64}(aa \times aa)$, $\frac{1}{64}(AA \times aa) + \frac{1}{64}(aa \times AA)$, etc. The mating correlation tables for the first five generations of sib mating are given in Table 37. Note that, in the first generation $(n = 1)$,

TABLE 37

CORRELATIONS BETWEEN MATES UNDER SIB MATING

	First Generation			Second Generation			Third Generation		
	2	1	0	2	1	0	2	1	0
2	1	2	1	9	6	1	53	22	5
1	2	4	2	6	20	6	22	52	22
0	1	2	1	1	6	9	5	22	53
	4	8	4	16	32	16	80	96	80
		$m=0$			$m=\frac{1}{2}$			$m=\frac{3}{5}$	

	Fourth Generation			Fifth Generation			Limit		
	2	1	0	2	1	0	2	1	0
2	269	70	13	1261	230	45	1	0	0
1	70	180	70	230	564	230	0	0	0
0	13	70	269	45	230	1261	0	0	1
	352	320	352	1536	1024	1536	1	0	1
		$m=\frac{8}{11}$			$m=\frac{19}{24}$			$m=1$	

the population is $(\frac{1}{4}, \frac{1}{2}, \frac{1}{4})$, with $m = 0$. From then on the correlation coefficient between mates (m) increases with the degree of inbreeding and finally reaches the limiting value of unity when complete homozygosis is obtained. This method, however, becomes tedious when the inbreeding system becomes more complicated. A far more effective method of obtaining the value of m will be given in Chapters 13 and 14.

In Table 36 are listed also the combined frequencies of all segregating crosses, $S = x + y + z$. The recurrence relation of the S series is, of course, also of the form (6). Its limiting value is zero; that is, eventually all the matings in the population will breed true.

Next let us examine the correlation tables between mates (Table 37) in a different manner. The frequencies of the various kinds of matings between genotypes may be converted into those of uniting gametes. For instance, one $AA \times AA$ mating is equivalent to one union of an A gamete with another A gamete; one $Aa \times Aa$ mating is equivalent to $\frac{1}{4}$ union of an A gamete with another A gamete and $\frac{1}{2}$ union of an A gamete with an a gamete, etc. Let an A gamete take the value 1 and an a gamete 0. Then the 3×3 correlation tables between genotypes may be converted into 2×2 tables for uniting gametes (Table 38). We shall use F to denote the correlation coefficient between such uniting gametes.

TABLE 38

CORRELATIONS BETWEEN UNITING GAMETES
UNDER SIB MATING
(Converted from Table 37)

First Generation			Second Generation			Third Generation	
	1	0		1	0		1	0

	1	0
1	4	4
0	4	4
	8	8

$F = 0$

	1	0
1	20	12
0	12	20
	32	32

$F = \frac{1}{4}$

	1	0
1	88	40
0	40	88
	128	128

$F = \frac{3}{8}$

| Fourth Generation | | | Fifth Generation | | | Limit | |

	1	0
1	384	128
0	128	384
	512	512

$F = \frac{8}{16}$

	1	0
1	1632	416
0	416	1632
	2048	2048

$F = \frac{19}{32}$

	1	0
1	1	0
0	0	1
	1	1

$F = 1$

It is clear that Tables 37 and 38 are merely two different ways of presenting the same facts embodied in Table 36. Hence, the m series: $\frac{1}{2}, \frac{3}{5}, \frac{8}{11}, \frac{19}{24}, \ldots$, for successive generations is equivalent to the F series: $\frac{1}{4}, \frac{3}{8}, \frac{8}{16}, \frac{19}{32}, \ldots$, for corresponding generations. In other words, m and F are two different indexes of the same effect of inbreeding. However, in most cases, it is more convenient to work with F than m, as will be shown in subsequent chapters, because a new technique makes it easy to find the recurrence relation of F for any system of inbreeding and because F bears a direct relation to H in the population.

§ 4. Panmictic Initial Population

A special case is that of the initial population $(p^2, 2pq, q^2)$, with $H_0 = 2pq$. This does not affect any of the recurrence relations above, which are independent of initial conditions (and thus of gene frequencies). But the general expressions for the nth term of the x, y, z, H, or S series may have some different constant coefficients of the λ's because of this particular set of initial conditions:

$$\left.\begin{aligned}
w_0 &= p^4 + q^4 &&= 1 - 2H_0 + \tfrac{1}{2}H_0^2\,, \\
x_0 &= 2p^2q^2 &&= \tfrac{1}{2}H_0^2\,, \\
y_0 &= 4pq(p^2 + q^2) &&= 2H_0 - 2H_0^2\,, \\
z_0 &= 4p^2q^2 &&= \phantom{1 - 2H_0 + \tfrac{1}{2}} H_0^2\,.
\end{aligned}\right\} \tag{12}$$

In the first generation of sib mating the frequencies of the four groups of mating will be, from (1) and (12),

$$\left.\begin{aligned}
w_1 &= w_0 + \tfrac{1}{4}y_0 + \tfrac{1}{8}z_0 = 1 - \tfrac{3}{2}H_0 + \tfrac{3}{8}H_0^2\,, \\
x_1 &= \phantom{w_0 + \tfrac{1}{4}y_0 +} \tfrac{1}{8}z_0 = \phantom{1 - \tfrac{3}{2}H_0 +} \tfrac{1}{8}H_0^2\,, \\
y_1 &= \tfrac{1}{2}y_0 + \tfrac{1}{2}z_0 = H_0 - \tfrac{1}{2}H_0^2\,, \\
z_1 &= x_0 + \tfrac{1}{4}y_0 + \tfrac{1}{4}z_0 = \tfrac{1}{2}H_0 + \tfrac{1}{4}H_0^2\,.
\end{aligned}\right\} \tag{12A}$$

Hence,

$$H_1 = \tfrac{1}{2}y_1 + z_1 = H_0\,, \qquad\qquad H_2 = \tfrac{1}{2}H_1 + \tfrac{1}{4}H_0 = \tfrac{3}{4}H_0\,,$$

$$H_3 = \tfrac{1}{2}H_2 + \tfrac{1}{4}H_1 = \tfrac{5}{8}H_0\,, \qquad H_4 = \tfrac{8}{16}H_0\,, \text{ etc.}$$

The coefficients of H_0 form a Fibonacci series with initial terms, $1, 1, \tfrac{3}{4}, \tfrac{5}{8}, \tfrac{8}{16}$, $\ldots$. Therefore, the general expression of the coefficients is (Chap. 5, Appendix, Example 4)

$$\frac{H_n}{H_0} = \frac{5 + 3\sqrt{5}}{10}\left(\frac{1 + \sqrt{5}}{4}\right)^n + \frac{5 - 3\sqrt{5}}{10}\left(\frac{1 - \sqrt{5}}{4}\right)^n. \tag{13}$$

The zygotic proportions among the offspring of first-generation sib matings from a random-mating population may be obtained easily from the sib-mating frequencies given in (12A). To facilitate the calculation of their offspring, we may write out the six sib matings separately, as in Table 39. Of particular im-

TABLE 39

FREQUENCY OF FIRST-GENERATION SIB MATINGS AND RESULTANT OFFSPRING, ASSUMING AN INITIAL RANDOM-MATING POPULATION

FREQUENCY OF SIB MATING (IN AN INITIAL PANMICTIC POPULATION)		SIB'S OFFSPRING		
		AA	Aa	aa
$w_1 \begin{cases} (AA \times AA) \\ (aa \times aa) \end{cases}$	$\begin{aligned} p^4 + p^3q + \tfrac{1}{4}p^2q^2 \\ q^4 + pq^3 + \tfrac{1}{4}p^2q^2 \end{aligned}$	$\begin{aligned} 1 \\ 0 \end{aligned}$	$\begin{aligned} 0 \\ 0 \end{aligned}$	$\begin{aligned} 0 \\ 1 \end{aligned}$
$x \quad (AA \times aa)$	$\tfrac{1}{2}p^2q^2$	0	1	0
$y \begin{cases} (AA \times Aa) \\ (aa \times Aa) \end{cases}$	$\begin{aligned} 2p^3q + p^2q^2 \\ 2pq^3 + p^2q^2 \end{aligned}$	$\begin{aligned} \tfrac{1}{2} \\ \cdots\cdots \end{aligned}$	$\begin{aligned} \tfrac{1}{2} \\ \tfrac{1}{2} \end{aligned}$	$\begin{aligned} \cdots\cdots \\ \tfrac{1}{2} \end{aligned}$
$z_1 \ (Aa \times Aa)$	$p^3q + pq^3 + 3p^2q^2$	$\tfrac{1}{4}$	$\tfrac{1}{2}$	$\tfrac{1}{4}$
Total sib's offspring.		$p^2 + \tfrac{1}{4}pq$	$2pq - \tfrac{1}{2}pq$	$q^2 + \tfrac{1}{4}pq$

portance is the proportion (R) of recessive offspring among sib matings, since in practice dominance is often involved. The student should be familiar with the different forms given to R in various literatures:

$$R = q^2 + \tfrac{1}{4}pq = \tfrac{3}{4}q^2 + \tfrac{1}{4}q = \tfrac{1}{4}q(1 + 3q) . \qquad (14)$$

This is a special case of a more general theorem which would give us the proportion of recessive offspring among matings of any kind of relatives in a random-mating population. It will be discussed in subsequent chapters.

§ 5. *Sex-linked Genes and Other Cases*

Since for sex-linked genes there is no heterozygous individual among the males (XO or XY), we shall consider only the proportion of heterozygous individuals among the females (XX). The six types of mating may be col-

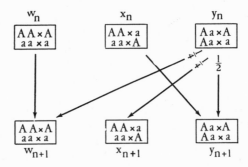

FIG. 12.—Relations between frequencies of types of mating in two successive generations with sib mating, for sex-linked genes.

lected into three groups according to their segregation properties under sib mating (Fig. 12). Hence, the transformation equations are (Haldane, 1937a):

$$\left. \begin{aligned} w_{n+1} &= w_n + \tfrac{1}{4}y_n \\ x_{n+1} &= \tfrac{1}{4}y_n \\ y_{n+1} &= x_n + \tfrac{1}{2}y_n \end{aligned} \right\} .$$

The last two equations form an independent set. Note that the proportion of Aa among females is simply $H_n = y_n$. In order to solve the identity $l_1x_{n+1} + l_2y_{n+1} \equiv \lambda(l_1x_n + l_2y_n)$, we proceed exactly as before and find

$$f(\lambda) = \begin{vmatrix} -\lambda & 1 \\ \tfrac{1}{4} & \tfrac{1}{2} - \lambda \end{vmatrix} = \lambda^2 - \tfrac{1}{2}\lambda - \tfrac{1}{4} = 0 ,$$

whose two roots are $\lambda_1 = (1 + \sqrt{5})/4$ and $\lambda_2 = (1 - \sqrt{5})/4$. The recurrence relation of x, y, and H are all of the form (11). In other words, the properties of H among females are identical with those for autosomal genes under sib mating. The expression for the general term H_n depends on the initial conditions of the population. If the initial cross is $AA \times a$ (Table 40), so that $x_0 = 1$, $w_0 = y_0 = 0$, the y_n ($=H_n$) forms a Fibonacci series whose general term is identical with (10). The S series, 1, 1, $\frac{3}{4}$, $\frac{5}{8}$, ..., has a general term identical with (13).

For sex-linked multiple alleles the maximum number of alleles in a sib-mating population is three, derived from families of the type $A_1A_2 \times A_3$. For autosomal genes there could be, at most, four alleles involved in one family such as $A_1A_2 \times A_3A_4$. The recurrence relation of H in each case has been found (Hal-

TABLE 40

SIB MATING FOR SEX-LINKED GENES

No. of Generations	Types and Frequencies of Mating in Population			Segregating Crosses
	$AA \times A$ $aa \times a$	$AA \times a$ $aa \times A$	$Aa \times A$ $Aa \times a$	$x+y$
n	w	x	$y=H$	S
0.........	0	1	0	1
1.........	0	0	1	1
2.........	$\frac{1}{4}$	$\frac{1}{4}$	$\frac{1}{2}$	$\frac{3}{4}$
3.........	$\frac{3}{8}$	$\frac{1}{8}$	$\frac{4}{8}$	$\frac{5}{8}$
4.........	$\frac{8}{16}$	$\frac{2}{16}$	$\frac{6}{16}$	$\frac{8}{16}$
5.........	$\frac{19}{32}$	$\frac{3}{32}$	$\frac{10}{32}$	$\frac{13}{32}$
6.........	$\frac{43}{64}$	$\frac{5}{64}$	$\frac{16}{64}$	$\frac{21}{64}$
...	...	...	...	...
∞	1	0	0	0

dane, 1937a) to be the same as (11). Hence, $H_{n+2} = \frac{1}{2}H_{n+1} + \frac{1}{4}H_n$ seems to be a universal property of sib mating for all diploids. The general expressions of H_n for certain initial conditions have also been given by Haldane (1937a). The largest root of the λ equation is $(1 + \sqrt{5})/4 = 0.809$. So that, after a sufficiently large number of generations of sib mating, the value of H will decrease by approximately 19.1 per cent per generation, because then $H_{n+1} = 0.809H_n$.

The effect of sib mating on autotetraploids has been investigated by Bartlett and Haldane (1934), who found that the approach to homozygosis is very slow. Ten generations of sib mating are needed to halve the proportion of heterozygotes, and thirty-one generations to reduce it to one-tenth. The greatest root of the λ equation is 0.92356. The methods used for these more complicated cases are exactly the same as the one we have used here, but the algebra is more involved.

Notes and Exercises

1. The zygotic proportions of the following three populations are all alike, each consisting of $\frac{1}{6}AA + \frac{4}{6}Aa + \frac{1}{6}aa$; but their distributions of sibships are

different:

$$Z_1: \tfrac{1}{24}\{AA\} + \tfrac{5}{12}\{Aa\} + \tfrac{1}{24}\{aa\} + \tfrac{1}{2}\{\tfrac{1}{4}AA + \tfrac{1}{2}Aa + \tfrac{1}{4}aa\}$$

$$Z_2: \tfrac{1}{3}\{\tfrac{1}{2}AA + \tfrac{1}{2}Aa\} + \tfrac{1}{3}\{Aa\} + \tfrac{1}{3}\{\tfrac{1}{2}Aa + \tfrac{1}{2}aa\}$$

$$Z_3: \tfrac{1}{6}\{AA\} + \tfrac{2}{3}\{Aa\} + \tfrac{1}{6}\{aa\} .$$

The members of a sibship are shown in braces. If all matings are confined to members of the same sibship, show that the zygotic proportions in the next generation are:

$$Z_1' = (\tfrac{13}{48}, \tfrac{22}{48}, \tfrac{13}{48}) ; \quad Z_2' = (\tfrac{7}{24}, \tfrac{10}{24}, \tfrac{7}{24}) ; \quad Z_3' = (\tfrac{1}{3}, \tfrac{1}{3}, \tfrac{1}{3}) .$$

2. The recurrence relation of H for sib mating may be directly obtained from the transformation set (1). Thus,

$$H_{n+2} = \tfrac{1}{2}y_{n+2} + z_{n+2} = \tfrac{1}{2}(\tfrac{1}{2}y_{n+1} + \tfrac{1}{2}z_{n+1}) + x_{n+1} + \tfrac{1}{4}y_{n+1} + \tfrac{1}{4}z_{n+1}$$

$$= \tfrac{1}{2}(\tfrac{1}{2}y_{n+1} + z_{n+1}) + \tfrac{1}{4}(\tfrac{1}{2}y_n + z_n) = \tfrac{1}{2}H_{n+1} + \tfrac{1}{4}H_n .$$

Perhaps this derivation may more readily convince students that the recurrence relation of H is purely a property of the mating system which determines (1) and is independent of the composition of a population and its gene frequencies.

3. Let f_1 be the frequency of mating $AA \times AA$, etc., and $\Sigma f = 1$. Verify the recurrence relation (11), using the following scheme.

Present Condition		Next Generation	Second Generation
$(AA \times AA)$	f_1	$f_1' = f_1 + \tfrac{1}{4}f_4 \ + \ \tfrac{1}{16}f_6$	$f_1'' =$ Expressions same
$(aa \times aa)$	f_2	$f_2' = f_2 + \tfrac{1}{4}f_5 \ + \ \tfrac{1}{16}f_6$	$f_2'' =$ as in previous
$(AA \times aa)$	f_3	$f_3' = \qquad\qquad\ \tfrac{1}{8}f_6$	$f_3'' =$ column except
$(AA \times Aa)$	f_4	$f_4' = \qquad \tfrac{1}{2}f_4 \ + \ \tfrac{1}{4}f_6$	$f_4'' =$ that $f_1, f_2, \ldots,$
$(aa \times Aa)$	f_5	$f_5' = \qquad \tfrac{1}{2}f_5 \ + \ \tfrac{1}{4}f_6$	$f_5'' =$ are replaced by
$(Aa \times Aa)$	f_6	$f_6' = f_3 + \tfrac{1}{4}(f_4 + f_5 + f_6)$	$f_6'' = f_1', f_2', \ldots .$
$H_0 = \tfrac{1}{2}(f_4 + f_5) + f_6$		$H_1 = \tfrac{1}{2}(f_4' + f_5') + f_6'$	$H_2 = \tfrac{1}{2}(f_4'' + f_5'') + f_6''$

Carry out the numerical calculations for the arbitrary case:

$$f_1 = 0.05, \quad f_2 = 0.09, \quad f_3 = 0.10, \quad f_4 = 0.20, \quad f_5 = 0.24, \quad f_6 = 0.32 .$$

4. Given an initial random-mating population (.04, .32, .64), calculate the frequencies of the six types of mating for the next three generations assuming sib mating. What will be the ratio of H_3/H_0? Check your answer by (13).

5. With the above initial population, what are the zygotic proportions among the offspring of the first generation of sib mating? Check your numerical calculations with (14).

6. For a pair of sex-linked genes a random-mating population in equilibrium is (p, q) and $(p^2, 2pq, q^2)$. Let it begin practicing sib mating. Calculate the frequencies of the six types of mating for the next three generations and show that the recurrence relation of H among females is identical with that for autosomal genes. Also calculate the zygotic proportions among the offspring of first-generation sib matings. Carry out the calculations for the numerical case $(.20, .80)$ and $(.04, .32, .64)$ as the initial population.

7. In the case for three sex-linked alleles, there are six genotypes for females and three for males. The eighteen different matings may be collected into four groups according to their segregation behaviors. Let the frequencies of the four groups of mating in the nth generation of sib mating be as follows:

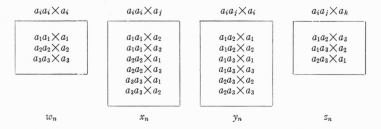

$a_i a_i \times a_i$	$a_i a_i \times a_j$	$a_i a_j \times a_i$	$a_i a_j \times a_k$
$a_1 a_1 \times a_1$	$a_1 a_1 \times a_2$	$a_1 a_2 \times a_1$	$a_1 a_2 \times a_3$
$a_2 a_2 \times a_2$	$a_1 a_1 \times a_3$	$a_1 a_2 \times a_2$	$a_1 a_3 \times a_2$
$a_3 a_3 \times a_3$	$a_2 a_2 \times a_1$	$a_1 a_3 \times a_1$	$a_2 a_3 \times a_1$
	$a_2 a_2 \times a_3$	$a_1 a_3 \times a_3$	
	$a_3 a_3 \times a_1$	$a_2 a_3 \times a_2$	
	$a_3 a_3 \times a_2$	$a_2 a_3 \times a_3$	
w_n	x_n	y_n	z_n

The fundamental transformation set is then

$$w_{n+1} = w_n + \tfrac{1}{4}y_n ,$$
$$x_{n+1} = \phantom{w_n + {}} \tfrac{1}{4}y_n ,$$
$$y_{n+1} = x_n + \tfrac{1}{2}y_n + \tfrac{1}{2}z_n ,$$
$$z_{n+1} = \phantom{x_n + \tfrac{1}{2}y_n + {}} \tfrac{1}{2}z_n .$$

Therefore, the characteristic equation is

$$f(\lambda) = \begin{vmatrix} -\lambda & 1 & 0 \\ \tfrac{1}{4} & \tfrac{1}{2} - \lambda & 0 \\ 0 & \tfrac{1}{2} & \tfrac{1}{2} - \lambda \end{vmatrix} = (\tfrac{1}{2} - \lambda)(\lambda^2 - \tfrac{1}{2}\lambda - \tfrac{1}{4}) = 0 .$$

The recurrence relation of $H = y + z$ is also (11). If the initial cross is $a_1 a_2 \times a_3$, so that $z_0 = 1$, and $w_0 = x_0 = y_0 = 0$, the successive values of H will be

$$1, 1, \tfrac{3}{4}, \tfrac{5}{8}, \tfrac{8}{16}, \tfrac{13}{32}, \dots ,$$

and its general expression is (13). The recurrence relation of y is $y_{n+3} = y_{n+2} - \tfrac{1}{8}y_n$ (same as that of x) because $f(\lambda) = \lambda^3 - \lambda^2 + \tfrac{1}{8} = 0$.

8. Show that the F series (Table 38) $0, \tfrac{1}{4}, \tfrac{3}{8}, \tfrac{8}{16}, \tfrac{19}{32}, \dots$, has a recurrence relation $F_{n+2} = \tfrac{1}{2}F_{n+1} + \tfrac{1}{4}F_n + \tfrac{1}{4}$, and thus its next two terms will be $\tfrac{43}{64}$ and $\tfrac{94}{128}$.

CHAPTER 11

Equilibrium Populations with Inbreeding

THE Hardy-Weinberg Law is a rather special case of a more general kind of equilibrium condition that involves a certain amount of inbreeding. We shall examine some of the properties of inbreeding equilibrium populations in this chapter.

§ 1. *Correlation between Uniting Gametes*

In the preceding chapter on sib mating it was shown that inbreeding leads to correlation between uniting gametes. In a population with $p(A)$ and $q(a)$ the probability that two A gametes should unite is p^2 under random mating and

TABLE 41

CORRELATION BETWEEN UNITING GAMETES

g	g'		TOTAL
	1	0	
1.........	$p^2+\epsilon$	$pq-\epsilon$	p
0.........	$pq-\epsilon$	$q^2+\epsilon$	q
Total....	p	q	1

will be greater than p^2 if there is a certain degree of inbreeding in the population. Let $p^2 + \epsilon$ be this probability, where ϵ is a positive fraction. Since the gene frequencies are not affected by inbreeding, the correlation table for the uniting gametes will take the form of Table 41, in which, as before, we let the variable $g = 1$ for A gametes, $g = 0$ for a gametes, and g' be the corresponding variable in the other sex.

From Table 41 we have $\bar{g} = \bar{g}' = p$, $\sigma_g^2 = \sigma_{g'}^2 = pq$ and $\sigma_{gg'} = p^2 + \epsilon - p^2 = \epsilon$. Hence the correlation coefficient between g and g' is

$$F = \frac{\sigma_{gg'}}{\sigma_g \sigma_{g'}} = \frac{\epsilon}{pq}; \qquad \text{i.e.,} \qquad \epsilon = Fpq. \tag{1}$$

The zygotic proportions in this population are thus (Wright, 1921b, 1922a)

$$D = p^2 + Fpq, \qquad H = 2pq(1-F), \qquad R = q^2 + Fpq, \qquad (2)$$

where $D + H + R = 1$. If F remains constant from generation to generation (through some regular or irregular mating system), the zygotic proportions D, H, R will also remain constant. The proportions shown in (2) may be called Wright's Equilibrium Law. This law is a generalization of the Hardy-Weinberg Law (for which $F = 0$), and it is one of the most important formulas in population genetics. We shall deal with its properties in more detail in subsequent sections. It should be clear that F is completely independent of gene frequencies: the gene frequencies tell us what proportion of each allele there is in the population, while F tells us how they are associated in pairs.

§ 2. *The Zygotic Proportions*

The zygotic proportions (2) are intermediate between those of completely random-mating populations (p^2, $2pq$, q^2) and those of completely inbred populations (p, 0, q) for any given value of gene frequency. From Figure 13 it is

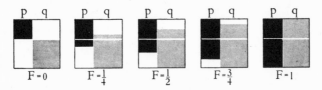

FIG. 13.—Zygotic proportions of populations with various degrees of inbreeding for given values of gene frequencies. (Solid black = AA; shaded = aa; white = Aa.)

clear that Wright's proportions may be expressed in two equivalent ways: one as deviations from the case $F = 0$ and another as deviations from the case $F = 1$. A third way of expressing them arises from the fact that $p^2 + Fpq = (1 - F)p^2 + Fp$, etc. Thus, (2) may be rewritten as

$$(1 - F)(p^2, 2pq, q^2) + F(p, 0, q). \qquad (2')$$

In other words, the population may be thought of as consisting of two components—a panmictic component which consists of $(1 - F)$ of the entire population and a fixed (completely inbred) component which consists of F of the whole population. The above three different but equivalent ways of expressing the zygotic proportions are summarized in Table 42 (Wright, 1951).

Since the correlation coefficient F measures the degree of fixation, it is usually known as the *coefficient of inbreeding*. It is more useful than any other single index in describing the properties of a population relative to those of panmixia. The index $(1 - F)$ measures the relative amount of heterozygosis as compared with that in a panmictic population. Thus,

$$H_F = (1 - F)H_0,$$

where H_F and H_0 denote the proportions of heterozygotes of populations with and without inbreeding, respectively.

When there is complete dominance, the proportion of recessives in a population is of particular interest. Letting $R_F = q^2 + Fpq$ and $R_0 = q^2$, we see that the ratio R_F/R_0 is always greater than unity. For any given value of F, this ratio is near unity when q is of moderate magnitude but becomes very large when q is small (Table 43). Hence, the proportion of rare recessives in a panmictic population will be increased many fold by inbreeding (mating between relatives), while that of common recessives will be relatively little affected. This is a familiar phenomenon in human genetics.

TABLE 42

ZYGOTIC PROPORTIONS EXPRESSED IN
THREE EQUIVALENT WAYS
(Wright, 1951, p. 323)

Genotype	Deviation from Panmixia	Panmictic and Fixed Components	Deviation from Fixation
AA	p^2+Fpq	$(1-F)p^2+Fp$	$p-(1-F)pq$
Aa	$2pq-2Fpq$	$2(1-F)pq$	$2(1-F)pq$
aa	q^2+Fpq	$(1-F)q^2+Fq$	$q-(1-F)pq$
Total	$1+0$	$(1-F)+F$	$1-0$

TABLE 43

RATIO OF RECESSIVES WITH INBREEDING TO THOSE
WITH RANDOM MATING FOR VARIOUS GENE FRE-
QUENCIES AND TWO INBREEDING INTENSITIES

PROPORTION OF RE-CESSIVES IN A PANMICTIC POPU-LATION R_0	RECESSIVE-GENE FREQUENCIES q	VALUE OF R_F/R_0 WHEN INBREEDING COEFFICIENT	
		$F=\frac{1}{16}$	$F=\frac{1}{32}$
0.000001*	0.001	63.44	32.22
.00001	.00316	20.70	10.85
.0001*	.010	7.19	4.09
.0004	.020	4.06	2.53
.0025	.050	2.19	1.59
.0100	.100	1.56	1.28
.0400	.200	1.25	1.125
0.2500	0.500	1.06	1.03

* Values to be compared with two-factor recessives (§ 13).

§ 3. *Bernstein's Coefficient of Inbreeding*

It is desirable to mention here one other attempt at devising an index to measure the degree of inbreeding in a population. It is Bernstein's α-coefficient, which is defined in the following manner for populations with gene frequencies p and q.

Let $P\{A \mid A\} = P$ be the *conditional* probability of uniting with an A gamete when the *given* gamete is known to be A. Similarly, $P\{a \mid a\} = Q$ is the conditional probability of a *given* a gamete uniting with another a gamete. Now, since the probability that any given gamete should be A is p, and that it be a is q, the (absolute) probability that any zygote be AA is $p \times P$ and that it be aa is $q \times Q$. Further, the probability that any zygote be Aa or aA is $2p(1 - P)$ or $2q(1 - Q)$. These last two quantities must be equal, yielding the equation

$$\frac{1 - P}{q} = \frac{1 - Q}{p}.$$

Note that, in a random-mating population, P and Q are independent of the given gamete; viz., whatever the given gamete, its chance of uniting with an A gamete is p and with an a gamete is q. In other words, $P = p$ and $Q = q$ in a random-mating population, and the expression above reduces to unity. If, however, the uniting gametes are associated so that P is greater than p, the value $(1 - P)/q$ will be less than unity. Bernstein's α-coefficient is defined by

$$\frac{1 - P}{q} = 1 - \alpha = \frac{1 - Q}{p},$$

where α is a positive fraction. Solving for the conditional probabilities, we obtain

$$P = p + \alpha q, \qquad Q = q + \alpha p.$$

Hence, the zygotic proportions in the population are

$$
\begin{aligned}
AA: & \qquad pP & = p(p + \alpha q) \\
Aa: 2p(1 - P) &= 2q(1 - Q) & = 2pq(1 - \alpha) \\
aa: & \qquad qQ & = q(q + \alpha p),
\end{aligned}
$$

which are identical with (2). Thus we see that Bernstein's α-coefficient is the same as Wright's F-coefficient.

§ 4. *Graphical Representation of Populations*

In chapter 1 the parabola $4DR - H^2 = 0$ was used in homogeneous coordinates within an equilateral triangle to represent all random-mating populations. In exactly the same manner Wright's proportions (2) may be plotted within the same triangle for various gene frequencies with a given (fixed) value of F. As a very simple example, suppose $F = \frac{1}{4}$; then the zygotic proportions for various values of gene frequencies will be as shown in Table 44. The zygotic proportions for $p > 0.5$ may be obtained by interchanging the values of p and q and thus also those of D and R. When the points (D, H, R) are plotted inside the triangle (Fig. 14), it will be found that they also lie on a parabola but under that for random-mating populations, owing to the increase of homozygosis (perpendiculars to the two sides of the triangle) at the expense of heterozygosis (perpendicular to the base). Inspection of (2) shows that the equation of this parabola is (Haldane and Moshinsky, 1939):

$$4\,DR - H^2 = 4Fpq = F\,(2\,D + H)\,(H + 2R)$$

or

$$= \frac{F}{1-F} \cdot 2H\,. \tag{3}$$

Adopting the form given in Exercise 15 of Chapter 1, however, we see that (3) may be put into a simpler form:

$$\frac{D}{D+\frac{1}{2}H} + \frac{R}{R+\frac{1}{2}H} = \frac{D}{p} + \frac{R}{q} = 1 + F\,. \tag{3'}$$

TABLE 44

ZYGOTIC PROPORTIONS IN A POPULATION WITH $F = 0.25$

p	q	D	H	R	$\dfrac{D}{p}$	$\dfrac{R}{q}$	Sum
0.1	0.9	0.0325	0.1350	0.8325	0.325	0.925	1.25
.2	.8	.0800	.2400	.6800	.400	.850	1.25
.3	.7	.1425	.3150	.5425	.475	.775	1.25
.4	.6	.2200	.3600	.4200	.550	.700	1.25
0.5	0.5	0.3125	0.3750	0.3125	0.625	0.625	1.25

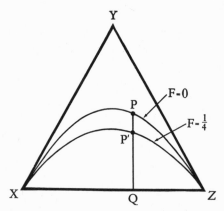

FIG. 14.—The upper parabola represents all random-mating populations, while the lower parabola represents those populations in which $F = \frac{1}{4}$. The two populations, P and P', have the same gene frequencies, whose ratio is $q:p = XQ:QZ$. The point P' cuts the projection PQ so that $PP':P'Q = F:(1 - F)$. (Modified from Haldane and Moshinsky, 1939.)

It is left to the student to show that (3) and (3′) are equivalent. The chief advantage of the latter form is that it can be readily generalized to the case of multiple alleles. The right-hand half of Table 44 gives a numerical illustration of the relation (3′).

The effect of inbreeding, as illustrated in Figure 14, is to move the population point P to a lower position P', along the projection PQ, so that the gene frequencies remain the same. (Inbreeding itself does not change the gene frequencies, as shown in the two previous chapters.) Generally speaking, the effect of inbreeding is to press the parabola down toward the base of the triangle. In the extreme case when $F = 1$, the parabola is so flattened that it coincides with the base; so that $D = p$, $H = 0$, $R = q$. In the intermediate positions, since $H_F = (1 - F)H_0$, as pointed out in Section 2, the point P' cuts the projection PQ in the proportions $PP' : P'Q = F : (1 - F)$. It may be added that a change in gene frequency (such as by the force of selection) means the moving of P along a parabola, while inbreeding moves it in the vertical direction along a projection to the base.

§ 5. *General Theorem for Equilibrium Populations*

Before we go further into the properties of equilibrium with inbreeding, let us prove a very general but simple theorem which applies to all equilibrium populations. Associate the subscripts 2, 1, 0 with genotypes AA, Aa, aa, respectively; let u_{22} be the frequency of $AA \times AA$ matings, etc., in an equilibrium population; and, further, assume reciprocal crosses equally numerous and thus $u_{10}(Aa \times aa) = u_{01}(aa \times Aa)$. The sum of the nine u's in Table 45 is unity;

TABLE 45

FREQUENCIES OF MATINGS IN AN
EQUILIBRIUM POPULATION

Mates	AA (2)	Aa (1)	aa (0)	Total
AA (2).....	u_{22}	u_{21}	u_{20}	D
Aa (1).....	u_{21}	u_{11}	u_{10}	H
aa (0).....	u_{20}	u_{10}	u_{00}	R
Total...	D	H	R	1

and the sums of its three rows, as well as those of its columns, are the zygotic proportions of the parental population.

The offspring proportions may be easily calculated from the frequencies of parental matings. For example, the $2u_{21}(AA \times Aa)$ matings, reciprocals included, will contribute $u_{21}AA$ offspring to the next generation. Thus we have

(Haldane and Moshinsky, 1939):

> Freq. of AA parents: $u_{22} + u_{21} + u_{20}$,
>
> Freq. of AA offspring: $u_{22} + u_{21} + \frac{1}{4}u_{11}$.

Since the population is in equilibrium, the zygotic proportions of the parental and offspring generations must be the same. Hence, we obtain the relation

$$u_{11} = 4u_{20} = 2(u_{20} + u_{02}) .\qquad(4)$$

In other words, in any equilibrium population, $Aa \times Aa$ matings are *twice* as frequent as those between the two different homozygotes ($AA \times aa$ and $aa \times AA$). This relation is independent of gene frequencies or amount of inbreeding. It is clearly true for panmictic populations (Chap. 1).

The reason that this theorem was demonstrated in the above manner is that we shall use it to deduce some further theorems in later sections. This property of equilibrium was actually first noted by Fisher (1918, pp. 410–11). His argument is especially simple. Of the six types of mating in the population, four types ($AA \times AA$, $aa \times aa$, $AA \times Aa$, $aa \times Aa$) yield offspring of the same genotypic proportions as their parents. On the other hand, in $AA \times aa$ matings the two homozygous parents are replaced by heterozygotes in the next generation; while in $Aa \times Aa$ matings only half of the offspring regain the homozygous condition. Therefore, in the equilibrium state, the mating $Aa \times Aa$ must be twice as frequent as $AA \times aa$ (reciprocals included).

§ 6. *Genetic Variance with Inbreeding*

Assigning the values 2, 1, 0 to AA, Aa, aa, whose frequencies in the population are D, H, R, respectively, we see that the mean is $2D + H = 2p$ and that the variance is

$$\sigma^2_F = 4D + H - (2D + H)^2 = 4DR - H^2 + H .\qquad(5)$$

Note that, when $4DR - H^2 = 0$, the variance is reduced to $\sigma^2_0 = H = 2pq$, using the symbol σ^2_0 to denote the genetic variance of a corresponding completely panmictic population with the same gene frequencies. Substituting the values of D, H, R as given by (2) in (5), we have

$$\sigma^2_F = 4(p^2 + Fpq) + 2pq(1 - F) - (2p)^2$$
$$= 2pq(1 + F) = \sigma^2_0(1 + F) .\qquad(5')$$

This expression shows that the inbreeding coefficient F also measures the percentage increase of genetic variance of a population due to inbreeding (see Chap. 9, Ex. 7). It is important to remember that the variance (5') refers to the entire population. The variance of a subgroup, induced by inbreeding, is *decreased* by a proportion F, assuming the value $2pq(1 - F)$, as is to be explained in Section 3 of Chapter 21. In a pure line the genetic variance is zero.

§ 7. *Relationship between* m *and* F

As in the preceding chapter, we use m to denote the correlation coefficient between *mates*. The coefficient F has been in popular use largely because of its convenience in calculation and the fact that $1 - F$ directly measures the relative decrease in heterozygosis in a stock that has been subjected to inbreeding. But it should be realized that in actuality it is the correlation between mating individuals that leads to a correlation between uniting gametes. In this section we shall find the relation between m and F of the same population, as well as express them in terms of zygotic proportions.

The value of m may be readily calculated from the mating frequencies (Table 45). The variance of the population was given by (5') in the last section. The covariance for mates is:

$$\text{Cov.} = 4u_{22} + 4u_{21} + u_{11} - (2p)^2 .$$

Noting that

$$u_{11} = 4u_{20} \quad \text{and} \quad u_{22} + u_{21} + u_{20} = D = p^2 + Fpq ,$$

we obtain:

$$\text{Cov.} = 4(p^2 + Fpq) - 4p^2 = 4Fpq .$$

Hence,

$$m = \frac{4Fpq}{2pq(1+F)} = \frac{2F}{1+F}, \quad \text{or} \quad F = \frac{m}{2-m}. \tag{6}$$

This is a well-known theorem in population genetics, first arrived at by Wright (1921b) through a different method. The values of m are always higher than F except when they are both 0 or both 1. For example, when $F = 0.25$, $m = 0.40$.

The values of F and m may all be directly calculated from the zygotic proportions of a population. Thus, from (3),

$$F = \frac{4DR - H^2}{(2D+H)(H+2R)} = \frac{4DR - H^2}{4DR - H^2 + 2H}. \tag{7}$$

And, if we express the covariance for mates in terms of D, H, R instead of in terms of p and q, we obtain, with the help of (5),

$$m = \frac{4D - (2D+H)^2}{4DR - H^2 + H} = \frac{4DR - H^2}{4DR - H^2 + H}. \tag{8}$$

It is easy to show (Li, 1953a) that the expressions (7) and (8) conform with the relation (6). The student should verify the various results of the last two sections for the population (.22, .36, .42).

§ 8. *Combination of Random Mating and Selfing*

Many plants, under natural conditions, practice both random mating and selfing in each generation. A cotton flower may be either self-pollinated or cross-pollinated. Let ω_1 be the fraction of the population practicing self-fertilization in each generation and let $1 - \omega_1$ represent the remaining plants that practice random mating. It should be clear that the ω_1 here is *not* the F of (2), in which the panmictic and fixed components are regarded as though they were two *separate* groups of individuals, each group with its own mating system. Here, as exemplified by cotton, *any* individual may mate at random (with probability $1 - \omega_1$) or be self-pollinated (with probability ω_1) in each generation; and the offspring, likewise, may either open-cross or self.

Under this combined system of mating any arbitrary initial population will eventually reach an equilibrium condition whose zygotic proportions will be somewhere between those of complete fixation and complete panmixia. Let the equilibrium status be (D, H, R) and, as before, let u_{22} be the frequency of $AA \times AA$, etc. The frequencies of the various types of matings in this equilibrium population will be $(1 - \omega_1)$ times the frequencies of random mating plus ω_1 times the selfing frequencies (see mating table, Ex. 16). Hence,

$$AA \times aa:\ 2u_{20} = 2DR(1 - \omega_1)\ ;$$

$$Aa \times Aa:\ u_{11} =\ \ H^2(1 - \omega_1) + \omega_1 H\ .$$

But $u_{11} = 4u_{20}$ at equilibrium; hence the following equation:

$$4\,DR - H^2 = \frac{\omega_1}{1 - \omega_1}\,H\ .$$

Comparing this expression with (3), we see that

$$\frac{2F}{1 - F} = \frac{\omega_1}{1 - \omega_1},$$

which is just another form of (6) with $\omega_1 = m$ (Ex. 7). Therefore,

$$F = \frac{\omega_1}{2 - \omega_1},\tag{9}$$

whatever the original initial population (which is relevant only in determining gene frequencies). Substituting (9) in (2), we obtain the equilibrium zygotic proportions of the population under this system of mating. This result was first reached by Haldane (1924), later given by Haldane and Moshinsky (1939), and more recently again by Garber (1951) for the particular case of a panmictic initial population. But none of these authors noted that $\omega_1 = m$ at equilibrium; and, consequently, they failed to recognize that this result is merely a special case of the more general relation $F = m/(2 - m)$ reached by Wright in 1921.

An interesting and practical application in plant breeding may be obtained immediately from what has been demonstrated. If we choose a "marker gene" without complete dominance in cotton or wheat and maintain a random plot of the crop for a number of generations, the values of F or m may be calculated from the zygotic proportions of the random plot (by [7] or [8]), and thus the percentage of natural self-fertilization may be estimated. For instance, should we find $F = 0.081$ in a cotton plot, it would indicate 15 per cent natural self-fertilization in cotton plants. This method may prove more accurate than the artificial devices employed by plant breeders, as well as more economical.

§ 9. *Combination of Random Mating and Sib Mating*

For a system that combines random mating and sib mating the relationships are similar to those described in the preceding section. If there is a constant amount of sib mating in each generation, the population will eventually reach an equilibrium state. Proceeding as before, let ω_2 be the fraction of the population practicing sib mating and $1 - \omega_2$ that practicing random mating. The frequencies of the various types of matings will then be $(1 - \omega_2)$ times those under panmixia, plus ω_2 times those of sib mating. According to Figure 11, we have

$$AA \times aa: 2u_{20} = 2DR(1 - \omega_2) + \tfrac{1}{8}u_{11}\omega_2 ;$$

$$Aa \times Aa: u_{11} = H^2(1 - \omega_2) + (2u_{20} + \tfrac{1}{4}u_{11} + \tfrac{1}{4}2u_{21} + \tfrac{1}{4}2u_{10})\omega_2 .$$

Since $u_{11} = 4u_{20}$ at equilibrium, substituting and simplifying, and remembering that $H = u_{21} + u_{11} + u_{10}$, we have

$$4 DR - H^2 = \frac{\omega_2}{1 - \omega_2} \tfrac{1}{2}H .$$

Equating this to the second expression of (3), we obtain

$$\frac{\omega_2}{1 - \omega_2} = \frac{4F}{1 - F};$$

$$\therefore F = \frac{\omega_2}{4 - 3\omega_2}, \tag{10}$$

whatever the original initial population. The equilibrium zygotic proportions under this system of mating may be obtained by substituting (10) in (2). The equivalent amounts of selfing and sib mating in a population may be obtained by comparing this result with the previous one (9). Thus, when equilibrium is reached,

$$F = \frac{m}{2 - m} = \frac{\omega_1}{2 - \omega_1} = \frac{\omega_2}{4 - 3\omega_2}; \tag{9.10}$$

$$\therefore m = \omega_1 = \frac{\omega_2}{2 - \omega_2}. \tag{11}$$

For example, 15 per cent self-fertilization is equivalent to 26 per cent sib mating in a population in the sense that they would give the same values of F and m and the same final zygotic proportions in the population. It is interesting to note that ω_1 is the same function of ω_2 as F is of m.

§ 10. *Numerical Illustration and Other Results*

The following numerical picture may help to clarify the algebraic relations established in the foregoing sections and will also provide the student an opportunity to verify the results of mixed systems of mating. Suppose that in a given initial population, with gene frequencies $p = 0.20$ and $q = 0.80$, we let 40 per cent of the individuals practice selfing and the rest mate at random in each generation. The population will rapidly reach the equilibrium state (0.08, 0.24, 0.68). The correlation between uniting gametes and between mating individuals at equilibrium are shown in the following Tables 46 and 47.

<table>
<tr><td colspan="3" align="center">TABLE 46</td><td colspan="4" align="center">TABLE 47</td></tr>
<tr><td colspan="3" align="center">UNITING GAMETES</td><td colspan="4" align="center">MATING INDIVIDUALS</td></tr>
<tr><td></td><td align="center">A</td><td align="center">a</td><td></td><td align="center">AA</td><td align="center">Aa</td><td align="center">aa</td></tr>
<tr><td align="center">A</td><td>0.08</td><td>0.12</td><td align="center">AA</td><td>0.03584</td><td>0.01152</td><td>0.03264</td></tr>
<tr><td align="center">a</td><td>0.12</td><td>0.68</td><td align="center">Aa</td><td>.01152</td><td>.13056</td><td>.09792</td></tr>
<tr><td></td><td></td><td></td><td align="center">aa</td><td>0.03264</td><td>0.09792</td><td>0.54944</td></tr>
<tr><td></td><td>0.20</td><td>0.80</td><td></td><td></td><td></td><td></td></tr>
<tr><td></td><td></td><td></td><td></td><td>0.08000</td><td>0.24000</td><td>0.68000</td></tr>
</table>

Table 46 gives $F = 0.25$, while Table 47 yields $m = 0.40 = \omega_1$, confirming the general relation (6). The frequencies of matings shown in Table 47 are the sum of 60 per cent random mating plus 40 per cent selfing frequencies. The student may verify that the offspring population remains (0.08, 0.24, 0.68) under the same system of mating. By virtue of (10), we see that the same result would have been obtained if we had allowed $\omega_2 = \frac{4}{7} = 57$ per cent sib mating instead of 40 per cent selfing.

The correlations between parent and offspring (r_{PO}) and between full sibs (r_{OO}) in an inbreeding equilibrium population depend upon the intensiveness of inbreeding in the population; in other words, they depend on the value of m or F at the equilibrium state. Let us find the values of r_{PO} and r_{OO} for the numerical case above. The frequencies of the various parent-offspring and sib-sib combinations may be calculated from the frequencies of mating given in Table 47 by methods outlined in Chapter 2. If we do this, we obtain Tables 48 and 49.

<table>
<tr><td colspan="4" align="center">TABLE 48</td><td colspan="4" align="center">TABLE 49</td></tr>
<tr><td colspan="4" align="center">PARENT-OFFSPRING COMBINATIONS</td><td colspan="4" align="center">SIB-SIB COMBINATIONS</td></tr>
<tr><td></td><td align="center">AA</td><td align="center">Aa</td><td align="center">aa</td><td align="center">AA</td><td align="center">Aa</td><td align="center">aa</td></tr>
<tr><td align="center">AA</td><td>0.0416</td><td>0.0384</td><td>0</td><td>0.04976</td><td>0.02208</td><td>0.00816</td></tr>
<tr><td align="center">Aa</td><td>0.0384</td><td>.1200</td><td>0.0816</td><td>.02208</td><td>.15264</td><td>.06528</td></tr>
<tr><td align="center">aa</td><td>0</td><td>0.0816</td><td>0.5984</td><td>0.00816</td><td>0.06528</td><td>0.60656</td></tr>
<tr><td></td><td>0.0800</td><td>0.2400</td><td>0.6800</td><td>0.0800</td><td>0.2400</td><td>0.6800</td></tr>
</table>

From Tables 48 and 49 it may be readily calculated that $r_{PO} = r_{OO} = 0.70$. In general, the relations of these correlations with m at equilibrium state are

(Wright, 1921):

$$r_{PO} = r_{OO} = \tfrac{1}{2}(1 + m) . \tag{12}$$

The relation (12) may of course also be demonstrated algebraically, using Table 45 and the relations (4) and (6). When $m = F = 0$, these correlations become $\tfrac{1}{2}$, as given in Chapter 3. The relation (12) has also been demonstrated by Fisher (1918) through a different method.

§ 11. *Multiple Alleles*

Let q_i be the frequency of the allele $A_i(i = 1, \ldots, k)$ in a population, and $\Sigma q_i = 1$. The zygotic proportions in an equilibrium population with inbreeding coefficient F are

$$(1 - F)\left(\sum_i q_i A_i \right)^2 + F \left(\sum_i q_i A_i A_i \right)$$
$$= \sum_i \{ (1 - F) q_i^2 + F q_i \} A_i A_i + 2 (1 - F) \sum_{i<j} q_i q_j A_i A_j . \tag{13}$$

As before, these zygotic proportions may be arranged in the form of a combination table of uniting gametes. Such a tabulation, illustrating the case of three ($k = 3$) alleles, appears in Table 50. The correlation coefficient between the

TABLE 50

UNITING GAMETES FOR MULTIPLE ALLELES

	A_1	A_2	A_3	
A_1	$(1-F)q_1^2+Fq_1$	$(1-F)q_1q_2$	$(1-F)q_1q_3$	q_1
A_2	$(1-F)q_2q_1$	$(1-F)q_2^2+Fq_2$	$(1-F)q_2q_3$	q_2
A_3	$(1-F)q_3q_1$	$(1-F)q_3q_2$	$(1-F)q_3^2+Fq_3$	q_3
	q_1	q_2	q_3	1

uniting gametes of the table will be found to be F, no matter what arbitrary values are assigned to the alleles A_1, A_2, A_3.

If we let x_{ii} denote the proportion of A_iA_i, and $2x_{ij}$ be that of $A_iA_j(i < j)$, so that $\Sigma_j x_{ij} = q_i$, then the equation representing all equilibrium populations, analogous to (3′) for two alleles, is (Li, 1953b)

$$\sum_i \frac{x_{ii}}{q_i} = 1 + (k - 1) F . \tag{14}$$

For example, when $k = 3$, $q_1 = x_{11} + x_{12} + x_{13}$, etc.;

$$\frac{x_{11}}{q_1} + \frac{x_{22}}{q_2} + \frac{x_{33}}{q_3} = 1 + 2F . \tag{14′}$$

The student should verify this relation, using Table 50. The total proportion of heterozygotes in a completely panmictic population is $H_0 = 2\Sigma q_i q_j(i < j)$, while that in a population with inbreeding (13) is

$$2(1 - F)\Sigma q_i q_j = H_F = (1 - F)H_0 \,. \tag{15}$$

This relation is independent of the number of alleles concerned. In other words, $(1 - F)$ measures the relative deficiency of heterozygosis due to inbreeding, regardless of multiple alleles. This is another feature of F that makes it so useful in population genetics.

§ 12. *Sample Estimates of* F

Suppose that we have a random sample of G individuals of which a are A_1A_1, b are A_1A_2, and c are A_2A_2. The estimate of the frequency of A_1 is $q_1 = (2a + b)/2G$. The estimate of F, in view of (3), will be given by

$$f = \frac{4\,a\,c - b^2}{(2\,a + b)\,(b + 2\,c)} \,, \tag{16}$$

in which f denotes the sample estimate of F. It may be readily verified that (16) is also the maximum likelihood estimate. Comparing (16) with (2′) of Chapter 2, we see that

$$\chi^2 = f^2\,G\,; \qquad \therefore\, f = \sqrt{\left(\frac{\chi^2}{G}\right)}, \tag{16′}$$

where χ^2 is calculated on the assumption of complete panmixia. The estimation of F based on the value of χ^2 may be extended to the case of multiple alleles. Using the proportions (13) as the "observed" and those of complete panmixia as the "expected" numbers, it may be shown that (Li and Horvitz, 1953)

$$f^2 = \frac{\chi^2}{G\,(k - 1)} \,. \tag{17}$$

When multiple alleles are involved, another simple estimate of F may be made according to the relation (15). Thus

$$f = \frac{H_0 - H_F}{H_0} = 1 - \frac{H_F}{H_0}, \tag{18}$$

where H_F is the observed proportion of heterozygotes and H_0 is calculated assuming panmixia. When there are only two alleles, (18) reduces to (16).

When dominance is present, so that there are only two distinguishable phenotypes for two alleles, there is no direct way of estimating either the gene frequencies or the inbreeding coefficient, because the proportion of recessives is a function of both q and F. In order to obtain an estimate of either, the dominants must be distinguished as homozygotes or heterozygotes by whatever test crosses are convenient. When recessives are available, backcrossing to recessives is better than selfing or crosses *inter se*, because it offers a better chance of identifying a heterozygote than do the last two methods.

Suppose that in a sample of G individuals, of which d are dominants and c are recessives $(d + c = G)$, a number of the dominants have been tested and a of them found to be homozygotes and b to be heterozygotes. The number $a + b$

is usually smaller than d, because the dominants are not necessarily all identified successfully. From the information thus obtained we may form the following two equations:

$$\frac{c}{G} = q^2 + fpq, \qquad \frac{b}{a} = \frac{2(1-f)pq}{p^2 + fpq}.$$

Solving simultaneously (first eliminating f by the substitution $fpq = c/G - q^2$ in the second equation), we obtain

$$p = \frac{d(2a+b)}{2G(a+b)}, \qquad f = \frac{c - Gq^2}{Gpq}, \qquad (19)$$

which is equivalent to an expression given by Li (1948). If all the d dominants in the sample are successfully identified (i.e., $a + b = d$), it reduces to the case without dominance; and (19) reduces to (16).

Finally, it should be said that, when the proportions of homozygotes turn out to be higher than those expected on the basis of complete panmixia, it does not necessarily imply that this is due to the effect of inbreeding. There may be other causes leading to the same apparent result. The foregoing is a method of estimating the degree of inbreeding of a natural population in which there *is* inbreeding.

§ 13. *Two-Factor Recessives*

If a trait is due to two pairs of recessive genes ($aabb$), its proportion in a panmictic population is $R_0 = q^2 v^2$, where q and v are the frequencies of the recessive genes a and b, respectively. If there is inbreeding, its proportion will be increased to

$$R_F = (q^2 + Fpq)(v^2 + Fuv).$$

Table 51 gives some of the values of the ratio R_F/R_0 for various values of q and v

TABLE 51

RATIO OF TWO-FACTOR RECESSIVES WITH INBREEDING TO
THOSE WITH RANDOM MATING
(Compare with Table 43)

PROPORTION OF RECESSIVES IN A PANMICTIC POPULATION	RECESSIVE-GENE FREQUENCIES		VALUE OF $\dfrac{R_F}{R_0} = \dfrac{(q+Fp)(v+Fu)}{qv}$ WHEN INBREEDING COEFFICIENT	
R_0	q	v	$F = \frac{1}{16}$	$F = \frac{1}{32}$
$0.000001\ (qv = 0.001)\ldots$	$\begin{cases} 0.100 \\ .050 \\ 0.0316 \end{cases}$	$\begin{matrix} 0.010 \\ .020 \\ 0.0316 \end{matrix}$	$\begin{matrix} 11.23 \\ 8.89 \\ 8.49 \end{matrix}$	$\begin{matrix} 5.25 \\ 4.03 \\ 3.83 \end{matrix}$
$0.000100\ (qv = 0.01)\ldots$	$\begin{cases} 0.50 \\ .20 \\ 0.10 \end{cases}$	$\begin{matrix} 0.02 \\ .05 \\ 0.10 \end{matrix}$	$\begin{matrix} 4.32 \\ 2.73 \\ 2.44 \end{matrix}$	$\begin{matrix} 2.61 \\ 1.79 \\ 1.64 \end{matrix}$

(assuming that none of them is close to unity). A comparison of these ratios with those of Table 43, showing the *same* proportion of recessives in the general population, reveals that inbreeding does not increase the proportion of two-factor recessives as much as it does that of unit-factor recessives, even when the recessive trait is rare. For instance, when $F = \frac{1}{16}$, recessives increase 63.44 times in a unit-factor case as compared with only 11.23, 8.89, or 8.49 times in a two-factor case—even though the trait be very rare. This leads to a conclusion important in human genetics: If a not-too-rare human abnormality is due to multiple recessive factors, its incidence would hardly be increased to any appreciable extent by consanguineous matings.

Notes and Exercises

1. In a population with gene frequencies p and q, and with H heterozygotes, the correlation table between uniting gametes may be put into the following form, which is equivalent to Table 41.

	A	a	
A	$p-\frac{1}{2}H$	$\frac{1}{2}H$	p
a	$\frac{1}{2}H$	$q-\frac{1}{2}H$	q
	p	q	1

   Show that $F = 1 - H/2pq$ and $H = 2pq(1 - F)$.

2. If the frequency of union of two A gametes is D, in a population with gene frequencies p and q, the correlation coefficient between uniting gametes may also be calculated from the following table:

	A	a	
A	D	$p-D$	p
a	$p-D$	$q-p+D$	q
	p	q	1

   Show that $F = (D - p^2)/pq$ and $D = p^2 + Fpq$. In this problem D was given, while in the previous problem H was given. The results are equivalent.

3. Calculate the value of F for each of the following:

	A	a		A	a		A	a		A	a		A	a
A	0.828	0.072		0.672	0.128		0.532	0.168		0.408	0.192		0.300	0.200
a	0.072	0.028		0.128	0.072		0.168	0.132		0.192	0.208		0.200	0.300
	0.90	0.10		0.80	0.20		0.70	0.30		0.60	0.40		0.50	0.50

   ANS.: $F = 0.20$ in each case.

4. Show that $2H/[(2D + H)(H + 2R)] = 1 - F$.

5. Referring to Table 43, show that $R_F = 2R_0$ when

(i) $q = 1/17 = .0588$ with $F = 1/16$;

(ii) $q = 1/33 = .0303$ with $F = 1/32$.

6. Plot the curve (6), noting that m is greater than F.

m....	0.10	0.20	0.30	0.40	0.50	0.60	0.70	0.80	0.90
F....	0.053	0.111	0.176	0.250	0.333	0.429	0.538	0.667	0.818

m....	0.182	0.333	0.462	0.571	0.667	0.750	0.824	0.889	0.947
F....	0.10	0.20	0.30	0.40	0.50	0.60	0.70	0.80	0.90

7. Show that the relation (6) may be written as

$$\frac{2F}{1-F} = \frac{m}{1-m}.$$

8. Show that

$$H = 2pq\,(1 - F) = 4pq\left(\frac{1-m}{2-m}\right)$$

at equilibrium.

9. If wheat has 1 per cent open-cross and 99 per cent selfing each year, what are the values of m and F in a natural wheat population? Calculate the three genotypic proportions in a wheat field with $p = q = \frac{1}{2}$.

10. Given an initial random-mating population (.16, .48, .36), in which 60 per cent of the individuals are allowed to practice random mating in each generation and the rest to practice selfing, show that the equilibrium state will be (.22, .36, .42), with $F = 0.25$ and $m = 0.40$. Further, show that $r_{PO} = r_{OO} = 0.70$. Carry out the arithmetic of the following four tabulations.

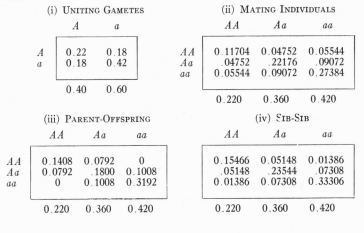

(i) UNITING GAMETES

	A	a
A	0.22	0.18
a	0.18	0.42
	0.40	0.60

(ii) MATING INDIVIDUALS

	AA	Aa	aa
AA	0.11704	0.04752	0.05544
Aa	.04752	.22176	.09072
aa	0.05544	0.09072	0.27384
	0.220	0.360	0.420

(iii) PARENT-OFFSPRING

	AA	Aa	aa
AA	0.1408	0.0792	0
Aa	0.0792	.1800	0.1008
aa	0	0.1008	0.3192
	0.220	0.360	0.420

(iv) SIB-SIB

	AA	Aa	aa
	0.15466	0.05148	0.01386
	.05148	.23544	.07308
	0.01386	0.07308	0.33306
	0.220	0.360	0.420

11. Given an initial panmictic population $(p^2, 2pq, q^2)$, in which a fraction ω of the population practices selfing and $(1 - \omega)$ mate at random (subscript of ω being dropped for simplicity), the next generation will be

$$(1 - \omega)(p^2, 2pq, q^2) + \omega(p^2 + \tfrac{1}{2}pq, \quad pq, \quad q^2 + \tfrac{1}{2}pq)$$
$$= [p^2 + \tfrac{1}{2}\omega pq, \quad 2pq(1 - \tfrac{1}{2}\omega), \quad q^2 + \tfrac{1}{2}\omega pq].$$

Continuing this process, it will be found that the proportion of heterozygotes in the next generation is

$$H_2 = 2pq(1 - \omega) + \omega pq(1 - \tfrac{1}{2}\omega) = 2pq\{1 - (\tfrac{1}{2}\omega) - (\tfrac{1}{2}\omega)^2\}.$$

After n generations of this system of mating,

$$H_n = 2pq\{1 - (\tfrac{1}{2}\omega) - (\tfrac{1}{2}\omega)^2 - \ldots - (\tfrac{1}{2}\omega)^n\}.$$

Therefore, at equilibrium $(n \to \infty)$,

$$H_\infty = 2pq \left\{1 - \frac{\tfrac{1}{2}\omega}{1 - \tfrac{1}{2}\omega}\right\} = 2pq \left\{1 - \frac{\omega}{2 - \omega}\right\}.$$

Hence, by (9)

$$F = \frac{\omega}{2 - \omega}.$$

It is evident that, the smaller the value of ω, the more rapidly the population will reach the equilibrium state.

12. If $D = 0.432$ and $p = 0.60$, what is the value of F in the population? Calculate its zygotic proportions.
    ANS.: $F = 0.30$, $(.432, .336, .232)$.

13. For a sample of 180 individuals $(92, 56, 32)$, estimate the values of p, q, and F.
    ANS.: $p = \tfrac{2}{3}$, $F = 0.30$.

14. Suppose that we have a sample of 90 individuals, of which 74 are dominants and 16 recessives. The dominants have been tested by backcrossing to recessives, and it has been found that 23 of them are homozygous and 14 heterozygous. Estimate the gene frequencies and the inbreeding coefficient.
    ANS.: Use (19). $p = \tfrac{2}{3}$, $f = 0.30$.

15. Show that the correlation coefficient of Table 50 is F by assigning convenient values to A_1, A_2, A_3 (for instance, 1, 2, 3).

16. It should be noted that any table of the *form* of Table 50 will yield a correlation coefficient equal to the fraction of nonrandom combination, whatever the marginal variables may be. Thus, if $1 - \omega$ of a population (D, H, R) practices random mating and ω practices selfing, the correlation coefficient

between mating individuals will be simply ω. Verify this result, using the following table of mating frequencies:

Mates	AA (2)	Aa (1)	aa (0)	Total
AA (2)......	$(1-\omega)D^2+\omega D$	$(1-\omega)DH$	$(1-\omega)DR$	D
Aa (1)	$(1-\omega)DH$	$(1-\omega)H^2+\omega H$	$(1-\omega)HR$	H
aa (0)......	$(1-\omega)DR$	$(1-\omega)HR$	$(1-\omega)R^2+\omega R$	R
Total....	D	H	R	1.00

HINT: Covariance $= \omega(4DR - H^2 + H)$; use (5).

17. A sample of 400 individuals is found to contain:

$$32 \; A_1A_1 \; ; \qquad 36 \; A_1A_2 \; ; \qquad 60 \; A_1A_3 \; ;$$

$$57 \; A_2A_2 \; ; \qquad 90 \; A_2A_3 \; ; \qquad 125 \; A_3A_3 \; .$$

Estimate the frequencies of the three alleles. Estimate the value of F by (i) arranging the data into the form of a gametic combination table and calculating its correlation coefficient; (ii) calculating the value of χ^2, assuming complete panmixia and using (17); (iii) using equation (14'); and (iv) finding the total proportion of heterozygotes and using relation (18). ANS.: $q_1 = 0.20$, $q_2 = 0.30$, $q_3 = 0.50$, $f = \frac{1}{4}$.

CHAPTER 12

The Theory of Path Coefficients

THE algebraic methods employed in previous chapters become cumbersome when used for the more complex or irregular inbreeding systems or for more than one pair of genes. Professor Sewall Wright has developed an entirely different technique which has proved extremely effective for many problems in theoretical genetics and for practical applications in animal breeding as well as in the statistical analysis of cause and effect in a system of correlated variables. His theory of path coefficients gives us, among many other things, a simple and flexible method of solving a wide variety of inbreeding problems. We shall consider briefly only those few theorems that are applicable to the particular purposes of this book. Readers who are interested in the general statistical properties of path coefficients should consult Wright's original papers, particularly the following: *Journal of Agricultural Research*, **20** (1921); *Genetics*, **6** and **8** (1921, 1923); and *Annals of Mathematical Statistics*, **5** (1934).

The theory of path coefficients will be presented as a general statistical method in this chapter, and its specific applications to genetics will be given in the next chapter. Before proceeding with the theory itself, it may be helpful to the student to review some points in elementary statistics.

§ 1. *Statistical Memoranda*

The correlation coefficient.—The correlation coefficient between two variables, A and B, with mean values $\bar{A}$ and $\bar{B}$, respectively, is defined as

$$r_{AB} = \frac{\Sigma (A - \bar{A})(B - \bar{B})}{\sqrt{[\Sigma (A - \bar{A})^2 \Sigma (B - \bar{B})^2]}} = \frac{\sigma_{AB}}{\sigma_A \sigma_B}. \tag{1}$$

For N pairs of values of A and B, we take $\sigma_A^2 = \Sigma(A - \bar{A})^2/N$ and $\sigma_{AB} = \Sigma(A - \bar{A})(B - \bar{B})/N$. A numerical example is given in Table 52. It may be noted that, if the variances of A and B are equal ($\sigma_A^2 = \sigma_B^2$), the correlation coefficient reduces to the ordinary linear regression coefficient of A on B (or of B on A):

$$r_{AB} = \frac{\sigma_{AB}}{\sigma_A^2} = \frac{\sigma_{AB}}{\sigma_B^2} = b_{AB} = b_{BA}. \tag{2}$$

By definition (1) the correlation coefficient between any variable and itself is always unity; thus, $r_{AA} = 1$, because here σ_{AA} is identical with σ_A^2.

The expression (1), as it stands, is symmetrical with respect to A and B, yielding a numerical measurement of the degree of linear association between the deviations of A and B. This symmetry is one of the chief properties of a correlation coefficient. It is sometimes called the "total correlation" between two variables, because it includes all the known and unknown agents that make the two variables correlated, but it does not necessarily imply any causal relationship. It is well known, however, that r_{AB}^2 is that fraction of the variance of A that is "determined" by that of B (or vice versa), in the sense that this fraction would disappear if B were constant. If A and B are independent, $r_{AB} = 0$; for then the sum of the products of their corresponding deviations vanishes: $\Sigma(A - \bar{A})(B - \bar{B}) = 0$. For example, the A and B in Table 53 are two such independent variables.

The sum of variables.—If $X = A + B$,

$$\sigma_X^2 = \sigma_A^2 + \sigma_B^2 + 2\sigma_{AB} = \sigma_A^2 + \sigma_B^2 + 2r_{AB}\sigma_A\sigma_B. \tag{3}$$

When A and B are uncorrelated, (3) reduces to

$$\sigma_X^2 = \sigma_A^2 + \sigma_B^2. \tag{4}$$

This last relation is illustrated in Table 53.

TABLE 52

CORRELATION BETWEEN A AND B

									Total	Mean
A.........	16	8	17	3	44	59	42	51	240	$\bar{A}=30$
B.........	2	4	5	7	10	13	14	17	72	$\bar{B}=9$

$\Sigma(A-\bar{A})^2=3200,\qquad \Sigma(B-\bar{B})^2=200,\qquad \Sigma(A-\bar{A})(B-\bar{B})=672$
$\sigma_A=\sqrt{400}=20,\qquad \sigma_B=\sqrt{25}=5,\qquad \sigma_{AB}=84$

$$r_{AB} = \frac{672}{\sqrt{(3200\times200)}} = \frac{84}{20\times5} = 0.84$$

TABLE 53

SUM OF TWO INDEPENDENT VARIABLES

									Total	Mean
A.........	34	3	40	28	14	25	31	25	200	$\bar{A}=25$
B.........	2	4	5	7	10	13	14	17	72	$\bar{B}=9$
X.........	36	7	45	35	24	38	45	42	272	$\bar{X}=34$

$\Sigma(A-\bar{A})^2=956,\qquad \Sigma(B-\bar{B})^2=200,\qquad \Sigma(X-\bar{X})^2=1156$
$\sigma_A^2=119.5,\qquad \sigma_B^2=25,\qquad \sigma_X^2=144.5$

More generally speaking, if X is any linear combination of two independent variables, for instance, if $X = l_1 A + l_2 B$, where l_1 and l_2 are constants, $\sigma_X^2 = l_1^2 \sigma_A^2 + l_2^2 \sigma_B^2$. The quantity $l_1^2 \sigma_A^2$ is still associated with the variance of A. Therefore, for the sum of independent factors, we may describe this situation by saying that

$$\frac{\sigma^2 \text{ due to } A}{\sigma_X^2} + \frac{\sigma^2 \text{ due to } B}{\sigma_X^2} = 1 . \tag{5}$$

The foregoing three relations, (3), (4), and (5), may be extended to any number of factors.

Next, consider the correlation between the sum and one of its component independent variables, for instance, r_{XA}, where $X = A + B$ and $\sigma_{AB} = 0$. Now, since $\bar{X} = \bar{A} + \bar{B}$,

$$\begin{aligned}
\Sigma (X - \bar{X})(A - \bar{A}) &= \Sigma (A + B - \bar{A} - \bar{B})(A - \bar{A}) \\
&= \Sigma \{(A - \bar{A}) + (B - \bar{B})\}(A - \bar{A}) \\
&= \Sigma (A - \bar{A})^2 + \Sigma (B - \bar{B})(A - \bar{A}) = \Sigma (A - \bar{A})^2 \quad (6)
\end{aligned}$$

because of the fact that the sum-of-product term vanishes on the assumption of independence between A and B. Hence, we conclude that $\sigma_{XA} = \sigma_A^2$, from which it follows that

$$\left. \begin{aligned}
r_{XA} &= \frac{\sigma_{XA}}{\sigma_X \sigma_A} = \frac{\sigma_A}{\sigma_X} ; \qquad r_{XA}^2 = \frac{\sigma_A^2}{\sigma_X^2} ; \\[2mm]
r_{XB} &= \frac{\sigma_{XB}}{\sigma_X \sigma_B} = \frac{\sigma_B}{\sigma_X} ; \qquad r_{XB}^2 = \frac{\sigma_B^2}{\sigma_X^2} .
\end{aligned} \right\} \tag{7}$$

The last relation, together with (4), gives us the important theorem

$$r_{XA}^2 + r_{XB}^2 = 1 . \tag{8}$$

Verify the relations (6), (7), (8), using the numerical values of Table 53. Theorem (8) may be extended to any number of independent component factors.

Multiplying independent variables.—If $X = A \times B$, and A and B are independent, $\bar{X} = \bar{A} \times \bar{B}$; and the variance of the product variable is

$$\sigma_X^2 = \bar{B}^2 \sigma_A^2 + \bar{A}^2 \sigma_B^2 + \frac{1}{N} \Sigma (A - \bar{A})^2 (B - \bar{B})^2 . \tag{9}$$

Since the proof of this relation is not found in elementary statistical textbooks, a simple demonstration will be given here. Suppose there are n distinct values of A, and m distinct values of B. Further, assume that every value of B occurs to a given value of A and vice versa, so that A and B are independent for the $N = nm$ pairs of values (A, B). Note that the variance of A may be calculated either from its n distinct values or from its nm repeated values, the sum of squares of the latter being m times greater than that of the former. Now, consider the nm values of the product $X = AB$ (Table 54). In order to find its variance, we note that each deviation of X may be written as

$$X - \bar{X} = AB - \overline{AB} = (A - \bar{A})(B - \bar{B}) + \bar{A}\cdot B + \bar{B}\cdot A - 2\bar{A}\cdot\bar{B}$$
$$= (A - \bar{A})(B - \bar{B}) + \bar{A}(B - \bar{B}) + \bar{B}(A - \bar{A}) .$$

Squaring each X-deviation, adding the $N = nm$ squares of deviations together, and dividing by N, we obtain the formula (9), because, on summation, all the three cross-product terms vanish. To see this, let us take the term

TABLE 54

MULTIPLYING INDEPENDENT VARIABLES

A			B			$N = 3 \times 5 = 15$
	10	11	12	13	14	
4........	40	44	48	52	56	$\bar{A} = 5$
5........	50	55	60	65	70	$\bar{B} = 12$
6........	60	66	72	78	84	$\bar{X} = 60$

$$\Sigma(X - \bar{X})^2 = \bar{B}^2\Sigma(A - \bar{A})^2 + \bar{A}^2\Sigma(B - \bar{B})^2 + \Sigma(A - \bar{A})^2(B - \bar{B})^2$$

$$
\begin{aligned}
2210 &= (12)^2(2 \times 5) &+ (5)^2(10 \times 3) &+ 20 \\
&= 1440 &+ 750 &+ 20 \\
\sigma_X^2 = 147.3 &= 96.0 &+ 50.0 &+ 1.3
\end{aligned}
$$

$\Sigma(A - \bar{A})(B - \bar{B})^2$, where the summation means the sum of nm values. We add them column by column (Table 54); and, for each column, $(B - \bar{B})^2$ is a constant and $\Sigma(A - \bar{A}) = 0$; hence the sum over the nm values is also zero. A numerical illustration of (9) is given in Table 54.

It will be noted that the term $\Sigma(A - \bar{A})^2(B - \bar{B})^2$ is much smaller than $\bar{B}^2\Sigma(A - A)^2$ or $\bar{A}^2\Sigma(B - B)^2$, as is usually the case when the variation of A and B are not large in comparison with their mean values. Then (9) becomes

$$\sigma_X^2 = \bar{B}^2\sigma_A^2 + \bar{A}^2\sigma_B^2, \text{ approx.}$$

This is of the same form as though X were a *linear* combination of the two independent variables, A and B. Hence, our assertion (5) would still hold approximately. If not, a logarithmic transformation of the multiplicative variables will render them additive; thus, $\log X = \log A + \log B$. The demonstration above shows that in many cases it is safe, for practical purposes, to treat multiplicative variables as additive ones. In this chapter we shall deal with additive variables only.

Partial correlations.—Suppose there are four correlated variables: X_1, X_2,

X_3, X_4. The partial correlation coefficient between X_1 and X_2, for instance, when one of the remaining variables (X_3, say) is kept constant (i.e., the influence of its variation is eliminated), is known as the partial correlation coefficient of the *first order*. The notations, derivations, and properties of partial correlation coefficients are too long to be outlined here. However, an excellent elementary account is to be found in Yule and Kendall (1950, Chap. 12). One of the properties of the partial correlation coefficients is that they can be expressed in terms of correlation coefficients of lower orders. Thus, the first-order coefficient we mentioned above is

$$r_{12.3} = \frac{r_{12} - r_{13}r_{23}}{\sqrt{[\,(1 - r_{13}^2)\,(1 - r_{23}^2)\,]}}\,, \tag{10}$$

where the total correlations, r_{12}, etc., may be considered as of "zero" order. Similarly, the partial correlation between X_1 and X_2, when the effects of X_3 and X_4 are eliminated, is of the *second order:*

$$r_{12.34} = \frac{r_{12.3} - r_{14.3}r_{24.3}}{\sqrt{[\,(1 - r_{14.3}^2)\,(1 - r_{24.3}^2)\,]}}\,. \tag{11}$$

The subscripts 3 and 4 may be interchanged. This method of calculating partial correlations may be extended to that of third and higher orders.

§ 2. *Causation and Path Coefficient*

Cause and effect.—We shall not consider the philosophical problem of what constitutes "cause" and what "effect." Suffice it to say that there are many cases where we do have a priori or experimental grounds for postulating that certain variables are causes of variation in others or that certain pairs of variables are correlated as effects of a certain common cause. For example, the yield of wheat obviously depends upon the amount of fertilizers applied rather than vice versa. Hence, we take fertilizers as the independent variable (cause) and yield as the dependent variable (effect or result) in any statistical analysis of their relationship. Here, however, we would prefer the regression method rather than the correlation method, because the latter, being symmetrical with respect to yield and amount of fertilizers, is inadequate to describe the cause-and-effect relationship.

In many cases, moreover, there is an obvious mathematical relationship between variables. For example, the final weight (X) of an animal at the end of four weeks is the sum of its initial weight (A) plus its gain in weight (B) during the period of four weeks. Hence, we have $X = A + B$. Furthermore, the initial weight and the subsequent gain in weight may be correlated for various reasons such as the size of litter, the health of dam, genetical constitution, etc. This situation may be represented by the following diagram, in which the arrows indicate the directions of influence, and a double-arrowed line indicates (symmetrical) correlation.

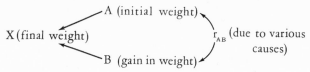

The arrows connecting "causes" and "effects" in a network of related variables are referred to as "paths." In trying to determine the relative importance of each path of causation, we shall assign a numerical index (coefficient) to each path to measure the direct influence along that path in a system of related variables. In doing so, we shall find also the degree to which the variation of a given effect is determined by each particular cause.

Path coefficient and determination.—Let X be the dependent effect and A, B, C, etc., be the causes, so that X is a linear combination of $A, B, C, \ldots$. Further, let σ_X be the total standard deviation of X and $\sigma_{X:A}$ denote the standard deviation of X due to the influence of A, while all the other causes (except A) are kept constant, but the variation of A is still as great as before. How to assign the value of $\sigma_{X:A}$ is another matter and will be explained for each specific case in the next section. The *path coefficient* for the path from cause A to X is defined as

$$p\,(X \leftarrow A) = p_{X \cdot A} = \frac{\sigma_{X:A}}{\sigma_X}. \tag{12}$$

When this definition is given, it is assumed that the direct influence along a given path can be measured by the standard deviation remaining in X after all other paths of influence are eliminated, while the variation of the cause back of the given path (A's variation) is kept as great as ever regardless of its relations to the other causes which have been made constant.

It is clear from definition (12) that the path coefficient $p_{X \cdot A}$ is an absolute number without any physical unit—whatever the actual units of measurement used for the variables. In this respect it is similar to correlation coefficients. On the other hand, it has a *direction* (from A to X); and expression (12) shows that it is similar to regression coefficients (which are also "directional" but have physical units attached, e.g., grams/inch). Indeed, it may be shown that path coefficients are equivalent to those "standardized" regression coefficients which refer to "standardized" variables rather than to variables in original physical units (see "Notes and Exercises").

Next, we will define another index: the *coefficient of determination* of X by cause A. This index is denoted by the symbol $d_{X \cdot A}$ and is defined as that fraction of complete determination of X for which the cause A is directly responsible in a given system of related variables. It follows from this definition that, if *all* causes are accounted for, the sum of such coefficients must equal unity:

$$d_{X \cdot A} + d_{X \cdot B} + d_{X \cdot C} + \ldots = 1. \tag{13}$$

The degree of determination of one variable by another is most easily found when the variables are connected by a mathematical expression.

§ 3. *Systems of Relationship*

Now let us consider some simple causal schemes and see how the method of path coefficients works and what kind of results we obtain by its use. We start with the simplest scheme in which all the causes are uncorrelated with each other.

Independent causes.—Let A and B be two uncorrelated determining variables ($r_{AB} = 0$), both influencing the dependent variable X. The simplest case is that of the relationship $X = A + B$, as illustrated in Figure 15 and exemplified in Table 53. From (4), we have $\sigma_X^2 = \sigma_A^2 + \sigma_B^2$. Now, if B were a constant

FIG. 15.—Independent causes

and thus $\sigma_B^2 = 0$, the variance of X would be simply that of A. Hence, we say that "the variance of X due to the influence of A" is $\sigma_{X:A}^2 = \sigma_A^2$. It follows from definition (12) that the path coefficient from A to X is

$$p_{X \cdot A} = \frac{\sigma_{X:A}}{\sigma_X} = \frac{\sigma_A}{\sigma_X}. \tag{14p}$$

The degree to which the variation of X is determined by that of A is $d_{X.A} = \sigma_A^2/\sigma_X^2$; and hence, conforming with (13),

$$d_{X \cdot A} + d_{X \cdot B} = \frac{\sigma_A^2}{\sigma_X^2} + \frac{\sigma_B^2}{\sigma_X^2} = 1. \tag{14d}$$

From the relations in (7) we see that $p_{X \cdot A} = r_{XA}$ and $d_{X \cdot A} = r_{XA}^2$ and that (14d) is the same as (8). The expressions (14p) and (14d) may be summed up into one as follows:

$$\sqrt{d_{X \cdot A}} = p_{X \cdot A} = r_{X A} = \frac{\sigma_A}{\sigma_X}. \tag{14}$$

The student should verify these results, using the numbers given in Table 53, and should place the numerical values of $p_{X \cdot A}$ and $p_{X \cdot B}$ on the appropriate paths of Figure 15. For example, $p_{X \cdot A} = \sqrt{(956/1156)} = \sqrt{0.827} = 0.909$.

Formula (14) still holds for the more general case where X is a linear combination of $A, B, C, \ldots$, as long as all the causes are independent of each other.

In this case the deviations of X are additive, which means that a given amount of change in one cause always determines the same change in the effect (X), regardless of its own absolute value or that of the other causes.

Chains of independent causes.—In a chain system of cause-and-effect schemes (Fig. 16) in which $X = A + B$ and in turn $A = C + D$ (where A and B are

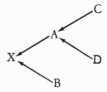

FIG. 16.—Chain of independent causes

independent and so are C and D), the relation is clearly equivalent to having three independent causes of the effect X. Thus, when

$$X = A + B = C + D + B, \qquad \sigma_X^2 = \sigma_A^2 + \sigma_B^2 = \sigma_C^2 + \sigma_D^2 + \sigma_B^2.$$

Applying the results of the previous section, we have immediately

$$d_{X \cdot A} = \frac{\sigma_A^2}{\sigma_X^2}, \qquad d_{A \cdot C} = \frac{\sigma_C^2}{\sigma_A^2}, \qquad d_{X \cdot C} = \frac{\sigma_C^2}{\sigma_X^2}.$$

From this our theorem about chains of independent causes follows:

$$\left.\begin{array}{c} d_{X \cdot C} = d_{X \cdot A} d_{A \cdot C} \, ; \\[4pt] \therefore \quad p_{X \cdot C} = p_{X \cdot A} p_{A \cdot C} \, . \\[4pt] r_{XC} = r_{XA} r_{AC} \, . \end{array}\right\} \qquad (15)$$

Also,

The corresponding relations between X and D are similar except that C is replaced by D in (15). More generally speaking, the degree of determination, the path coefficient, and the correlation coefficient between the effect and an independent cause are all equal to the *product* of the corresponding individual values along the chain which connects the cause with the effect. Another obvious result is that, since $d_{A \cdot C} + d_{A \cdot D} = 1$, $d_{X \cdot A} = d_{X \cdot C} + d_{X \cdot D}$.

Common causes and correlation.—Let all the four causes A, B, C, D in Figure 17 be independent of each other; that is, $r_{AB} = r_{AC} = r_{AD} = r_{BC} = r_{BD} = r_{CD} = 0$. Consider the two effects, X and Y, where X is influenced by A, B, C and Y by B, C, D. Therefore, X and Y will be correlated because of the influences of the two common causes, B and C. We wish to find an expression for r_{XY} in terms of the path coefficients from their common causes to X and Y. Obviously, A and D do not contribute to r_{XY} at all.

Since the student is by now familiar with the notations of path coefficients, we shall henceforth further simplify them by writing small letters corresponding to the causes; thus, $p(X \leftarrow A) = p_{X \cdot A} = a$ (Fig. 17). The paths to the other effect, Y, may be distinguished by primed small letters; thus, $p(Y \leftarrow D) = p_{Y \cdot D} = d'$. Now, since B and C are independent, we have, from (14),

$$b = p_{X \cdot B} = r_{XB}, \qquad c = p_{X \cdot C} = r_{XC} \quad \text{(solid arrows)} ;$$

$$b' = p_{Y \cdot B} = r_{YB}, \qquad c' = p_{Y \cdot C} = r_{YC} \quad \text{(dotted arrows)} .$$

If the common influence of the cause B is eliminated by keeping it constant, the first-order partial correlation between X and Y will be, according to (10),

$$r_{XY \cdot B} = \frac{r_{XY} - r_{XB} r_{YB}}{\sqrt{[\,(1 - r_{XB}^2)(1 - r_{YB}^2)\,]}} = \frac{r_{XY} - b b'}{\sqrt{[\,(1 - b^2)(1 - b'^2)\,]}} .$$

If both B and C are kept constant, the second-order partial correlation be-

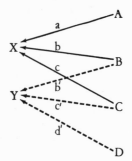

FIG. 17.—Common independent causes

tween X and Y will then be, according to (11),

$$r_{XY \cdot BC} = \frac{r_{XY \cdot B} - r_{XC \cdot B} r_{YC \cdot B}}{\sqrt{[\,(1 - r_{XC \cdot B}^2)(1 - r_{YC \cdot B}^2)\,]}} ,$$

where

$$r_{XC \cdot B} = \frac{r_{XC} - r_{XB} r_{BC}}{\sqrt{[\,(1 - r_{XB}^2)(1 - r_{BC}^2)\,]}} = \frac{r_{XC}}{\sqrt{(1 - r_{XB}^2)}} = \frac{c}{\sqrt{(1 - b^2)}} ,$$

remembering that $r_{BC} = 0$. The expression for $r_{YC \cdot B}$ is similar except that X is replaced by Y; thus, $r_{YC \cdot B} = c'/\sqrt{(1 - b'^2)}$. Substituting and simplifying, we obtain

$$r_{XY \cdot BC} = \frac{r_{XY} - b b' - c c'}{\sqrt{[\,(1 - b^2 - c^2)(1 - b'^2 - c'^2)\,]}} .$$

When the influences of all the common causes have been eliminated, there will be no correlation left between X and Y; and we should have $r_{XY \cdot BC} = 0$. Hence, we have the following theorem:

$$r_{XY} = bb' + cc' \tag{16}$$

$$= p_{X \cdot B} p_{Y \cdot B} + p_{X \cdot C} p_{Y \cdot C} .$$

This kind of analysis may be extended to any number of independent common causes. Generally speaking,

$$r_{XY} = \sum_i p_{X \cdot i} p_{Y \cdot i} , \tag{16'}$$

where i is a common cause. This is one of the most important theorems in the theory of path coefficients, and we may restate it thus: The total correlation between two effects is equal to the sum of the products of pairs of path coefficients connecting the two effects with each common cause (when all the common causes are independent). We have partitioned the total correlation into its component parts, each part due to a common cause. Exercise 7 gives a numerical illustration of this relation.

Correlated causes.—Now we pass on to the case in which the causes themselves are correlated. Again let $X = A + B;$ but this time A and B are corre-

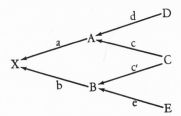

Fig. 18.—Correlated causes

lated by their common cause, C (Fig. 18). We assume that the remote causes, C, D, E, are independent of each other. We shall first investigate the relation between X and its immediate causes (A and B) and then the relation between X and its remote causes (C, D, E).

Since A and B are correlated, σ_A^2 will diminish to $\sigma_A^2(1 - r_{AB}^2)$ when the variable B is kept constant. But now we must recall the definition of $\sigma_{X:A}$ given in Section 2 (p. 149). There it was stated that $\sigma_{X:A}$ is the standard deviation of X due to the influence of A, when those of all other variables (except A) are eliminated but A still varies as much as before. The undiminished σ_A should be taken as the value of $\sigma_{X:A}$, disregarding its reduction after the influence of B is eliminated. Thus, we have

$$a = p_{X \cdot A} = \sigma_A/\sigma_X , \qquad b = p_{X \cdot B} = \sigma_B/\sigma_X .$$

It should be noted that these expressions are *not* the same as formula (14), which we used for independent causes and in which the path coefficient is equal to the corresponding correlation coefficient. Here this is not true, and $a \neq r_{XA}$.

The variance of $X = A + B$ is given by (3), from which it is seen that the coefficients of determination of X by causes A and B are:

$$d_{X \cdot A} = \frac{\sigma_A^2}{\sigma_X^2} = a^2$$

$$d_{X \cdot B} = \frac{\sigma_B^2}{\sigma_X^2} = b^2$$

$$d_{X \cdot AB} = \frac{2 r_{AB} \sigma_A \sigma_B}{\sigma_X^2} = 2 a b r_{AB}$$

$$\left. \begin{array}{l} \\ \\ d_{X \cdot A} + d_{X \cdot B} + d_{X \cdot AB} \\ = a^2 + b^2 + 2 a b r_{AB} = 1 . \\ \\ \\ \end{array} \right\} \quad (17)$$

The expression (17) is the theorem for complete determination by correlated causes and is clearly a generalization of (14d).

Next, let us extend our attention to the remote causes, C, D, E. In reading the following passages, it will be helpful to make constant reference to Figure 18, because many of the subsequent expressions are almost self-evident from inspection of the causal scheme diagramed there. Since C is the only common cause of A and B, we have $r_{AB} = p_{A \cdot C} p_{B \cdot C} = cc'$ from (16). Note that the effect X may also be considered as a linear combination of the independent causes, C, D, E, if we omit the intermediate variables A and B from the scheme. As it stands, however, C is connected with X through two paths: one by way of A and one by way of B. Our chief purpose here is to find the value of the path from C to X in terms of the intermediate individual "steps."

Since C, D, E are independent of each other, we have

$$d_{X \cdot C} + d_{X \cdot D} + d_{X \cdot E} = 1 ,$$

$$d_{A \cdot D} + d_{A \cdot C} = 1, \quad \text{and} \quad d_{B \cdot E} + d_{B \cdot C} = 1 .$$

From the theorem on chains of independent variables, we write

$$d_{X \cdot A} = d_{X \cdot A}(d_{A \cdot D} + d_{A \cdot C}) = d_{X \cdot D} + d_{X \cdot A} d_{A \cdot C} ,$$

$$d_{X \cdot B} = d_{X \cdot B}(d_{B \cdot E} + d_{B \cdot C}) = d_{X \cdot E} + d_{X \cdot B} d_{B \cdot C} .$$

The value of the coefficient of determination of X by C may be found easily by making the above substitutions in the following equation:

$$d_{X \cdot A} + d_{X \cdot B} + d_{X \cdot AB} = d_{X \cdot C} + d_{X \cdot D} + d_{X \cdot E} = 1 ;$$

$$\therefore \quad d_{X \cdot C} = (d_{X \cdot A} + d_{X \cdot B} + d_{X \cdot AB}) - d_{X \cdot D} - d_{X \cdot E}$$

$$= d_{X \cdot A} d_{A \cdot C} + d_{X \cdot B} d_{B \cdot C} + d_{X \cdot AB}$$

$$= a^2 c^2 + b^2 c'^2 + 2abcc' = (ac + bc')^2 ;$$

$$\therefore \quad p_{X \cdot C} = ac + bc' .$$

Furthermore, since C is independent of D and E, the path coefficient from C to X is also the correlation coefficient between C and X from theorem (14); that is,

$$p_{X \cdot C} = r_{XC} = ac + bc' = p_{X \cdot A} p_{A \cdot C} + p_{X \cdot B} p_{B \cdot C} . \qquad (18)$$

Thus, we obtain the important theorem: The combined path coefficient for all paths connecting an effect with a remote cause equals the sum of products of the intermediate individual path coefficients along all connecting paths. This principle can be extended to cases in which a multiple-step remote cause acts upon an effect through any number of intermediate causes. Exercise 8 gives a numerical illustration of (18).

§ 4. *General Theorems*

In the previous sections we have investigated four elementary causal schemes: independent causes, chains of causes, common causes, and correlated causes. Combining these elementary theorems, we obtain more general theorems in a complex system of relationships. In this section we shall summarize the theory of path coefficients under two main theorems: one concerned with the

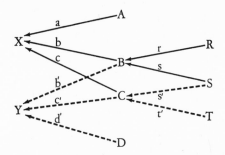

Fig. 19.—Correlated common causes

total correlation between two effects and another with the complete determination of a variable.

Consider the system shown in Figure 19, where the remote causes, R, S, T, are independent. The total correlation between X and Y is due primarily to their immediate common causes, B and C, which are, however, also correlated owing to the common influence of S. It will be recalled that, if B and C were independent (Fig. 17), the correlation between X and Y would be simply $r_{XY} = bb' + cc'$ according to (16). Now, since the causes B and C are themselves correlated with $r_{BC} = ss'$, the value of r_{XY} will be higher than just $bb' + cc'$. This should be clear intuitively because here the common causes, B and C, are more alike than if they were independent; and thus they make X and Y more correlated. Our problem is to express this r_{XY} in terms of relevant path coefficients.

Let us examine the system in Figure 19 in a slightly different manner. If we ignore the intermediate variables (B and C), our problem becomes simply that of finding the value of r_{XY} due to three independent common causes, R, S, T. Thus our theorem (16′) becomes directly applicable, letting $i = R, S, T$. Hence,

$$r_{XY} = p_{X \cdot R} p_{Y \cdot R} + p_{X \cdot S} p_{Y \cdot S} + p_{X \cdot T} p_{Y \cdot T}.$$

Each of these path coefficients consists of two or more component steps. Applying our theorems concerning chains and correlated causes, respectively, we have, from (15),

$$p_{X \cdot R} = br \,,$$

$$p_{Y \cdot R} = b'r, \text{ etc.} \,,$$

and, from (18),

$$p_{X \cdot S} = bs + cs' \,,$$

$$p_{Y \cdot S} = b's + c's' \,.$$

Substituting, we obtain

$$r_{XY} = br \cdot b'r + (bs + cs')(b's + c's') + ct' \cdot c't'$$

$$= bb'(r^2 + s^2) + cc'(s'^2 + t'^2) + bss'c' + cs'sb' \,.$$

Since R, S, T are independent of each other, $r^2 + s^2 = 1$, $s'^2 + t'^2 = 1$, and $ss' = r_{BC}$, from our previous elementary theorems. So the final expression for the correlation between X and Y is

$$r_{XY} = bb' + cc' + br_{BC}c' + cr_{BC}b' \,. \tag{19}$$

This is clearly an extension of (16) and is the first general theorem we have established in this section.

In tracing out the expression (19) in Figure 19, we see that, as far as the correlation between X and Y is concerned, the system of relations may be simplified considerably by omitting the remote causes, R, S, T, from the diagram and instead connecting B and C with a double-arrowed line indicating correlation, as shown in Figure 20. The last two terms of (19) show that a double-arrowed correlation line is a "two-way" path, and such a double-arrowed line has been used twice in two different directions (from B to C and from C to B). Therefore, the two effects X and Y are connected by *four* different paths, viz., X–B–Y, X–C–Y, X–B–C–Y, X–C–B–Y; and this is precisely what formula (19) says. We may state this theorem in more general terms: The correlation between two variables is the sum of the products of the chains of individual path coefficients along all the paths by which they are connected.

This theorem may be applied to any two variables in a causal scheme. For instance, A and Y are not connected by any path in Figure 20; hence, $r_{AY} = 0$. Similarly, $r_{DX} = 0$. On the other hand, B and Y are connected by *two* paths: one directly from B to Y and the other from B to C and then to Y. Thus,

$$r_{BY} = b' + r_{BC}c' \,; \qquad r_{CY} = c' + r_{BC}b' \,.$$

Substituting in (19), we obtain an alternative form:

$$r_{XY} = ar_{AY} + br_{BY} + cr_{CY} \,. \tag{20}$$

In the particular scheme under consideration (Fig. 20), its first term vanishes because $r_{AY} = 0$. The expression (20) says that, if a variable X is influenced by a number of other variables (A, B, C, etc., some of which may be correlated among themselves), the correlation between X and another variable Y is a linear combination of correlations between that variable (Y) and those influencing variables (A, B, C, etc.) with path coefficients as coefficients of the terms. A more general presentation of this relation is given in "Notes and Exercises" at the end of this chapter. But it should be emphasized that (19) and (20), despite their apparent differences in appearance and in verbal interpretation, are entirely equivalent. The practical convenience of an expression depends largely

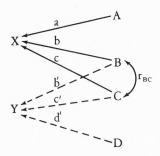

FIG. 20.—Simplification of Figure 19 by omitting the remote causes

upon how the causal scheme between the variables is formulated (compare Fig. 20 with Fig. 25).

Next, let us consider the degrees of determination of X by its influencing factors. Since X is completely determined by A, B, and C (Fig. 20), where A is independent of B and C but the latter two are correlated, we have, from (14d) and (17),

$$a^2 + b^2 + c^2 + 2bcr_{BC} = 1 . \tag{21}$$

This is the second general theorem established in this section. It follows directly from our definition of coefficients of determination. However, it may also be obtained from a different consideration. It will be recalled from Section 1 (p. 145) that the correlation between any variable and itself is always unity. Now, if we try to express the correlation between X and itself in terms of path coefficients according to our general formula (19), replacing b' and c' by b and c, and taking into account the cause A, we will obtain the same expression (21) for $r_{XX} = 1$. Therefore, the expression (21) may be regarded as a limiting form of (19). Similarly, the alternative form (20) would reduce to

$$r_{XX} = ar_{AX} + br_{BX} + cr_{CX} = 1 , \tag{22}$$

where X is completely determined by A, B, and C, some of which may be correlated among themselves. In conclusion, the theory of path coefficients may be summarized by the two expressions (19) and (21), which combine all the preliminary theorems developed in the last section.

§ 5. *Tracing Connecting Paths*

The practical application of the techniques of path coefficients can be facili-
tated by a few rules for tracing a connecting path between two variables in a
causal scheme. Consider the simplest system, shown in Figure 15, where A and
B are independent. The effect X is connected with A by a single path and also
connected with B by a single path; but we cannot regard A and B as being connected by way of X. That is to say, in tracing a connecting path, it is not permissible to trace first forward (along with the direction of an arrow, e.g., from A
to X) and then backward (against the direction of an arrow, e.g., from X to B).
Therefore, our first rule is: No "first-forward-and-then-backward" motion in
tracing any connecting path. Thus, the route $A–X–B$ in Figure 15 is *not* a connecting path between A and B, which are independent.

On the other hand, the reverse motion, first-backward-and-then-forward, is
the correct way of tracing a connecting path. Thus, in Figure 17, the route
from X to B (first backward) and then from B to Y (second forward) is a connecting path between X and Y. Similarly, the route $X–C–Y$ in the same figure
is also a connecting path.

Our third rule follows from the theorem about chains of variables: If one is
tracing backward, one can continue to trace backward (no change in direction)
for as many steps as are available, and then forward for as many steps as are
available, without changing direction. Thus, in Figure 18, the route from X to
A to C (two backward steps) is a connecting path between X and C; and, in
Figure 19, $X–B–S$ (two backward steps) and then $S–C–Y$ (two forward steps)
is a connecting path between X and Y.

Finally, it is necessary to point out an important precaution in using a
double-arrowed correlation line. Such a line is a two-way path and can be used
in either direction, but it does not possess the "chain" property of path coefficients. For a system such as $A \rightarrow B \rightarrow C$ it has been demonstrated that A and C
are connected by a path whose coefficient is equal to the product of the two
single-step coefficients; but for a system such as $A \leftrightarrow B \leftrightarrow C$ it is a well-known
fact that, if A and B are correlated and B and C are correlated, it does *not* imply
that A and C are also correlated. Indeed, they may be independent. Therefore
the system $A \leftrightarrow B \leftrightarrow C$ does not have a connecting path between A and C. In
a sense, this situation is equivalent to the system of Figure 15, in which A and X
are correlated and in turn X and B are also correlated, but A and B are independent. In brief, lacking the chain property, a series of double-arrowed correlation lines does not by itself constitute a connecting path. When A and C are
correlated, they should be connected by a separate correlation line ($A \leftrightarrow C$)
with a value of r_{AC}, which usually is not at all equal to $r_{AB}r_{BC}$.

Tracing connecting paths is a process preliminary to calculating the total
correlation between two variables, because this correlation is the sum of all
paths connecting these two variables in a causal scheme. Having laid down the

rules for tracing paths, we shall now examine some illustrations of their application to calculating correlations in a more complex scheme as shown in Figure 21. The results to be observed are as follows:

(i) $r_{46} = 0$.—This follows from the discussion in the previous paragraph. The two correlations, r_{45} and r_{56}, do not constitute a connecting path between V_4 and V_6. The zigzag route 4–1–5–2–6 is not permissible, because it involves first-forward-and-then-backward turns.

(ii) $r_{36} = p_{3.6}$.—There is only one connecting path between V_6 and V_3, and it is the direct path from V_6 to V_3, whose coefficient is $p_{3.6}$.

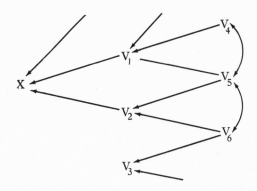

FIG. 21.—Correlations in a complex scheme

(iii) $r_{13} = p_{1.5} r_{56} p_{3.6}$.—The route is 1–5–6–3, which is the only connecting path between V_1 and V_3. They are connected only because V_5 and V_6 are correlated.

(iv) $r_{23} = p_{2.6} p_{3.6} + p_{2.5} r_{56} p_{3.6}$, there being two different connecting paths between V_2 and V_3: one by way of V_6 (a direct common cause) and another via V_5, using its correlation with V_6.

(v) $r_{12} = p_{1.5}\, p_{2.5} + p_{1.4} r_{45} p_{2.5} + p_{1.5} r_{56} p_{2.6}$.—The first connection between V_1 and V_2 is due to their direct common cause V_5, while the other two connections are due to the fact that V_5 is correlated with both V_4 and V_6. But note that the route 1–4–5–6–2 does not connect V_1 with V_2, because $r_{46} = 0$.

In tracing all the paths connecting two variables, we must take care to avoid duplication of chains. This may be illustrated best by the system shown in Figure 22, where R and S determine B, which is a common cause of X and Y. Therefore, R and S also are common causes of X and Y. However, the three connecting chains, X–R–Y, X–S–Y, and X–B–Y, are not independent. The remote factors, R and S, are common causes of X and Y only through the influence of B. The chain X–B–Y sums up all causes of correlation between X and Y in this scheme, and thus $r_{XY} = bb'$. Alternatively, we may omit B from the scheme and let R and S be two independent common causes of X and Y. Then we have, from (16′) and (15),

$$r_{XY} = p_{X \cdot R} p_{Y \cdot R} + p_{X \cdot S} p_{Y \cdot S}$$
$$= br \cdot rb' + bs \cdot sb'$$
$$= bb'(r^2 + s^2) = bb' ,$$

since $r^2 + s^2 = 1$, owing to the independence of R and S. It becomes clear that we may either use B without R and S *or* use the latter two without B, but not all three variables at the same time, because the influences of R and S are already represented by B.

The same precaution against duplication should be taken when we consider the degrees of determination of a variable by its various causes. For instance,

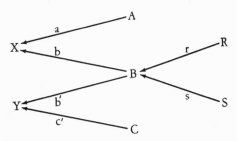

FIG. 22.—Duplication of connecting paths

the complete determination of X (Fig. 22) may be expressed either in terms of the influences of A and B *or* in terms of A, R, S. The two modes of expression are, respectively,

$$a^2 + b^2 = 1 , \qquad a^2 + (br)^2 + (bs)^2 = 1 .$$

This amounts to a subdivision of the total influence of B into its R- and S-components as $b^2 = (br)^2 + (bs)^2$.

§ 6. *Formulation of a Causal Scheme*

That a path coefficient must have a direction does not mean that either of two variables may not be considered as determining the other but merely that the reverse paths, $p_{X \cdot A}$ and $p_{A \cdot X}$, are in general not equal. This is obvious from our definition of a path coefficient (12). It is conceivable that there are various ways of formulating a causal scheme, depending upon what particular viewpoint is taken of the interrelationships between the variables involved. The important thing to be remembered is that, if we change the direction of a path, its value will also change; and, furthermore, the directions of other paths in the scheme should be changed accordingly, so that they are consistent with the particular viewpoint taken of their relationships.

As a simple illustration of the above principle, let us consider once more the scheme $X = A + B$ of Figure 15, in which A and B are independent ($r_{AB} = 0$).

For the sake of simplicity, let us further assume that A and B have equal standard deviations ($\sigma_A = \sigma_B$). Then, X is completely and equally determined by A and B (Fig. 15 is redrawn as the first scheme of Fig. 23). The variance of X is

$$\sigma_X^2 = \sigma_A^2 + \sigma_B^2 = 2\sigma_A^2 = 2\sigma_B^2 \ ;$$

$$d_{X \cdot A} = \ d_{X \cdot B} \ = \frac{\sigma_A^2}{\sigma_X^2} = \ \tfrac{1}{2} \ .$$

Therefore, from (14),

$$p_{X \cdot A} = p_{X \cdot B} = a = b = \sqrt{\tfrac{1}{2}} = r_{XA} = r_{XB} \ .$$

But we can just as legitimately turn the diagram around and regard A as the "effect" determined by causes X and B, which, however, are correlated (Fig. 23,

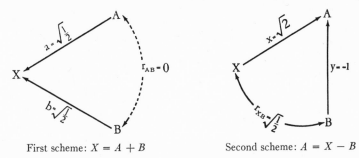

First scheme: $X = A + B$ Second scheme: $A = X - B$

Fɪɢ. 23.—Two different viewpoints of the same relationship. For explanation see text

second scheme). The causal relationship then becomes

$$A = X - B , \quad \text{with } r_{XB} = \sqrt{\tfrac{1}{2}} \ .$$

It should be emphasized that the correlation coefficient between two variables remains the same whatever viewpoint is taken of the paths. Let the path coefficients in this new scheme be $x = p_{A \cdot X}$ and $y = p_{A \cdot B}$. From (20), we have the following two equations:

$$r_{XA} = x + yr_{XB} = \sqrt{\tfrac{1}{2}} ,$$
$$r_{AB} = y + xr_{XB} = 0 .$$

Solving, we obtain the values of the new path coefficients

$$p_{A \cdot X} = x = \sqrt{2} , \quad p_{A \cdot B} = y = -1 .$$

Our theorem on complete determination of a variable by its causes (21) still holds in this new scheme with respect to A:

$$x^2 + y^2 + 2xyr_{XB} = 1 .$$

The important feature is that the reverse path coefficients are not equal, as demonstrated above: $a = \sqrt{\frac{1}{2}}$, while $x = \sqrt{2}$ (Fig. 23).

As a purely mathematical proposition we may look upon either one of two variables as a factor contributing toward the determination of the other. But, once a viewpoint has been taken of a particular path, it must be held consistently throughout the whole scheme.

The formulation of a causal scheme must be adequate and complete, as well as consistent, if it is to yield valid results in its subsequent analysis. Otherwise, the values of the path coefficients will be erroneous and misleading.

Finally, it may be added that an adequate scheme is not necessarily a complex network involving many remote variables. A complex system can always be reduced by stages to a simpler one, just as we simplified the system of Figure 19 to that of Figure 20. When two intermediate variables are correlated through some remote common causes, the products of the individual coefficients along the chains connecting the two variables can always be summed up in the total correlation between them, without destroying the adequacy and consistency of the scheme. Hence, the formulation of a scheme is a very flexible thing. The reducibility of a causal scheme renders the two main expressions (19) and (21) quite general.

§ 7. *Some Other Properties of Path Coefficients and Correlations*

The following properties are treated separately because, although they are important enough to be noted in path analysis, they are not likely to be encountered in genetics.

1. The example shown in Figure 23 brings out two interesting points. First, a path coefficient may take values greater than unity, as well as negative values. It can be greater than unity because we did not put any restrictions on the relative magnitudes of the variances of an effect and a cause. When the variance of a cause is greater than that of an effect, some other path coefficient has to take a negative value.

2. Second, two variables may not be correlated, and yet the path coefficient from one variable to the other is not zero. Thus, in Figure 23, A and B are "independent" in the sense that $r_{AB} = 0$; and yet the path from B to A is $p_{A \cdot B} = y = -1$. This may well clarify the difference between a correlation coefficient and a path coefficient. The former gives an *absolute* measure of correlation between two variables in a given body of data, while the latter measured the influence of one variable on another from a particular viewpoint indicated in the causal scheme. Thus, on taking the viewpoint that $A = X - B$, it is obvious that the value of A is partly determined by that of B.

The values of x and y in Figure 23 are self-evident and may be obtained offhand without the formal derivations given in the last section. Since $\sigma_X^2 = 2\sigma_A^2$ by assumption, we have immediately $p_{A \cdot X} = \sqrt{(\sigma_X^2/\sigma_A^2)} = \sqrt{2}$; and, since

$\sigma_A^2 = \sigma_B^2$, the path coefficient from B to A obviously will take a numerical value of unity. That the path coefficient is negative can be interpreted as its taking the negative root of σ_B^2, on account of the negative relation between A and B.

3. Two variables may even be completely determined by the same common causes and yet be uncorrelated with each other. For example, let A and B be two independent common causes of X and Y (Fig. 24) and assume that A and B have *equal* variances. Let the causal scheme be

$$X = A + B, \qquad Y = A - B. \qquad (23)$$

We see that both X and Y are completely determined by the same causes. But

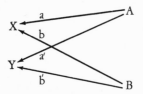

FIG. 24.—Two effects completely determined by two common causes

they are not correlated, as shown in the following:

$$\Sigma(X - \bar{X})(Y - \bar{Y}) = \Sigma(A + B - \bar{A} - \bar{B})(A - B - \bar{A} + \bar{B})$$
$$= \Sigma\{(A - \bar{A}) + (B - \bar{B})\}\{(A - \bar{A}) - (B - \bar{B})\} \qquad (24)$$
$$= \Sigma(A - \bar{A})^2 - \Sigma(B - \bar{B})^2 = 0,$$

since we assumed that A and B have equal variances. If we express the correlation between X and Y in terms of path coefficients in Figure 24, we have

$$r_{XY} = aa' + bb' = 0 ;$$
$$\therefore \quad aa' = -bb' .$$

Since $\sigma_A^2 = \sigma_B^2$ and $\sigma_X^2 = 2\sigma_A^2$, as in the previous example, we have $a = a' = b = \sqrt{\frac{1}{2}}$; $b' = -\sqrt{\frac{1}{2}}$; and $r_{XY} = 0$. A concrete example of this scheme is that the correlation between the sum and difference of pairs of random numbers is zero.

It should have been noted that for this particular system (23) the sum-of-product term, $\Sigma(A - \bar{A})(B - \bar{B})$, canceled off in (24). It follows that, even if A and B are correlated, r_{XY} will still be zero as long as A and B have equal variances. The accompanying tabulation is a numerical illustration of this situation.

This brief account of the theory of path coefficients must suffice for our purpose: applying it to genetical analysis in the next chapter. Further properties may be found in Wright (1934).

A........	16	8	17	3	44	59	42	51	$\bar{A}=30$
B........	8	16	20	28	40	52	56	68	$\bar{B}=36$

$$\Sigma(A-\bar{A})^2=\Sigma(B-\bar{B})^2=3200; \qquad r_{AB}=0.84$$

X........	24	24	37	31	84	111	98	119	$\bar{X}=66$
Y........	8	-8	-3	-25	4	7	-14	-17	$\bar{Y}=-6$

$$\Sigma(X-\bar{X})(Y-\bar{Y})=0; \qquad r_{XY}=0$$

Notes and Exercises

The theorem on total correlation between two variables (19) provides us with a method of partitioning the total correlation into its separate components, each component ascribable to a common cause by which the two variables are connected or to the joint influence of two correlated common causes. The (second) theorem on complete determination (21) may be regarded as a limiting form of (19). Hence, there is really only one fundamental formula in the theory of path coefficients as given in this chapter; and we shall consider (Exs. 1–5) a somewhat more general derivation of this fundamental theorem.

In most of the following arbitrary numerical exercises there are only five to eight values for each variable; and they are intended solely to make the student familiar with the arithmetic of path coefficients and to provide him with an opportunity to verify the various relations described in the text. In any actual case, however, the data would be far more voluminous.

1. Consider the expression (1) for correlation between A and B. If we "standardize" the variables, taking $A' = (A - \bar{A})/\sigma_A$ and $B' = (B - \bar{B})/\sigma_B$, so that the mean values of A' and B' are both zero, and their variances are both unity, we have, owing to the fact that correlation is independent of origin and units of measurement,

$$r_{AB} = r_{A'B'} = \sigma_{A'B'},$$

since $\sigma_{A'} = \sigma_{B'} = 1$. In other words, r_{AB} is the covariance of the standardized variables and may be called the "standardized" covariance of A and B.

As a numerical example, let us standardize the original values of Table 52 (p. 145). Thus:

A'......	-0.70	-1.10	-0.65	-1.35	$+0.70$	$+1.45$	$+0.60$	$+1.05$	0
B'......	-1.4	-1.0	-0.8	-0.4	$+0.2$	$+0.8$	$+1.0$	$+1.6$	0

$$\Sigma A'^2 = 8 \qquad \Sigma B'^2 = 8 \qquad \Sigma A'B' = 6.72$$
$$\sigma_{A'} = 1 \qquad \sigma_{B'} = 1 \qquad \sigma_{A'B'} = 0.84 = r_{AB}$$

2. In ordinary regression analysis the regression coefficient of X on A is $b_{XA} = \sigma_{XA}/\sigma_A^2$, as shown in all elementary textbooks of statistics. And the regression equation is

$$(X - \bar{X}) = b_{XA}(A - \bar{A}).$$

Standardizing the variables, it becomes

$$\left(\frac{X - \bar{X}}{\sigma_X}\right) = b_{XA} \cdot \frac{\sigma_A}{\sigma_X}\left(\frac{A - \bar{A}}{\sigma_A}\right),$$

in which the new regression coefficient is

$$b_{XA}\frac{\sigma_A}{\sigma_X} = \frac{\sigma_{XA}}{\sigma_A^2} \cdot \frac{\sigma_A}{\sigma_X} = \frac{\sigma_{XA}}{\sigma_A \sigma_X} = r_{XA} = r_{X'A'} = \sigma_{X'A'},$$

where X' and A' are standardized values of X and A, respectively. Note that this regression coefficient is the *path* coefficient from A to X for independent causes (14). Hence, the regression equation in terms of standardized variables is

$$X' = p_{X \cdot A} A'.$$

From this point of view the *path coefficient may be called a "standardized" linear regression coefficient.* Our first preliminary theorem (14) simply says that, if we choose to work with standardized variables, the linear regression coefficient is equal to the correlation coefficient between the two variables concerned.

3. More generally speaking, if X is influenced by A, B, C, . . . , the multiple regression equation of X on the causes is

$$(X - \bar{X}) = b_{XA}(A - \bar{A}) + b_{XB}(B - \bar{B}) + b_{XC}(C - \bar{C}) + \ldots .$$

Standardizing the variables and, writing X' for $(X - \bar{X})/\sigma_X$, etc., the regression equation above becomes

$$X' = p_{XA}A' + p_{XB}B' + p_{XC}C' + \ldots ,$$

in which the new regression coefficients

$$p_{Xi} = b_{Xi} \cdot \frac{\sigma_i}{\sigma_X},$$

where $i = A, B, C, \ldots$. These "standardized" linear regression coefficients are called "path coefficients" (from i to X). This conforms with our original definition (12), since $b_{Xi}\sigma_i$ may be regarded as the "standard deviation of X due to the influence of i." Hence, in the following, we write p_{XA} for $p_{X \cdot A}$, dropping the dot between the subscripts to conform with the usual notation for regression coefficients.

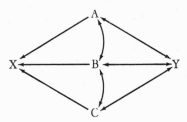

FIG. 25.—The total correlation between X and Y. Note that, if A were independent of B and C, as well as of Y, this scheme would be equivalent to that of Figure 20.

4. Suppose that Y is another variable also influenced by A, B, C (Fig. 25). The total correlation between X and Y is, for N pairs of values,

$$r_{XY} = r_{X'Y'} = \sigma_{X'Y'} = \frac{1}{N} \Sigma X' Y' \qquad \text{from Ex. 1}$$

$$= \frac{1}{N} \Sigma (p_{XA} A' + p_{XB} B' + p_{XC} C') \, Y' \qquad \text{from Ex. 3}$$

$$= p_{XA} r_{AY} + p_{XB} r_{BY} + p_{XC} r_{CY}. \qquad \text{i.e., } (20)$$

This is our fundamental theorem (20) which reduces to (19) if $r_{AY} = 0$. When the causes A, B, C are independent, it becomes (16'), since r_{AY} would reduce to $p_{Y \cdot A}$, etc.

Since p_{Xi} is the regression coefficient of X' on i', it is an absolute number without physical unit. This is also evident from the definition $p_{Xi} = b_{Xi}(\sigma_i/\sigma_X)$, all units being canceled off. It also indicates that the sign of p is the same as that of b. Hence, in a system such as $X = A + B - C$, the path from C to X will assume a negative value.

5. The theorem on complete determination of a variable may be obtained immediately by correlating X with itself; that is, replacing Y by X in the previous formula. Thus,

$$r_{XX} = p_{XA} r_{AX} + p_{XB} r_{BX} + p_{XC} r_{CX} = 1.$$

Or, more generally, noting that $r_{Xi} = p_{Xi} + \Sigma_j p_{Xj} r_{ij}$ (the sum of all connecting paths between X and i for $i = A, B, C, \ldots, j \neq i$ [Fig. 25]), we may write

$$r_{xx} = \sum_i p_{xi} r_{xi}$$

$$= \sum_i p_{xi} \left(p_{xi} + \sum_j p_{xj} r_{ij} \right)$$

$$= \sum_i p_{xi}^2 + 2 \sum_{i,j} p_{xi} p_{xj} r_{ij} = 1 \qquad (i < j) \ .$$

This is a generalized form of (22). In the case $r_{AB} = r_{AC} = 0$, it reduces to (21).

6. *Chains of independent causes (Fig. 16).*—Let $X = A + B$ and $A = R + S$, where A, B as well as R, S are uncorrelated. In the following, "SSq" is the abbreviation for the "sum of squares" of deviations from the mean of the variable.

						Total	Mean	SSq
R..........	1	21	12	6	20	60	12	302
S..........	3	5	8	6	3	25	5	18
A..........	4	26	20	12	23	85	17	320
B..........	25	1	39	1	34	100	20	1304
X..........	29	27	59	13	57	185	37	1624

(i) For the $X = A + B$ part, calculate $d_{X \cdot A}$, r_{XA}, $p_{X \cdot A}$.

(ii) For the $A = R + S$ part, calculate $d_{A \cdot R}$, r_{AR}, $p_{A \cdot R}$.

(iii) Taking $X = R + S + B$, show that $d_{X \cdot R} + d_{X \cdot S} + d_{X \cdot B} = 1$.

(iv) Show that $d_{X \cdot R} = d_{X \cdot A} d_{A \cdot R}$ and $p_{X \cdot S} = p_{X \cdot A} p_{A \cdot S}$.

7. *Uncorrelated common causes (Fig. 17).*—Let the causal scheme be $X = B + C$ and $Y = B + 3C$, whereas $r_{BC} = 0$.

						Total	Mean	SSq
B..........	4	26	20	12	23	85	17	320
C..........	11	12	2	11	14	50	10	86
X..........	15	38	22	23	37	135	27	406
Y..........	37	62	26	45	65	235	47	1094

Sum of products of deviations of pairs of variables:
$(XB) = 320 \qquad (XC) = 86 \qquad\qquad (XY) = 578 = 320 + 258$
$(YB) = 320 \qquad (YC) = 258 = 3 \times 86$

First, calculate the correlation coefficient between X and Y directly from the last two rows of values shown in the tabulation. Next, find the values of the four path coefficients: b, b', c, c'. Finally, verify the relation $r_{XY} = bb' + cc'$.

8. *Correlated causes (Fig. 18).*—Let the causal scheme be $X = A + B$, where $A = D + C$ and $B = C + E$, so that the immediate causes A and B are correlated by their common cause, C.

						Total	Mean	SSq
D........	1	21	12	6	20	60	12	302
C........	3	5	8	6	3	25	5	18
E........	58	36	65	1	40	200	40	2486
A........	4	26	20	12	23	85	17	320
B........	61	41	73	7	43	225	45	2504
X........	65	67	93	19	66	310	62	2860

(i) First calculate the four path coefficients: a, b, c, c'.

(ii) Calculate r_{AB} directly and then verify: $r_{AB} = cc'$.

(iii) Verify numerically formula (3) concerning the variance of X.

(iv) Taking $X = D + 2C + E$, find the values of $d_{X \cdot D}$, $d_{X \cdot C}$, and $d_{X \cdot E}$ and see whether they add up to unity.

(v) Find the value of $p_{X \cdot C}$ directly from the data, as though the causal scheme were $X = D + 2C + E$; and then verify:

$$r_{XC} = p_{X \cdot C} = ac + bc',$$

as given by (18).

ANS.: (i) $a = 0.3345$, $b = 0.9357$, $c = 0.2372$, $c' = 0.0848$. (ii) $r_{AB} = 18/\sqrt{(320 \times 2504)} = 0.0201 = (0.2372)(0.0848)$. (iii) $N\sigma_X^2 = 320 + 2504 + 2(18) = 2860$. (iv) $\sigma_X^2 = \sigma_D^2 + 4\sigma_C^2 + \sigma_E^2$; hence, $d_{X \cdot C} = 4(18)/2860$, etc. (v) $r_{XC} = \sqrt{d_{X \cdot C}} = 0.15867 = ac + bc'$. (Here, $ac = bc'$. Why?)

9. Let C, D, E be three uncorrelated variables. If $A = C + D$ and $B = C + E$, show that

$$\Sigma(A - \bar{A})(B - \bar{B}) = \Sigma(C - \bar{C})^2.$$

10. *Correlated common causes (Fig. 20).*—Let A, B, C, D be four causes, where B and C are correlated and all the other pairs of causes uncorrelated. Suppose the causal scheme is $X = A + B + C$, and $Y = 10B + 3C + D$.

									Total	Mean	SSq
A....	34	3	40	28	14	25	31	25	200	25	956
B....	2	4	5	7	10	13	14	17	72	9	200
C....	16	8	17	3	44	·59	42	51	240	30	3200
D....	211.6	160.0	160.0	156.7	118.9	160.0	8.9	303.9	1280	160	47,901.08
X....	52	15	62	38	68	97	87	93	512	64	5700
Y....	279.6	224.0	261.0	235.7	350.9	467.0	274.9	626.9	2720	340	137,021.08

(i) Find the values of the six paths in Figure 20 as well as that of r_{BC}.

(ii) For the complete determination of X, verify (21). Write out the corresponding expression for complete determination of Y and verify it numerically.

(iii) Calculate r_{XY} directly from the values of X and Y and then show that $r_{XY} = bb' + cc' + (bc' + cb')r_{BC}$.

Ans.: $a^2 = 956/5700 = 0.16772$, etc. You will find it convenient to arrange your calculations in a systematic manner, as in the following:

$a^2=0.16772$	$d'^2=0.34959$	$a=0.4095$	$d'=0.5912$	$bc=0.14034$	$b'c'=0.17515$
$b^2=0.03509$	$b'^2=0.14596$	$b=0.1873$	$b'=0.3821$	$bb'=0.07157$	$bc'=0.08586$
$c^2=0.56140$	$c'^2=0.21019$	$c=0.7493$	$c'=0.4584$	$cc'=0.34384$	$cb'=0.28631$

$2bcr_{BC}=0.23578$	$2b'c'r_{BC}=0.29426$	$r_{BC}=0.840$	$(bc'+cb')r_{BC}=0.31262$

$*[X]=1.00$	$[Y]=1.00$	$r_{XY}=0.07157+0.34384+0.31262=0.72767$

$$\text{Directly, } r_{XY} = \frac{20{,}336}{\sqrt{(5700 \times 137{,}021.08)}} = \frac{20{,}336}{27{,}946.7} = 0.72767$$

* $[X]$ = complete determination of X, confirming (21).

11. *Sum of uncorrelated variables (Fig. 15).*—In the simple scheme $X = A_1 + A_2$, where the two causes are uncorrelated, there is an important special case in which the two causes have equal variances. Then X is equally determined by A_1 and A_2. For the following two sets of data show that $a_1 = a_2 = a = \sqrt{\frac{1}{2}}$.

A_1	1	1	1	1	1	1	0	0	0	6	$\frac{2}{3}$
A_2	1	1	1	1	0	0	1	1	0	6	$\frac{2}{3}$
X	2	2	2	2	1	1	1	1	0	12	$\frac{4}{3}$

A_1	1	1	1	1	1	1	1	1	1	1	1	1	0	0	0	0	12	$\frac{3}{4}$
A_2	1	1	1	1	1	1	1	1	1	1	0	0	0	1	1	1	0	12	$\frac{3}{4}$
X	2	2	2	2	2	2	2	2	2	2	1	1	1	1	1	1	0	24	$\frac{3}{2}$

12. As in the previous problem, let $X = A_1 + A_2$, where the two causes have equal variances but are correlated, with $r_{A_1A_2} = r$.

A_1	1	1	1	1	1	1	0	0	0
A_2	1	1	1	1	0	1	1	0	0
X	2	2	2	2	1	2	1	0	0

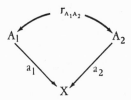

(i) First find the value of $r = r_{A_1A_2}$.

(ii) Find the values of the two path coefficients, a_1 and a_2. Are they equal? If so, why? Call its value $a = a_1 = a_2$.

(iii) Show that for the complete determination of X we have, from (17),

$$2a^2 + 2a^2r = 1,$$

and verify it numerically.

ANS.: $r = \frac{1}{2}$, $a = \sqrt{\frac{1}{3}}$.

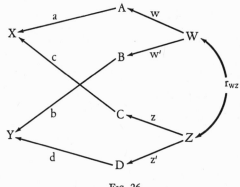

FIG. 26

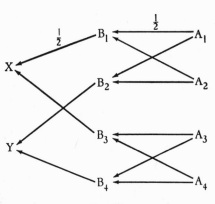

FIG. 27

13. Given the system of relations in Figure 26, in which the path coefficients are denoted by small letters, (i) find the expressions for r_{XW}, r_{XZ}, r_{YW}, r_{YZ}, and r_{XY} in terms of path coefficients; (ii) if $w = w' = z = z'$ and $a = b = c = d$, what would be the expressions for these correlation coefficients?
ANS.:

(i) $\begin{cases} r_{XW} = aw + czr_{WZ}, \text{ etc.}, \\ r_{XY} = aw.w'b + cz.z'd + awr_{WZ}z'd + czr_{WZ}w'b, \end{cases}$

$$\text{(ii)} \begin{cases} r_{XW} = r_{XZ} = r_{YW} = r_{YZ} = aw + awr_{WZ} = aw(1 + r_{WZ}), \\ r_{XY} = 2aw \cdot wa + 2awr_{WZ}wa = 2a^2w^2(1 + r_{WZ}). \end{cases}$$

14. Find the correlation coefficient between X and Y in the system of relationships in Figure 27, assuming *all* path coefficients equal to $\frac{1}{2}$.

ANS.: $r_{XY} = 4 \times (\frac{1}{2})^4 = \frac{1}{4}$.

CHAPTER 13

Path Relations between Parent
and Offspring

BEFORE we study the properties and results of continued inbreeding, it is well to formulate the relationships between parents and their offspring in terms of path coefficients. In applying the method of path analysis in genetics, we must regard all the gametes and zygotes as variables which take numerical values corresponding to their genic make-up. This can be done easily if the effects of genes are additive. In genotypic analysis we may let the gametic variable g take the value 1 if the gamete is A, and $g = 0$ if the gamete is a. Consequently, the zygotic variable Z takes the values 2, 1, 0, corresponding to AA, Aa, aa, respectively. Adopting this scale of measurement, the method of path coefficients can be readily applied to genetics. Furthermore, when a number of pairs of genes are involved, as long as all genic effects are additive (but not necessarily of the same magnitude for the different loci), the following arguments and results are valid for any number of loci that may be involved in determining the gametic and zygotic values. The substance of this chapter is based upon the account given by Wright (1921b).

§ 1. *Zygote Determined by Uniting Gametes*

First of all, we note that a zygote (short for "zygotic value") may be considered to be *linearly*, *completely*, and *equally* determined by the two gametes which have united to produce the zygote. This relation may be represented by the simple causal scheme (Fig. 28)

$$Z \text{ (zygote)} = g_1 \text{ (sperm)} + g_2 \text{ (egg)} .$$

Since Z is equally determined by g_1 and g_2 for autosomal genes, the two path coefficients, one from egg to zygote and the other from sperm to zygote, must be equal. Using Wright's notations, we let a be the path coefficient from gamete (egg or sperm) to zygote and F be the correlation coefficient between uniting gametes. Then for the complete determination of a zygote we have (Ex. 12 of preceding chapter):

$$2a^2 + 2a^2F = 1 .$$

172

Therefore,

$$a^2 = \frac{1}{2\,(1+F)}\,, \qquad a = \sqrt{\frac{1}{2\,(1+F)}}\,. \tag{1}$$

The higher the value of F, the smaller will be the value of a. As F varies from 0 to 1, the values of a vary from 0.707 to 0.500, as shown in Table 55.

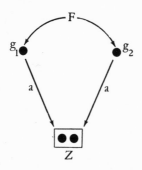

FIG. 28.—Path from gamete to zygote

TABLE 55

VALUES OF F AND a AND COMPONENTS OF
DETERMINATION OF THE ZYGOTE

F	a^2	a	$2a^2$	$2a^2F$
0	$\frac{1}{2}$	0.7071	1.0000	0
$\frac{1}{4}$	$\frac{2}{5}$	.6325	0.8000	0.2000
$\frac{1}{2}$	$\frac{1}{3}$	.5774	0.6667	.3333
$\frac{3}{4}$	$\frac{2}{7}$	.5345	0.5714	.4286
1	$\frac{1}{4}$	0.5000	0.5000	0.5000

The above equation does not, of course, apply to cases in which the parental contributions to inheritance are unequal, as with sex-linked genes. Modifications for the latter case are, however, very simple and will be given later.

Caution must also be taken in applying (1) to mated individuals that belong to different generations in a system of consanguineous mating. In such cases the two path coefficients from parental zygotes to their eggs and sperms will be different. We shall examine this case in Section 9.

§ 2. *Gamete Produced by Zygote*

The constitution of a gamete is, of course, determined by that of a parent; but the same parent can produce various kinds of gametes by the random process of segregation. Let b denote the path coefficient from a zygote to its gametes (Fig. 29). Thus,

$$b = p_0 \cdot z = r_0 z ,$$

where $r_0 z$ is the correlation between the zygote and any one of the gametes produced by that zygote. This correlation must be the same as that between the zygote and one of the gametes of the previous generation which contributed to the make-up of the zygote. Hence, we have the relation

$$b = r_v z = r_0' z = a' + a'F' = a'(1 + F') ,$$

the primes indicating the paths for the preceding generation of the zygote under consideration. We shall use this notation throughout this and the next few

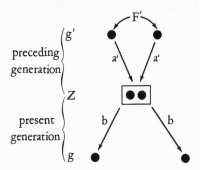

FIG. 29.—Path from zygote to gamete

chapters dealing with path coefficients. Substituting the value of a' as given by (1), we obtain

$$b = \sqrt{\frac{1}{2(1+F')}} \cdot (1+F') = \sqrt{\frac{1+F'}{2}} . \tag{2}$$

The value of the path from a zygote to its gametes depends solely upon the correlation between the uniting gametes (of the preceding generation) which formed the zygote. In this respect it is similar to a; but, unlike a, it increases with the value of F. For a derivation of (2) from another point of view see Exercise 1 at the end of this chapter.

§ 3. *Path for One Generation*

The path from zygote to gamete (b), or that from gamete to zygote (a), may be regarded as covering half a generation if we take one generation as from a parent to offspring. The compound path from a parental zygote to its offspring (from Z to O in Fig. 30) is, from (1) and (2),

$$ba = \frac{1}{2}\sqrt{\frac{1+F'}{1+F}} . \tag{3}$$

In many expressions in this and subsequent chapters, a and b appear in pairs, because the two together constitute the path for one *zygotic generation*.

Alternatively, we may regard the path from the gamete received by an individual to the gamete produced by that individual as one generation, whose path value is then (Fig. 30)

$$a'b = \sqrt{\frac{1}{2\,(1+F')}}\,\sqrt{\frac{1+F'}{2}} = \tfrac{1}{2}. \tag{4}$$

It is a remarkable fact that the path for one *gametic generation* is always $\tfrac{1}{2}$, being independent of the value of F and of the system of mating. We shall use this fact frequently in the next chapter when we deal with various mating systems.

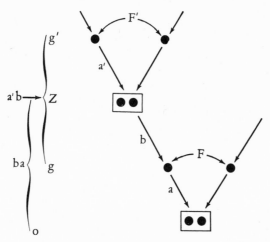

FIG. 30.—Path for one generation

§ 4. *Relation between* F *and* m

It was pointed out in Chapters 9 and 10 that it is the correlation between mated individuals (m) which leads to the correlation between uniting gametes (F); and at that time there was given an expression for their relations in equilibrium condition. Their general relation under *any* condition, however, is difficult to obtain by direct algebraic method but is almost self-evident from the viewpoint of causal paths. Figure 31 shows that

$$F = bmb = b^2m, \tag{5}$$

there being only one route connecting the two uniting gametes—that through the correlation between mates. Since $b^2 = (1 + F')/2$ according to (2), we have

$$F = \frac{(1+F')}{2}\,m, \qquad m = \frac{2F}{1+F'}. \tag{5'}$$

The values of a and b are all functions of F, which in turn depends upon m. Therefore m is the key value to all others. It is possible to express the correlations and path coefficients in each generation in terms of those of the preceding generation, provided that an explicit expression for m can be found. The latter is determined by the system of mating practiced in a population. For many regular systems of inbreeding the expression for m in terms of a', b', m' of the preceding generation can be written out quite easily; hence the subsequent results of a particular system of inbreeding may be obtained accordingly. This will be shown in the next chapter.

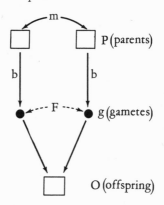

FIG. 31.—Correlation between uniting gametes (F) in terms of that between mates (m). The dotted double arrow of F is a duplicate of the chain bmb; either of them, but not both, may be retained in the causal scheme.

§ 5. Correlations between Family Members

It will be recalled that the correlations between immediate family members were given in Chapter 3 under the simple condition of panmixia. Here we shall deduce their general relations under *any* condition, of which our previous results are merely special cases. The causal scheme for family members is shown in Figure 32. Let r_{PP}, r_{PO}, r_{OO} be the correlations between parents, parent and offspring, and sibs, respectively. A consideration of Figure 32 (see also Chap. 12, Ex. 13 and Fig. 26) shows immediately that

$$
\left.
\begin{aligned}
r_{PP} &= m , \\
r_{PO} &= ab + abm = ab(1 + m) , \\
r_{OO} &= 2abba + 2abmba = 2a^2b^2(1 + m) .
\end{aligned}
\right\} \tag{6}
$$

It might be said that r_{PO} gives the correlation between either parent and any one offspring for autosomal genes. In tracing the connecting paths, we should restrict our attention to one specified parent and one specified offspring.

§ 6. Equilibrium Conditions

In terms of path analysis, an equilibrium condition merely implies that m (and thus F) remains constant from generation to generation; and, consequently, the paths a and b will also remain constant. Putting $m = m' =$ constant, we have $F = F'$; and, from (1) and (2), $a = a'$ and $b = b'$. Their values may all be expressed in terms of m. For instance, substituting (5) in (2) and dropping the prime, we have

$$b^2 = \tfrac{1}{2}(1 + F) = \tfrac{1}{2}(1 + b^2 m) \; ;$$

$$\therefore \; b^2 = \frac{1}{2 - m} \; ; \tag{2e}$$

and

$$F = b^2 m = \frac{m}{2 - m} \cdot \tag{5e}$$

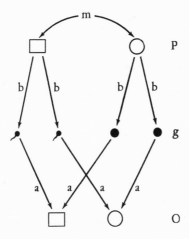

Fig. 32.—Correlations between family members

The latter relation may also be obtained by putting $F = F'$ in (5′). It will be recalled that we have already demonstrated these by direct algebraic method in Chapter 11 (p. 133). Expressing F in terms of m, we also obtain

$$a^2 = \frac{1}{2\,(1 + F)} = \frac{1}{2\left(1 + \dfrac{m}{2 - m}\right)} = \frac{2 - m}{4} \cdot \tag{1e}$$

Perhaps the most useful simplification due to equilibrium is that the path for one zygotic generation (3) reduces to

$$b a = \frac{1}{2} \sqrt{\frac{1 + F'}{1 + F}} = \tfrac{1}{2} , \tag{3e}$$

whatever the mating system and whatever the degree of inbreeding existing in the population. The correlations between family members also take a simpler form in equilibrium populations. Noting $2a^2 b^2 = 2(\tfrac{1}{2})^2 = \tfrac{1}{2}$, we have, from (6),

$$r_{\mathrm{PP}} = m = \text{const.} , \quad r_{\mathrm{PO}} = \tfrac{1}{2}(1 + m) , \quad r_{\mathrm{OO}} = \tfrac{1}{2}(1 + m) . \tag{6e}$$

These have previously been numerically verified (p. 136). The results of this section should be sufficient to show how genetic relations can be obtained in a very simple manner by the technique of path coefficients.

§ 7. *Correlations between Relatives under Panmixia*

At this stage it is well to consider a simple application of the preceding results to a panmictic population. Here, $m = F = 0$. Hence,

$$a = b = \sqrt{\tfrac{1}{2}}, \quad \text{and} \quad ab = \tfrac{1}{2}.$$

With the aid of path analysis, we shall readily find the correlation between any two relatives, once their relationships are translated into a causal scheme, no matter how remote or how irregular their relationships may be. The most general formula for finding this correlation will be given in Chapter 16, where we shall consider cases in which the mated individuals themselves may be

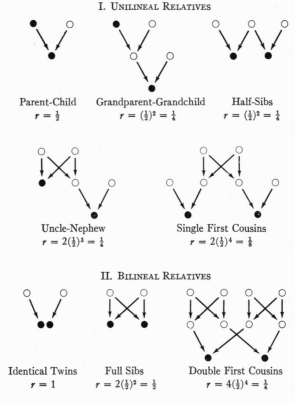

I. UNILINEAL RELATIVES

Parent-Child
$r = \tfrac{1}{2}$

Grandparent-Grandchild
$r = (\tfrac{1}{2})^2 = \tfrac{1}{4}$

Half-Sibs
$r = (\tfrac{1}{2})^2 = \tfrac{1}{4}$

Uncle-Nephew
$r = 2(\tfrac{1}{2})^3 = \tfrac{1}{4}$

Single First Cousins
$r = 2(\tfrac{1}{2})^4 = \tfrac{1}{8}$

II. BILINEAL RELATIVES

Identical Twins
$r = 1$

Full Sibs
$r = 2(\tfrac{1}{2})^2 = \tfrac{1}{2}$

Double First Cousins
$r = 4(\tfrac{1}{2})^4 = \tfrac{1}{4}$

FIG. 33.—Correlations between two human relatives are indicated by the two solid symbols. Other individuals are indicated by circles. Gametes are not shown in these figures. Each arrow covers one generation with a value of $\tfrac{1}{2}$. (Modified from Cotterman, 1941.)

correlated. In this section we shall merely deduce the correlation between some relatives whose parents are uncorrelated ($m = 0$). Figure 33 gives a few examples of close relatives (see also Chaps. 2 and 3). In calculating the correlation between two specified relatives, we trace all the connecting paths from one to the other, remembering that the path of any one generation is $ab = \frac{1}{2}$. The gametes have not been included in Figure 33. Tracing the connecting paths between two individuals is a simple and direct application of the important theorem developed in the last chapter—that on total correlation between two variables with common causes. A "common parent" is equivalent to a "common cause" in our old terminology. The similarity between Figure 33 and the causal schemes of the preceding chapter should be noted. For instance, the figure for grandparent-grandchild relations here is identical with that for chains of independent causes. Also, half-sibs are variables with one independent common cause; single first cousins are variables with two remote common causes; etc. Since each of the paths has a value of $ab = \frac{1}{2}$, the formula for total correlation between two variables (individuals here) reduces to

$$r = \Sigma(\tfrac{1}{2})^{L}, \tag{7}$$

where L is the number of "links" (arrows or generations) along one connecting chain between the two specified relatives and Σ is the summation over all such connecting chains. It is seen that r between any two relatives in a random-mating population may be obtained from (7), once their "causal scheme" is formulated.

§ 8. *A Summary of Formulas*

The correlations F and m have been treated in various earlier chapters. The only new feature in this chapter is the introduction of paths from gamete to zygote and from zygote to gamete. It is these two path values which have simplified so many problems in genetics. Since we shall continue to use the various expressions given in previous sections, it may be helpful to collect some of them into one table for quick reference. Many of the expressions listed in Table 56 were either demonstrated or numerically verified before we introduced the method of path analysis. But now we know that these expressions are applicable to any number of genes as long as their effects are additive.

§ 9. *Unequal Paths from Zygotes to Gametes*

It is obvious that the two paths from uniting gametes to a resultant zygote are always equal in value because the zygote is equally determined (for autosomal genes) by the gametes, regardless of their origin. However, since the uniting gametes are from two different individuals (Fig. 34), the paths (b) from the parental zygotes, X and Y, to their respective gametes, are not necessarily equal. This can be seen in (2), which says that the value of b depends upon that of F' of the preceding uniting gametes which formed the zygote under consideration. The larger the value of F', the larger will be the value of b.

In an irregular system of inbreeding, the two parents, X and Y, may have different degrees of inbreeding experience; in other words, F_X and F_Y in Figure 34 may not be equal. Consequently, their respective b's may not be equal. Thus. from (2),

$$b_X = \sqrt{\frac{1+F_X}{2}}, \qquad b_Y = \sqrt{\frac{1+F_Y}{2}}. \tag{8}$$

TABLE 56

SUMMARY OF FORMULAS

(Simplified from Wright, 1921b, p. 121, by Ignoring Environmental Influences and Assuming Complete Determination by Heredity)

Consanguineous Mating	Equilibrium	Panmixia
$m = \phi(a', b', m')$	$m = \text{const.}$	$m = 0$
$b^2 = \frac{1}{2}(1+F')$	$b^2 = 1/(2-m)$	$b^2 = \frac{1}{2}$
$F = b^2 m$	$F = m/(2-m)$	$F = 0$
$a^2 = \dfrac{1}{2(1+F)}$	$a^2 = \frac{1}{4}(2-m)$	$a^2 = \frac{1}{2}$
$ab = \dfrac{1}{2}\sqrt{\dfrac{1+F'}{1+F}}$	$ab = \frac{1}{2}$	$ab = \frac{1}{2}$
$r_{PP} = m$	$r_{PP} = \text{const.}$	$r_{PP} = 0$
$r_{PO} = ab(1+m)$	$r_{PO} = \frac{1}{2}(1+m)$	$r_{PO} = \frac{1}{2}$
$r_{OO} = 2a^2 b^2(1+m)$	$r_{OO} = \frac{1}{2}(1+m)$	$r_{OO} = \frac{1}{2}$

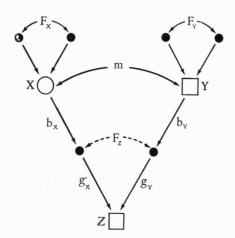

FIG. 34.—The two b's (b_X and b_Y) are unequal because $F_X \neq F_Y$

Therefore, the correlation between the uniting gametes, g_X and g_Y (Fig. 34), is

$$F_Z = b_X m b_Y = \tfrac{1}{2}m\sqrt{[(1 +F_X)(1 + F_Y)]} \, . \tag{9}$$

This is a more general expression for (5), in which the two b's have been assumed to be equal. Formula (8) is useful in tracing irregular inbreeding pedigrees (such as those of inbred livestock).

§ 10. *Zygotic Proportions in a Population*

It has been emphasized in earlier chapters that the correlations between relatives and the correlation between uniting gametes are all independent of gene frequencies in the population. In fact, all the values (F, m, a, b, r, etc.) and their relations listed in Table 56 are independent of gene frequencies in the population. They are properties solely of additive Mendelian inheritance and mating systems which may or may not lead to an equilibrium condition. The zygotic proportions in a population, however, depend upon the gene frequencies as well as upon F (or m).

As usual, let p and q be the frequencies of two allelic genes ($p + q = 1$). Then in any generation the proportion of heterozygotes is

$$H = 2pq(1 - F) \, ,$$

where F is the correlation between uniting gametes which formed the zygotes in that generation. The proportion of AA zygotes in the same generation is

$$D = p - \tfrac{1}{2}H = p^2 + Fpq \, .$$

These proportions shift from generation to generation as F increases with continued inbreeding. When equilibrium is reached, F and m remain constant and the zygotic proportions may be expressed in terms of these constants. Let the equilibrium value be $\hat{F} = \hat{m}/(2 - \hat{m})$; then the final proportion of heterozygotes is

$$\hat{H} = 2p\,q\,(1 - \hat{F}) = 4p\,q\left(\frac{1 - \hat{m}}{2 - \hat{m}}\right). \tag{10}$$

§ 11. *Paths for Sex-linked Inheritance*

Let the heterogametic sex be males, whom we may consider as haploid individuals with regard to sex-linked genes. Since the sperms produced by males are *completely* determined by their genotypes (for sex-linked genes), the only modification of our earlier formula needed here is to let $b = 1$ for male parental zygotes (Fig. 35). Note that, since sons do not receive any sex-linked genes from their fathers, the path from sperm to son is $a = 0$. In other words, a son receives his whole inheritance from his mother, and the path from egg to son is $a = 1$. On the other hand, a daughter receives one gamete from each parent, and the paths from gametes to a daughter remain the same as for autosomal genes.

With the modifications shown in Figure 35, the correlations between family members with respect to sex-linked traits may be obtained immediately, once the diagram of a family is formulated in the style of a causal scheme, just as was done with autosomal genes. From Figure 36 it is easy to see that

$$
\left.\begin{aligned}
r_{\text{FS}} &= 0, \\
r_{\text{FD}} &= a = \sqrt{\tfrac{1}{2}}, & r_{\text{SS}} &= b^2 = \tfrac{1}{2}, \\
r_{\text{MS}} &= b = \sqrt{\tfrac{1}{2}}, & r_{\text{DD}} &= a^2 + a^2b^2 = \tfrac{1}{2} + \tfrac{1}{4} = \tfrac{3}{4}, \\
r_{\text{MD}} &= ab = \tfrac{1}{2}, & r_{\text{SD}} &= ab^2 = \tfrac{1}{2}\sqrt{\tfrac{1}{2}}.
\end{aligned}\right\} \tag{11}
$$

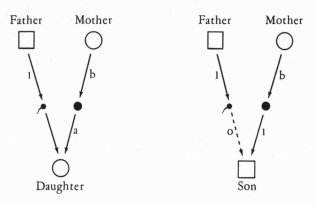

Fig. 35.—Paths from parents to offspring for sex-linked genes

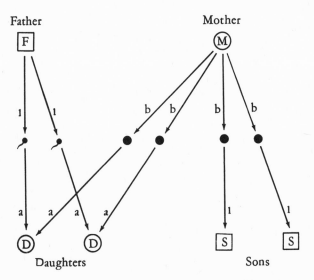

Fig. 36.—Correlations between family members for sex-linked inheritance

Note that these results are identical with those given in Chapter 5, where they were directly calculated from the frequencies of the various combinations in a random-mating population.

§ 12. *Multiple Factors and Environmental Influences*

It should be noted that in this chapter we did not use the single-factor scheme in deriving the various relations and genetic correlations. As long as genic effects are additive, so that a gametic value is the sum of the individual effects of the genes present in the gamete, and a zygotic value is the sum of the values of the two gametes that united to produce the zygote, the results of this and the next

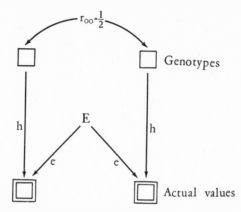

Fig. 37.—Correlation between full sibs, including environmental effects, in a random-mating population.

few chapters hold for any number of genes. Thus, in a random-mating population, the full-sib correlation for a metrical trait due to many pairs of genes is still $r_{OO} = \frac{1}{2}$ if the trait is entirely determined by additive hereditary factors.

To take account of environmental influences by the method of path coefficients, we merely introduce into the causal scheme an additional factor, E, representing environment. The principle stated above may be illustrated by considering full-sib correlation in a random-mating population (Fig. 37). The genetic correlation is $r_{OO} = \frac{1}{2}$. Let the path from the genetic make-up (genotype) to the actually observed value of an individual be h, and the path from E (a common cause) to an individual be e. The correlation between two full sibs is then

$$r^*_{OO} = \tfrac{1}{2}h^2 + e^2 . \tag{12}$$

The actually observed correlation is due partly to common heredity and partly to common environment. In Figure 37 we assumed that environmental influences are independent of genic effects. The first term of (12) represents the hereditary component; the second term, the environmental component of the total correlation. The fraction h^2 is usually known as the "heritability" of the trait under consideration. The value of r_{00}^* may deviate considerably from $\frac{1}{2}$, depending upon how strongly the common environmental factors influence the trait.

As was pointed out in the Preface, we shall not examine in detail metrical characters with environmental influences. The purpose of this section was to make the student aware of the possibilities of extending the method of path coefficients to include environmental influences in quantitative genetics, a field that has as one of its major concerns the evaluation of the relative magnitudes of h^2 and e^2. The results presented in this chapter are purely genetical ($h^2 = 1$ and $e^2 = 0$).

Notes and Exercises

1. The value of the path from zygote to gamete (b) may be obtained from a point of view different from that used in the text of this chapter. We know

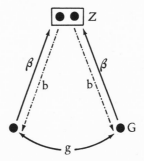

Fig. 38.—Another viewpoint of the bottom portion of Figure 29

that $r_{GZ} = p_{G \cdot Z} = b$. Using the argument advanced in Section 6 of Chapter 12, we may legitimately turn Figure 29 around and consider the zygote as determined by the gametes produced by that zygote (Fig. 38). Then the gametes produced will be correlated "causes" of Z. Let g denote this correlation between gametes produced by the same zygote. As far as one pair of alleles is concerned, it is obvious that the gametes produced by a single individual must have the same relation as those which have united to produce this individual. Hence,

$$g = F'.$$

Let β be the reverse path coefficients in Figure 38. Of course, β will not be equal to b; but the (absolute) correlation between Z and G will remain the same, whatever viewpoint has been taken toward the paths. From the theorems on complete determination and total correlation developed in Chapter 12, we have

$$2\beta^2 + 2\beta^2 g = 1 ,$$

$$\beta + \beta g \;\; = b = r_{GZ} .$$

Solving simultaneously and remembering that $g = F'$, we obtain

$$b = \sqrt{[\tfrac{1}{2}(1 + F')]} . \qquad\qquad \text{i.e., (2)}$$

2. Given $m = 0.40$ in an equilibrium population in which $p = q = \tfrac{1}{2}$, calculate the following values:

F	a	b	r_{PP}	r_{PO}	r_{OO}	D	H

3. In a certain inbreeding population $m = 0.50$ and $b = \sqrt{\tfrac{1}{2}}$. Suppose that m is increased to 0.60, owing to continued inbreeding, and verify the following results:

Present......	$m = 0.50$	$F = \tfrac{1}{4}$	$a = \sqrt{\tfrac{2}{5}}$	$b = \sqrt{\tfrac{1}{2}}$	$r_{PO} = \tfrac{3}{2}\sqrt{\tfrac{1}{5}}$	$r_{OO} = \tfrac{3}{5}$
Next........	$m = 0.60$	$F = \tfrac{3}{8}$	$a = \sqrt{\tfrac{4}{11}}$	$b = \sqrt{\tfrac{5}{8}}$	$r_{PO} = \tfrac{8}{5}\sqrt{\tfrac{5}{22}}$	$r_{OO} = \tfrac{8}{11}$

4. Show that, with the aid of (3) and (5'),

$$r_{PO} = ab + abm = \frac{1}{2} \frac{1 + 2F + F'}{\sqrt{[(1+F)(1+F')]}} .$$

5. Compare the diagram for double first cousins (Fig. 33) with that of Exercise 14 of Chapter 12. Do you see any similarities between them?

6. Given a population $(p - \tfrac{1}{2}H, H, q - \tfrac{1}{2}H)$ where $H = 2pq(1 - F)$, show that the genetic variance of this population is

$$\sigma_F^2 = 2pq(1 + F) = \sigma_0^2(1 + F) .$$

What does this expression mean? (Read § 6 of Chap. 11.)

7. Simplify Figure 36 for sex-linked genes by omitting the gametes from that figure (see Fig. 39). Then deduce the familial correlations (11).

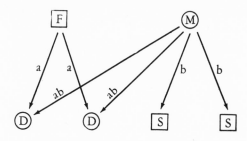

FIG. 39.—Simplified form of Figure 36

8. Hogben (1932*d*) obtained the following correlations for sex-linked genes by a direct method. Verify his results by the method of path coefficients.

Relatives	Aunt-Niece	Uncle-Niece	Aunt-Nephew	Uncle-Nephew
Maternal.....	$\dfrac{3}{8}$	$\dfrac{1}{4\sqrt{2}}$	$\dfrac{3}{4\sqrt{2}}$	$\dfrac{1}{4}$
Paternal......	$\dfrac{1}{4}$	$\dfrac{1}{2\sqrt{2}}$	0	0

HINT: Draw a simplified "causal scheme" for each type of relative. It may be further simplified by using the known correlations (11). For example, the maternal aunt-niece diagram may take either of the two forms shown in Figure 40. Hence, their correlation $= ab(a^2 + a^2b^2) = ab(r_{DD}) = \frac{3}{8}$.

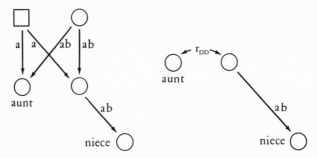

FIG. 40.—Two equivalent schemes for maternal aunt-niece relationship for sex-linked genes

9. In Figure 41, X and Y are half-sibs and so are Y and Z. Are X and Z correlated genetically? Do the rules of tracing a connecting path make good biological sense to you?

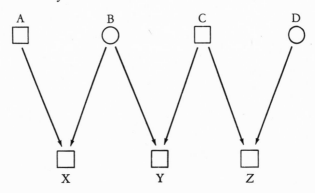

FIG. 41.—Independence between X and Z. Note that $r_{XY} = \frac{1}{4}$ and $r_{YZ} = \frac{1}{4}$, but $r_{XZ} = 0$. (Li and Sacks, 1954.)

10. It should be mentioned that many of the results reached in this chapter, especially those concerning correlations between relatives, are equivalent to those given by Fisher (1918), who used a different method and dealt with more general situations. If all genic effects are additive and environmental conditions remain absolutely uniform, it is easy to translate Fisher's formulas into the expressions given here.

The novel and simplifying feature of Wright's method, apart from the technique of path coefficients, is the introduction of the gametic variable into the analysis. In physical reality only a zygote can assume a measurable value (such as weight, height, etc.); consequently, only the correlations between zygotes can actually be observed. But, by introducing an abstract gametic variable and the abstract correlation between gametes, the analysis becomes much easier.

CHAPTER 14

Systems of Inbreeding

THE results brought about by some simple regular systems of inbreeding were presented in Chapters 9 and 10. As the system of inbreeding becomes more complex, it becomes desirable to replace the direct algebraic method with the method of path coefficients, which provides a concise and general analysis of the inbreeding results in a population. If gametes and zygotes are regarded as variables (on an additive scale), as in the preceding chapter, any system of mating can be represented by a diagram similar to the causal schemes to which path coefficients are applicable. In order to show the validity of the path method, we shall begin with the systems of selfing and sib mating. This will serve a dual purpose: to check on the path method for the known results of these systems given by direct methods and to illustrate the general procedure for adapting the path method to inbreeding problems.

§ 1. *Selfing*

Selfing is equivalent to mating between individuals of identical genotypes The correlation between mates is thus perfect; that is, $m = 1$, adopting the notations of the last chapter. The correlation between uniting gametes in any generation is

$$F = bmb = b^2 = \tfrac{1}{2}(1 + F'), \tag{1}$$

where the prime indicates the coefficient of the preceding generation. This is the recurrence relation of F in successive generations of selfing. It is seen that F increases with each generation of selfing.

Since heterozygosis (H) is proportional to $(1 - F)$, its recurrence relation may be found easily from that of F. If H_0 is the initial proportion of heterozygosis in a selfing population, then $H = H_0(1 - F)$ in any generation. Substituting (1), we obtain

$$H = H_0(1 - \tfrac{1}{2} - \tfrac{1}{2}F') = \tfrac{1}{2}H_0(1 - F') = \tfrac{1}{2}H', \tag{2}$$

which is the familiar expression $H_{n+1} = \tfrac{1}{2}H_n$ for selfing diploids (Chap. 9). Note that the recurrence relation of H is independent of the initial condition (H_0) of a population.

The general procedure for using the path method, as illustrated by the above example, may be outlined as follows: First, find an expression for m as specified by the mating system. Second, find the recurrence relation of F. Third, deduce the recurrence relation of H. The various values of paths and correlations belonging to the same generation may be calculated directly from the first column of Table 56 (p. 180). The details of this procedure are illustrated in the section on sib mating that follows.

§ 2. *Sib Mating*

A population practicing continued sib mating will become broken up into permanently separate but branching lines of descent (Fig. 42). The population consists of numerous "isolates," each isolate being a sibship. Since only sibs (brothers and sisters) will be mates, the correlation between mating individuals in any generation is simply that between full sibs of the preceding generation. From Section 5 or Table 56 of Chapter 13, we may write $r_{PP} = r'_{OO}$ (prime in-

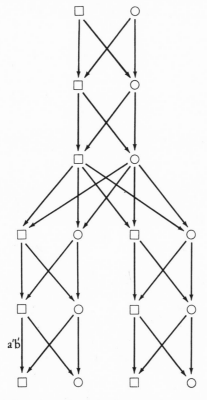

Fig. 42.—Continued sib mating. The paths shown are from parents to offspring, gametes being omitted.

dicating preceding generation), or

$$m = 2a'^2b'^2(1 + m') . \tag{3}$$

This is the key relation for the system of sib mating—all the properties of sib mating being derived from this fundamental relation. It is a specific form of $m = \phi(a', b', m')$, an expression mentioned in Chapter 13. Starting with this key formula, the values of the paths a and b, and correlations F, r_{PO}, etc., can be calculated generation by generation once the initial values of a, b, m are specified. The results shown in Table 57 are from a random-mating initial population in which $a = b = \sqrt{\frac{1}{2}}$ and $m = 0$. In order to show the successive

TABLE 57

RESULTS OF SIB MATING FROM A PANMICTIC
INITIAL POPULATION
(Wright, 1921b, p. 127)

Genera-tion	$m = r_{OO}' =$ $2a'^2b'^2(1+m')$	$b^2 =$ $\frac{1}{2}(1+F')$	$F =$ b^2m	$a^2 =$ $\dfrac{1}{2(1+F)}$	$H =$ $H_0(1-F)$
0........	0	$\frac{1}{2}$	0	$\frac{1}{2}$	$\frac{2}{4}$
1........	$\frac{1}{2}$	$\frac{2}{4}$	$\frac{1}{4}$	$\frac{2}{5}$	$\frac{3}{8}$
2........	$\frac{3}{5}$	$\frac{5}{8}$	$\frac{3}{8}$	$\frac{4}{11}$	$\frac{5}{16}$
3........	$\frac{8}{11}$	$\frac{11}{16}$	$\frac{8}{16}$	$\frac{8}{4}$	$\frac{8}{32}$
4........	$\frac{19}{24}$	$\frac{24}{32}$	$\frac{19}{32}$	$\frac{16}{51}$	$\frac{13}{64}$
5........	$\frac{43}{51}$	$\frac{51}{64}$	$\frac{43}{64}$	$\frac{32}{107}$	$\frac{21}{128}$
6........	$\frac{94}{107}$	$\frac{107}{128}$	$\frac{94}{128}$	$\frac{64}{222}$	$\frac{34}{256}$
. . .	. . .	. . .	. . .	. . .	. . .
10........	0.953	0.9297	0.886	0.265	0.057
15........	0.985	0.9756	0.9606	$.255$	$.020$
20........	0.995	0.9915	0.9863	$.252$	$.0068$
∞	1.0	1.0	1.0	0.250	0.0

values of H, we assume the frequencies of dominant and recessive alleles are equal, so that the initial proportion of heterozygotes in the population is $H_0 = 2pq = \frac{1}{2}$. This, however, does not at all affect the recurrence relation of H.

As an illustration of the general method, the results given in Table 57 are obtained row by row by repeated use of the relations shown at the head of each column. Note that the successive values of $m = 0, \frac{1}{2}, \frac{3}{5}, \frac{8}{11}, \ldots$, and of $F = 0, \frac{1}{4}, \frac{3}{8}, \frac{8}{16}, \ldots$, obtained here by the path method, are identical with those given by long-hand algebra in Tables 37 and 38 of Chapter 10. The recurrence relation of F under sib mating may also be found easily by the present method, so that its successive values may be written out separately for any number of generations without simultaneously calculating the values of other variables. The key formula for m may be put into the form

$$m = 2a'^2(b'^2 + b'^2m') = 2a'^2(b'^2 + F') . \tag{4}$$

Substituting the values of a'^2 and b'^2 (in terms of F' and F''), we obtain

$$m = \frac{1 + 2F' + F''}{2\,(1+F')}.$$

Hence,

$$F = b^2 m = \tfrac{1}{4}(1 + 2F' + F''), \tag{5}$$

which is the desired recurrence relation of F. Since $H = H_0(1 - F)$, the recurrence relation of H may be obtained immediately from that of F; thus,

$$\begin{aligned} H = H_0(1 - F) &= H_0(1 - \tfrac{1}{4} - \tfrac{1}{2}F' - \tfrac{1}{4}F'') \\ &= \tfrac{1}{2}H_0(1 - F') + \tfrac{1}{4}H_0(1 - F'') = \tfrac{1}{2}H' + \tfrac{1}{4}H'', \end{aligned} \tag{6}$$

which is our familiar expression $H_{n+2} = \tfrac{1}{2}H_{n+1} + \tfrac{1}{4}H_n$, as shown by direct algebraic methods. The values of other variables (m, a, b, r_{PO}, etc.) can also be expressed as functions either of F or of H. We have seen in the above that the path method gives precisely the same results as the long algebraic method. Convinced of the validity of this method, we shall pass on now to some other systems of inbreeding.

§ 3. *Parent-Offspring Mating*

In deriving the general relations between parent and offspring, we pointed out that, when mating individuals belong to different generations in a system of inbreeding, the values of path coefficients and correlations have to be modified. An analysis of the parent-offspring mating system illustrates nicely the flexibility of the method of path coefficients. Two simple systems of parent-offspring mating are considered in the following:

1. The first type of mating is between a fixed sire and his daughter, granddaughter, great-granddaughter, etc., as shown in Figure 43. Assuming that the two initial parents are from a panmictic population, the path from the sire to his sperm *always* takes the value $b = \sqrt{\tfrac{1}{2}}$. The parents of the individual D are S (sire) and C, whose correlation will be denoted by m. We are to express this m in terms of a', b', m' of their preceding generation. Inspection of Figure 43 shows that the key formula of this mating system is

$$m = a'\sqrt{\tfrac{1}{2}} + a'b'm', \tag{7}$$

where m' is the correlation between S and B (mother of C). The correlation between the two uniting gametes that produced the individual D is

$$F = bm\sqrt{\tfrac{1}{2}} = \tfrac{1}{2}\sqrt{2}\, bm. \tag{8}$$

The recurrence relation of F will be found when we express m in terms of F'. Thus, we rewrite the key formula for m as follows:

$$m = a'\sqrt{\tfrac{1}{2}}(1 + \sqrt{2}b'm') = a'\sqrt{\tfrac{1}{2}}(1 + 2F'); \tag{9}$$

$$\therefore \quad F = \sqrt{\tfrac{1}{2}}\, bm = \sqrt{\tfrac{1}{2}}\, b \cdot a' \sqrt{\tfrac{1}{2}}(1 + 2F') = \tfrac{1}{4}(1 + 2F') , \qquad (10)$$

remembering that $ba' = \tfrac{1}{2}$, whatever the mating system (p. 175). The last expression (10) is the required recurrence relation of F. The corresponding relation for H may be found in the usual manner; thus

$$H = H_0(1 - \tfrac{1}{4} - \tfrac{1}{2}F') = \tfrac{1}{4}H_0 + \tfrac{1}{2}H' . \qquad (11)$$

Note that, under the system of mating to a fixed individual who has never been inbred before, the proportion of heterozygosis among his offspring cannot ap-

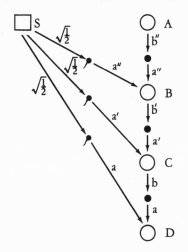

FIG. 43.—Backcrossing to a fixed sire

proach zero as the limiting value but has a minimum value of $\tfrac{1}{2}H_0$. Assuming $H_0 = 2pq = \tfrac{1}{2}$, and thus the initial value of $F = 0$, their successive values under this system of inbreeding are, according to (10) and (11), respectively,

F	$\frac{1}{4}$	$\frac{3}{8}$	$\frac{7}{16}$	$\frac{15}{32}$	. . .	$\frac{1}{2}$
H	$\frac{3}{8}$	$\frac{5}{16}$	$\frac{9}{32}$	$\frac{17}{64}$	. . .	$\frac{1}{4}$

which agrees with the results obtained by direct methods (Jennings, 1916).

2. The second type of parent-offspring mating is that in which each individual is mated successively with his (her) younger parent and with his (her) offspring, as shown in Figure 44. The correlation between the parents, S (sire) and D (dam), is

$$m = a'b' + a'b''m' , \qquad (12)$$

where m' is the correlation between the preceding mating individuals, viz., S and M (D's mother). The correlation between the uniting gametes forming the individual O (offspring) is

$$F = b \, m \, b' \quad \text{or} \quad \frac{F}{b} = m \, b' \, , \tag{13}$$

so that the key formula for m (12) may be written as

$$m = a' b' + a' \frac{F'}{b'} \, . \tag{14}$$

Thus, $F = bb'(a'b' + a'F'/b') = a'b(b'^2 + F')$

$$= \tfrac{1}{2}[\tfrac{1}{2}(1 + F'') + F'] = \tfrac{1}{4}(1 + 2F' + F'') \, , \qquad \text{i.e., (5)}$$

and therefore the recurrence relation of H is the same as (6). In other words, the consequences of mating with a younger parent are the same as those of mating with a full sib. These results also agree with those given by Jennings (1916).

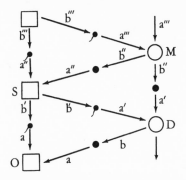

Fig. 44.—Mating with younger parent

§ 4. *Half-Sib Mating*

A number of systems of mating between half-sibs may be devised. We shall, however, consider only one of the simplest: one male is mated with an indefinite number of his half-sisters who are also half-sisters of each other (Fig. 45). The individuals A and B, who are to be mates, are connected by four chains: $A\overline{C}B$; $A\overline{CE}B$; $A\overline{DE}B$; $A\overline{DC}B$. The individuals C, E; D, E; and D, C; being half-sibs, are all correlated with the same coefficient m'. Summing the above four connecting chains, we find that the correlation between A and B is (Fig. 45)

$$m = a'^2 b'^2 (1 + 3m') \, , \tag{15}$$

which is the key formula for this type of half-sib mating. It may also be written in the form

$$m = a'^2 (b'^2 + 3 \, b'^2 m') = a'^2 \left(\frac{1 + F''}{2} + 3F' \right) . \tag{16}$$

The recurrence relation of F will be found immediately on substituting this value of m in

$$F = b^2 m = b^2 a'^2 \left(\frac{1+F''}{2} + 3F' \right),$$

where $ba' = \frac{1}{2}$. Therefore,

$$F = \tfrac{1}{8}(1 + 6F' + F'') . \tag{17}$$

Hence,

$$H = \tfrac{3}{4}H' + \tfrac{1}{8}H'' . \tag{18}$$

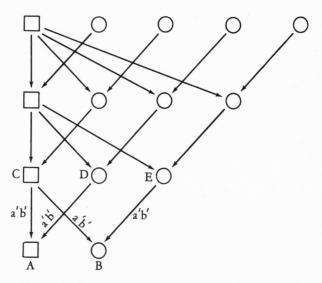

FIG. 45.—Mating between one male and his half-sisters (gametes not shown)

Assuming $H_0 = 2pq = \frac{1}{2}$ in a random-mating population, the student should verify the following series of values:

m	0	$\frac{1}{4}$	$\frac{7}{18}$	$\frac{1}{2}$	$\frac{195}{334}$	$\ldots$	1
F	0	$\frac{1}{8}$	$\frac{7}{32}$	$\frac{39}{128}$	$\frac{195}{512}$	$\ldots$	1
H	$\frac{2}{4}$	$\frac{7}{16}$	$\frac{25}{64}$	$\frac{89}{256}$	$\frac{317}{1024}$	$\ldots$	0

Each numerator of H is thrice the preceding plus twice the one before that, while the denominator is multiplied by four each generation. In livestock in which a great number of females may be mated to one sire, this system of inbreeding is perhaps the most rapid practical method of fixing characters, for the rate of increase in homozygosis is fairly rapid. It is slower than full-sib mating (Table 57), but full sibs are not available in large numbers and sometimes may not be available at all.

§ 5. *Rate of Decrease in Heterozygosis*

Reviewing the "Appendix on Recurrent Series" (Chap. 5), we see that H, with the recurrence relation (18), may be expressed as the sum of the corresponding terms of two geometric series whose common ratios are given by the roots of the equation:

$$\lambda^2 - \tfrac{3}{4}\lambda - \tfrac{1}{8} = 0 . \tag{19}$$

Solving, we find that its two roots are

$$\lambda_1 = \tfrac{1}{8}(3 + \sqrt{17}) = 0.89 , \quad \lambda_2 = \tfrac{1}{8}(3 - \sqrt{17}) = -0.14 .$$

After a sufficiently large number of generations, the term involving the smaller λ_2 will be so much smaller than the term involving the larger λ_1 that we may write, as an approximation,

$$H = \lambda_1 H' = 0.89\, H' . \tag{20}$$

This indicates that the eventual rate of decrease in H is $1 - \lambda_1 = 11$ per cent per generation under this system of half-sib mating (in contrast to the 19.1 per cent in full-sib mating).

The limiting ratio of two successive values of H may be found by another method. After a sufficiently large number of generations of continued inbreeding, we may put $H/H' = H'/H'' = L$, a certain positive constant smaller than unity. Substituting in (18), we have

$$\frac{\tfrac{3}{4}H' + \tfrac{1}{8}H''}{H'} = \frac{H'}{H''} ;$$

that is,

$$\frac{3}{4} + \frac{1}{8}\frac{1}{L} = L$$

or

$$\tfrac{3}{4}L + \tfrac{1}{8} = L^2 ,$$

which is identical with our previous λ-equation (19); thus $L = 0.89$. The method of putting $H/H' = H'/H''$, as employed by Wright, is the same as solving for the largest root of the λ-equation of the type (19).

§ 6. *Mating between Double First Cousins*

Double first cousins are those whose parents belong to two sibships. If all matings are confined to double first cousins in every generation, the population will be broken up into separate lines of descent ("isolates") which may bifurcate in any generation as in the case of sib mating. In the latter case, each line of descent involves only two individuals of one sibship, while in the former each isolate consists of four individuals of two sibships. The individuals C_1 and C_2 in Figure 46 are double first cousins because their fathers (the J's) are full sibs as well as their mothers (the I's). For autosomal genes it makes no difference if C_1's father is a brother of C_2's mother and vice versa. Now, C_1 and C_2 are to be mates; and they are connected by four chains:

$$C_1\overline{J_1J_2}C_2, \quad C_1\overline{I_1I_2}C_2, \quad C_1\overline{J_1I_2}C_2, \quad C_1\overline{I_1J_2}C_2.$$

Since the J's and the I's are all full sibs, their correlation is

$$r_{J_1J_2} = r_{I_1I_2} = r_{OO}'' = 2a''^2b''^2(1 + m'').$$

The correlation between J_1 and I_2 must be the same as that between J_1 and I_1, because the I's are full sibs and double first cousins of the J's. Hence, $r_{J_1I_2} =$

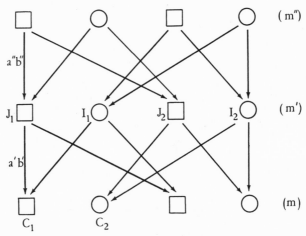

FIG. 46.—Continued mating between double first cousins (gametes not shown)

$r_{I_1J_2} = m'$. The values of the four connecting chains are:

$$C_1\overline{J_1J_2}C_2 \quad \text{or} \quad C_1\overline{I_1I_2}C_2 \quad : \quad a'^2b'^2 \cdot r_{OO}''.$$
$$C_1\overline{J_1I_2}C_2 \quad \text{or} \quad C_1\overline{I_1J_2}C_2 \quad : \quad a'^2b'^2 \cdot m'.$$

The correlation between the mating double first cousins (C_1 and C_2), being the sum of the values of the above four connecting chains, is thus (Fig. 46)

$$m = 2a'^2b'^2m' + 4a'^2b'^2a''^2b''^2(1 + m'') \tag{21}$$
$$= 2a'^2(b'^2m') + 4(a''^2b'^2)a'^2(b''^2 + b''^2m'')$$
$$= 2a'^2F' + a'^2[\tfrac{1}{2}(1 + F''') + F'']$$
$$= \tfrac{1}{2}a'^2(1 + 4F' + 2F'' + F'''). \tag{22}$$

The recurrence relations of F and H may be obtained immediately from the last expression for m. Thus,

$$F = b^2m = \tfrac{1}{8}(1 + 4F' + 2F'' + F'''), \tag{23}$$

and

$$H = H_0(1 - F) = H_0(1 - \tfrac{1}{8} - \tfrac{1}{2}F' - \tfrac{1}{4}F'' - \tfrac{1}{8}F''')$$
$$= H_0\{\tfrac{1}{2}(1 - F') + \tfrac{1}{4}(1 - F'') + \tfrac{1}{8}(1 - F''')\}$$
$$= \tfrac{1}{2}H' + \tfrac{1}{4}H'' + \tfrac{1}{8}H''' . \tag{24}$$

If the initial proportion of heterozygotes in the population is $H_0 = 2pq = \tfrac{1}{2}$, its succeeding values will be

$$H: \tfrac{1}{2}, \tfrac{2}{4}, \tfrac{4}{8}, \tfrac{7}{16}, \tfrac{13}{32}, \tfrac{24}{64}, \tfrac{44}{128}, \ldots, 0 .$$

Each numerator of H is the sum of the preceding three numerators if the denominator is doubled each generation. The limiting value of H is zero. After a sufficiently large number of generations the values of H will decrease at approximately a constant proportion. In the last section it was shown that putting $H/H' = H'/H'' = H''/H'''$ is equivalent to solving for the largest root of the equation

$$\lambda^3 - \tfrac{1}{2}\lambda^2 - \tfrac{1}{4}\lambda - \tfrac{1}{8} = 0 .$$

It will be found (Wright, 1933a; Fisher, 1949) that $\lambda = 0.91964$ is its largest positive root. Hence, $H = 0.920\ H'$, approximately, after a number of generations of continued double-first-cousin matings. The eventual rate of decrease in H is $1 - \lambda = 8$ per cent per generation.

§ 7. A General Result

Under the system of double-first-cousin matings, each breeding unit consists of $N = 4$ individuals of two sibships. Note that matings are *not* at random among the four individuals, as we specified that only the double first cousins could mate. The possible matings between full sibs (among the four individuals) are excluded, and so are the possibilities of selfing. As far as these four individuals are concerned, their most distant relationship is that of double first cousins. In other words, the mating system is such that close consanguineous matings are avoided as far as possible within a group of four individuals in each generation.

Similarly, continued exclusive quadruple-second-cousin matings (Wright, 1921b) will give rise to isolates of size $N = 8$, wherein the grandparents belong to four sibships. Any matings closer than this are excluded among the eight individuals. The general results of similar mating systems of larger groups are given in Table 58.

As the size of the breeding unit becomes larger, the rate of decrease in H becomes slower. The limiting value of H is, however, zero in each case. In a finite group of N individuals, the rate of decrease in heterozygosis is $1/4N$ per generation when close inbreeding is avoided as far as possible and all matings are between the most distantly related individuals.

If, on the other hand, close inbreeding is permitted on the basis of random mating within a group of N individuals, we should expect that the rate of decrease in H will be higher than $1/4N$ per generation. This case will be investigated in the next chapter.

TABLE 58

RECURRENCE RELATIONS OF H WHEN CLOSE INBREEDING IS
AVOIDED WITHIN GROUPS OF SIZE N
(Wright, 1921b, 1951)

Mating	Size of Group	Exact Value of H	Limiting Value Approximate H
Self-fertilization.......	1	$\frac{1}{2}H'$	$0.500\ H'$
Full sibs.............	2	$\frac{1}{2}H'+\frac{1}{4}H''$	$0.809\ H'$
Double first cousins...	4	$\frac{1}{2}H'+\frac{1}{4}H''+\frac{1}{8}H'''$	$0.920\ H'$
Quadruple second cousins...............	8	$\frac{1}{2}H'+\frac{1}{4}H''+\frac{1}{8}H'''+\frac{1}{16}H^{IV}$	$0.965\ H'$
Octuple third cousins..	16	$\frac{1}{2}H'+\frac{1}{4}H''+\frac{1}{8}H'''+\frac{1}{16}H^{IV}+\frac{1}{32}H^{V}$	$0.983\ H'$
More distant cousins..	N	(See Table 59)	$\dfrac{4N-1}{4N}H'$

§ 8. *Mating between (Single) First Cousins*

Under the systems of mating listed in Table 58, the entire population breaks up into numerous small and separate breeding units of a certain size. This is not the case with continued single-first- (or second-) cousin matings. In the latter cases the analysis is usually more complicated, and, most important of all, the limiting value of H is not necessarily zero if the mates are too distantly related. We shall examine the results of continued first-cousin matings in this section and those of second-cousin matings in the next.

The individuals C_1 and C_2 in Figure 47 are (single) first cousins because only two of their four parents are full sibs (P_1 and P_2); the other two parents (S_1 and S_2) are second cousins because two of their grandparents (G_1 and G_2) are full sibs. Now, C_1 and C_2 are to be mates; and they are connected by four chains, namely,

$$C_1\overline{P_1P_2}C_2\,, \qquad C_1\overline{S_1P_2}C_2\,, \qquad C_1\overline{P_1S_2}C_2\,, \qquad C_1\overline{S_1S_2}C_2\,.$$

Proceeding as before, let us examine first the correlations between the two intermediate individuals (indicated by bars) by whom C_1 and C_2 are connected. Since P_1 and P_2 are full sibs, their correlation will be denoted by r'_{00}. Next, the correlation between S_1 and P_2, being the same as that between S_1 and P_1 (who are first cousins and thus mates in the preceding generation), is simply m'. Similarly, the correlation between P_1 and S_2 (same as that between P_2 and S_2) is also m'. Finally, the two second cousins, S_1 and S_2, are themselves connected by four chains; let their correlation be denoted by r'_{22}. Hence, the correlation between the mates C_1 and C_2, being the sum of the four connecting chains, is

$$m = a'^2b'^2(r'_{00} + 2m' + r'_{22})\,, \tag{25}$$

where
$$r'_{22} = a''^2 b''^2 (m' + 2r''_{22} + r''_{33}) ,$$
and
$$r''_{33} = a'''^2 b'''^2 (r'''_{22} + 2r'''_{33} + r'''_{44}), \text{ etc.} ,$$

r_{33} being the correlation between third cousins, etc. There seems to be no method of obtaining the value of m other than that of carrying these auxiliary formulas

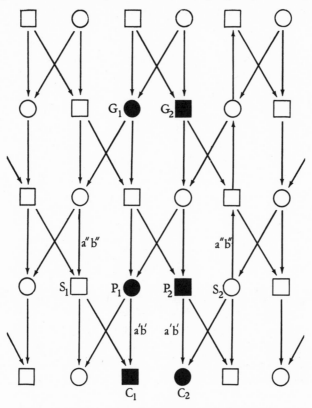

Fig. 47.—Continued mating between single first cousins

for cousin correlations (r_{nn}) back to a random-mating population. As before, assuming initial $H_0 = \frac{1}{2}$ and $m = 0$, their successive values under this system of mating are as follows:

	GENERATIONS								
	0	1	2	3	4 .	5	10	15	∞
m	0	0.125	0.176	0.221	0.261	0.294	0.407	0.477	1
H	0.500	0.469	0.453	0.439	0.427	0.416	0.374	0.344	0

The proportion of heterozygosis decreases rather slowly, falling only from 50 per cent to 34.4 per cent in fifteen generations. Nevertheless, its limiting value is zero (no equilibrium is possible short of complete homozygosis when $m = 1$).

§ 9. *Mating between Second Cousins*

In all the preceding regular systems of inbreeding the limiting value of H is zero. When the consanguinity is more remote than single first cousins, however, the proportion of heterozygosis in the population will approach some constant (not zero) as its limit, and, thus, the population will be in an equilibrium condition under the same system of mating. In the following the results of continued mating between second cousins will serve as an example of this situation.

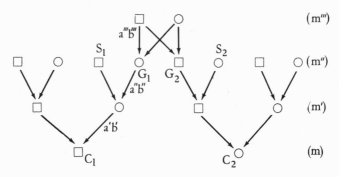

Fig. 48.—Mating between second cousins. Only *two* of the eight grandparents are full sibs

The individuals C_1 and C_2 in Figure 48 are second cousins because only two of their eight grandparents are full sibs (G_1 and G_2). Now, C_1 and C_2 are to be mates; and they are connected by three chains:

$$C_1\overline{G_1G_2}C_2\,, \qquad C_1\overline{S_1G_2}C_2\,, \qquad C_1\overline{G_1S_2}C_2\,.$$

The correlation between G_1 and G_2 (full sibs) is

$$r_{G_1G_2} = r''_{00} = 2a'''^2b'''^2(1 + m''')\,.$$

The correlations between S_1 and G_2 and G_1 and S_2, being the same as those between S_1 and G_1 and G_2 and S_2, who are mates, are all equal to m''. Note that the two grandparents S_1 and S_2 are independent and thus are no links between the cousins C_1 and C_2. The key formula for the correlation between the mates of the present generation (C_1 and C_2) is (Fig. 48)

$$m = a'^2b'^2.a''^2b''^2(r''_{00} + 2m'')\,. \tag{26}$$

Substituting the value of r''_{00} and simplifying by the relations $a''b' = \frac{1}{2}$, $b''^2m'' = F''$, etc., we obtain

$$m = \tfrac{1}{16}a'^2(1 + 8F'' + 2F''' + F''')\,. \tag{27}$$

Thus,

$$F = b^2 m = \tfrac{1}{64}(1 + 8F'' + 2F''' + F'''') , \qquad (28)$$

and

$$H = \tfrac{1}{64}(26 + 8H'' + 2H''' + H'''') . \qquad (29)$$

The limiting value of F is not unity. Putting $F = F'' = F'''$, etc., in (28), we obtain the equation $F = (1 + 11 F)/64$. Thus, $F = \frac{1}{53}$ is the equilibrium value under the system of continued second-cousin matings. That is to say, the value of F will then remain constant from generation to generation as long as the second-cousin matings are continued. This is an interesting and important result, showing that, even when all matings in a population are between relatives for an indefinite period, it leads not to complete homozygosis but instead to an equilibrium condition with a constant inbreeding coefficient. The equilibrium values, tabulated below, are all nearly equal to those in a random-mating population.

$F = \frac{1}{53} = 0.019$	$b^2 = \dfrac{1+F}{2} = \frac{27}{53}$	$a^2 = \dfrac{1}{2(1+F)} = \frac{53}{108}$
$m = \dfrac{F}{b^2} = \frac{1}{27}$	$ab = \sqrt{\frac{27}{108}} = \frac{1}{2}$	$r_{OO} = r_{PO} = \frac{1}{2}(1+m) = \frac{14}{27}$

$$H = H_0(1-F) = \tfrac{1}{2}(1 - \tfrac{1}{53}) = \tfrac{26}{53} = 49.06 \text{ per cent when } p = q = \tfrac{1}{2}$$

The situation for continued mating between half-first cousins (Ex. 6) is very similar to that above. The important conclusion is that continued matings between relatives more remote than first cousins cause only an insignificant decrease in heterozygosis of the population and, therefore, can hardly be considered as inbreeding as far as the population composition is concerned. It should be added, however, that consanguineous matings do give a better chance for the appearance of rare recessive traits than do random matings.

§ 10. *Mating between Remote Relatives*

Let us suppose that a population consists of nonoverlapping "generations," such that there is a correlation of m' between individuals of the parental generation. The correlation between two random individuals of the next generation will be (Fig. 49)

$$m = 4a'^2 b'^2 m' . \qquad (30)$$

Assuming random mating among the members of the same generation, this m will be the correlation between mates of the next generation. When equilibrium is reached $(m = m')$, we have $4a'^2 b'^2 = 1$, or $a'^2 b'^2 = \frac{1}{4}$, $a'b' = \frac{1}{2} = ab$. Also, since $F = F'$ at equilibrium, $F = b^2 m = \frac{1}{2}(1 + F)m$ or $F = m/(2 - m)$, as noted before. The values of a, b, and H are those given in the tabulation on page 180.

§ 11. *Inbreeding for Sex-linked Genes*

The method of path coefficients may be extended to cases of sex-linked genes, with the modifications explained on page 181. In the following we shall give, as an example, only the results of continued brother-sister mating for sex-linked genes (Wright, 1933a). Inspection of Figure 50 shows that the key formula for

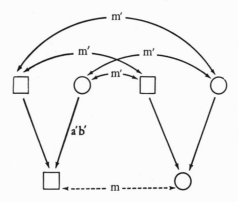

FIG. 49.—Correlation between remote relatives

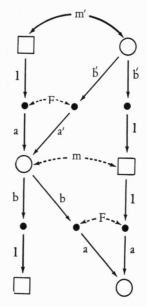

FIG. 50.—Continued brother-sister mating for sex-linked genes

the correlation between brother and sister (mates) is

$$m = b'^2a' + b'm'a' . \tag{31}$$

The values of a' and b' for sex-linked genes are the same as those for autosomal ones, so that $ba' = \frac{1}{2}$ for any gametic generation; but $F = bm$, $F' = b'm'$ for sex-linked genes (in contrast to b^2m for autosomal genes). The recurrence relation of F may be found by the usual procedure; thus

$$F = bm = b \cdot a'(b'^2 + b'm')$$
$$= \frac{1}{2}[\frac{1}{2}(1 + F'') + F']$$
$$= \frac{1}{4}(1 + 2F' + F'') , \qquad\qquad \text{i.e., (5)}$$

which is the same as that for autosomes. Hence, the recurrence relation of H will also be the same as (6), only here H denotes the proportion of heterozygotes among females. These results agree with those given in the earlier works of Jennings. It may be recalled that Haldane (1937a) obtained the equivalent result ($H = \frac{1}{2}H' + \frac{1}{4}H''$) by the algebraic methods shown in Chapter 10.

Notes and Exercises

1. Show that under continued brother-sister mating

$$r_{PP} = m = \frac{2F}{1 + F'}, \qquad r_{PO} = \frac{1 + 2F + F'}{2\sqrt{[(1+F)(1+F')]}};$$

and calculate their values for the first six generations (see Table 57).

2. Show that the recurrence relations of H for sib mating and double-first-cousin mating are, respectively,

$$H = H' - \frac{1}{8}H''' , \qquad H = H' - \frac{1}{16}H'''' . \qquad \text{i.e., (6), (24)}$$

3. In the system of backcrossing successive daughters to the same sire (Fig. 43), if the sire is known to be a purebred (homozygous for all loci), the path coefficient from S to his sperms will be $b = 1$ (instead of $\sqrt{\frac{1}{2}}$), since the constitution of these sperms is now completely determined by that of the sire. With this modification, derive the following relations:

$$m = a' + a'b'm'$$
$$F = bm = ba'(1 + b'm') = \frac{1}{2}(1 + F') . \qquad \text{i.e., (1)}$$

Hence, H will decrease in the same way as in the case of selfing; $H = \frac{1}{2}H'$. This system of inbreeding is of importance to livestock breeders. Since true self-fertilization is impossible in livestock, successive backcrossing to a purebred sire will give the same results as selfing, the quickest way of obtaining complete homozygosis.

4. Figure 51 shows another type of half-sib mating. One male (S) is mated with two of his half-sisters (D_1 and D_2), who are full sisters of each other (both being daughters of P and M_2). Under this system of mating, the population becomes broken into separate lines of descent, each consisting of three individuals. There are two matings in each generation: $P \times M_1$ and $P \times M_2$ in the parental generation; and $S \times D_1$ and $S \times D_2$ in the next. The correlations between mates are the same for the two matings of

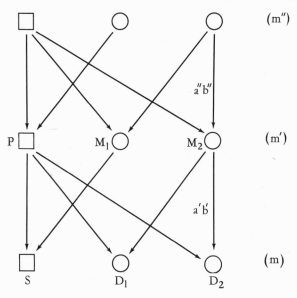

Fig. 51.—Continued mating between a half-brother and two full sisters

the same generation, so we need only to investigate the correlation between S and D_1. They are connected by four chains (Fig. 51):

$$S\overline{P}D_1, \quad S\overline{PM_1P}D_1, \quad S\overline{M_2}D_1, \quad S\overline{M_1M_2}D_1.$$

The first chain is directly through their father P. In the second chain the correlation between P and M_1 is m', as they are mates in the parental generation. The same is true for P and M_2. In the last chain the correlation between the two full sisters is $r_{\text{MM}} = r'_{\text{OO}} = 2a''^2b''^2(1 + m'')$, according to the usual formula for full sibs. With these, deduce the following relations:

$$m = a'^2b'^2(1 + 2m' + r'_{\text{OO}}),$$

$$F = \tfrac{1}{16}(3 + 8F' + 4F'' + F'''),$$

$$H = \tfrac{1}{2}H' + \tfrac{1}{4}H'' + \tfrac{1}{16}H''',$$

$$H: \tfrac{2}{4}, \tfrac{4}{8}, \tfrac{8}{16}, \tfrac{13}{32}, \tfrac{23}{64}, \tfrac{40}{128}, \tfrac{139}{512}, \ldots.$$

What is the eventual rate of decrease in H per generation?

5. With continued second-cousin matings we find that the equilibrium values are $F = \frac{1}{53}$ and $H = \frac{26}{53}$. Verify the relations (28) and (29) with these numerical values.

6. Half-first cousins are two individuals who have two of their parents related as half-sibs. In other words, two offspring of half-sibs (solid symbols in Fig. 52) will be mates in the next generation under the system of continued

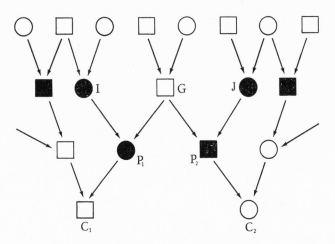

FIG. 52.—Mating between half first cousins

half-first-cousin mating. Thus, the individuals C_1 and C_2 are half-first cousins and will be mated; they are connected by three chains (Fig. 52):

$$C_1 P_1 \overline{G} P_2 C_2 , \qquad C_1 P_1 \overline{IG} P_2 C_2 , \qquad C_1 P_1 \overline{GJ} P_2 C_2 .$$

The first chain is directly through their parents P_1 and P_2, who have a common grandparent G. The other two chains are through I and G and G and J, who are mates and therefore are correlated with a value of m''. With these, deduce the following relations:

$$m = a'^2 b'^2 \cdot a''^2 b''^2 (1 + 2m'') ,$$

$$F = \tfrac{1}{32}(1 + 4F'' + F''') ,$$

$$H = \tfrac{1}{32}(13 + 4H'' + H''') .$$

Continued matings of this kind will lead to an equilibrium condition (other than complete homozygosis). Putting $m'' = m$, $F''' = F'' = F$, $H''' = H'' = H$, show that the equilibrium values are as follows:

$$F = \tfrac{1}{27} , \qquad m = \tfrac{1}{14} , \qquad r_{OO} = r_{PO} = \tfrac{15}{28} , \qquad H = \tfrac{13}{27} = 48.15 \text{ per cent} .$$

7. The modifications of path coefficients with respect to sex-linked genes are
of course applicable to any organism of the haploid-diploid type, such as
honeybees. The male bees (drones) develop from unfertilized eggs and thus
are haploids, while the females (queens) are ordinary diploids developed
from fertilized eggs. In other words, *all genes are sex linked in bees*. Therefore, the study of the effects of continued inbreeding in bees (which has
been made possible by suitable techniques of artificial insemination and

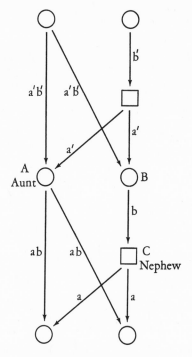

Fig. 53.—Continued aunt-nephew mating for sex-linked genes (or in bees)

the use of carbon dioxide to stimulate egg-laying by virgin but artificially
inseminated queens) is equivalent to studying such effects of sex-linked
genes in ordinary organisms.

The results of brother-sister mating for sex-linked genes (or bees) was
given in the text. The following is another example. Figure 53 presents the
system of continued aunt-nephew mating in which the gametic stages are
omitted for simplicity. Aunt (A) and nephew (C) are to be mates whose
correlation is m. Since A and B are full sisters, their correlation is

$$r_{AB} = r'_{DD} = a'^2 + a'^2 b'^2 + 2a'^2 b' m' ,$$

and

$$m = br'_{DD}$$

$$F = bm = b^2(a'^2 + a'^2b'^2 + 2a'^2b'm')$$
$$= \tfrac{1}{4}(1 + b'^2 + 2b'm')$$
$$= \tfrac{1}{4}[1 + \tfrac{1}{2}(1 + F'') + 2F']$$
$$= \tfrac{1}{8}(3 + 4F' + F'') .$$

This is the recurrence relation of F obtained by Crow and Roberts (1950), who also give

$$H = \tfrac{1}{2}H' + \tfrac{1}{8}H'' .$$

Solving the equation $\lambda^2 - \tfrac{1}{2}\lambda - \tfrac{1}{8} = 0$, we obtain its positive root $\lambda_1 = (1 + \sqrt{3})/4 = 0.683$. Hence, after a sufficiently large number of generations, the rate of decrease in H is $1 - 0.683 = 31.7$ per cent per "double generation" (i.e., a female generation from the preceding aunt to the next aunt in Fig. 53).

8. It should be noted that a recurrence relation can usually be written in various forms. Thus, (6) and (24) may also be written in the form shown in Exercise 2. If we write the recurrence relation of H in Exercise 7 as $\tfrac{1}{4}H' = \tfrac{1}{8}H'' + \tfrac{1}{32}H'''$, and subtract this from the original expression, we obtain another form:

$$H = \tfrac{3}{4}H' - \tfrac{1}{32}H''' .$$

Now, let $h = 1 - H$ be the proportion of homozygosis among the females. To obtain its recurrence relation, we merely write

$$(1 - h) = \tfrac{3}{4}(1 - h') - \tfrac{1}{32}(1 - h''')$$

or

$$h = \tfrac{3}{4}h' + \tfrac{1}{32}(9 - h''') .$$

This last expression is the result obtained by Kalmus and Smith (1948), using an entirely different method. The results of several other systems of inbreeding in bees are also given by Crow and Roberts (1950).

CHAPTER 15

Heterozygosis in Finite Groups

WE SHALL undertake here an analysis of the decrease of heterozygosis in a finite group of individuals, because it follows closely on what was demonstrated in the preceding chapter. Other properties of finite groups will be deferred until much later in the book. For this analysis let N be the number of mating individuals in a group and let the number N be a constant from generation to generation. Then we may begin by considering the results of the system of mating that breaks the entire population into isolates of a constant size N.

§ 1. *Maximum Avoidance of Inbreeding*

Continued octuple-third-cousin mating breaks the entire population into separate groups of size $N = 16 = 2^4$. Within each group inbreeding between cousins closer than octuple third cousins is excluded. In other words, all actual matings are between those with the remotest possible relation. The recurrence relation of H in this case is (Table 58)

$$H = (\tfrac{1}{2})H^{(1)} + (\tfrac{1}{2})^2 H^{(2)} + (\tfrac{1}{2})^3 H^{(3)} + (\tfrac{1}{2})^4 H^{(4)} + (\tfrac{1}{2})^5 H^{(5)} ,$$

writing $H^{(1)}$ for H', $H^{(2)}$ for H'', etc. Tracing one generation back and dividing by 2, we have

$$\tfrac{1}{2}H^{(1)} = (\tfrac{1}{2})^2 H^{(2)} + (\tfrac{1}{2})^3 H^{(3)} + (\tfrac{1}{2})^4 H^{(4)} + (\tfrac{1}{2})^5 H^{(5)} + (\tfrac{1}{2})^6 H^{(6)} .$$

Subtracting $\tfrac{1}{2}H^{(1)}$ from H, we obtain

$$H - \tfrac{1}{2}H^{(1)} = \tfrac{1}{2}H^{(1)} - (\tfrac{1}{2})^6 H^{(6)} ;$$

$$\therefore \quad H = H^{(1)} - (\tfrac{1}{2})^6 H^{(6)} .$$

When the recurrence relations of H are written in this latter form, the results of Table 58 may be rewritten in the form of Table 59. After a sufficiently large number of generations, the successive absolute values of H differ only slightly from each other, especially when N is moderately large. Hence,

$$H = \left(1 - \frac{1}{4N}\right) H' , \quad \text{approx.,} \tag{1}$$

indicating that H is decreasing at a rate of $1/4N$ per generation when close inbreeding is avoided within a group of N mating individuals. Therefore, it is the minimum rate of decrease in H for a finite group. If the N individuals mate entirely at random, the rate of "decay" of variability will be higher. This will be shown in the following.

§ 2. *Monoecious Diploids*

First, consider the simplest case of a group of N monoecious diploid individuals, whose gametes unite wholly at random in every generation, including even the possibility of self-fertilization. Now, the probability that a gamete should unite with a gamete from the same individual is $1/N$, and that from a

TABLE 59

ANOTHER FORM OF RECURRENCE RELATION OF H (SEE TABLE 58)

Size of Group	Value of H
$N=1$................	$H = H^{(1)} - (\frac{1}{2})^2 H^{(2)}$
$N=2$................	$H = H^{(1)} - (\frac{1}{2})^3 H^{(3)}$
$N=4=2^2$............	$H = H^{(1)} - (\frac{1}{2})^4 H^{(4)}$
$N=8=2^3$............	$H = H^{(1)} - (\frac{1}{2})^5 H^{(5)}$
$N=16=2^4$...........	$H = H^{(1)} - (\frac{1}{2})^6 H^{(6)}$
$\cdots$	$\cdots$
$N=2^k$..............	$H = H^{(1)} - (\frac{1}{2})^{2+k} H^{(2+k)} = H^{(1)} - \dfrac{1}{4N} H^{(2+k)}$

different individual is $(N-1)/N$. In the former case the correlation between mates is $m=1$; in the latter, $m = 4a'^2 b'^2 m'$ for two random individuals in the group (see [30], p. 201). The *average* value of m for the whole group is thus

$$m = \frac{1}{N} + \frac{N-1}{N}\, 4\,a'^2 b'^2 m' \; ;$$

$$\therefore F = b^2 m = \frac{1}{N}\, b^2 + \frac{N-1}{N}\, 4\,b^2 a'^2 b'^2 m' \, .$$

Simplifying by the familiar relations $ba' = \frac{1}{2}$, $b'^2 m' = F'$ and $b^2 = \frac{1}{2}(1 + F')$, we obtain (Wright, 1931, 1948, etc.)

$$F = \frac{1}{N}\, b^2 + \frac{N-1}{N}\, F' = \frac{1}{2N} + \frac{2N-1}{2N}\, F' \; ; \tag{2}$$

$$\therefore H = \frac{2N-1}{2N}\, H' = \left(1 - \frac{1}{2N}\right) H' \, . \tag{3}$$

This indicates that H is decreasing by $1/2N$ per generation, with complete random union of gametes within a group of N individuals. This rate is twice as high as in the case described in Section 1, in which inbreeding was specifically avoided.

For the case of complete random union of gametes (including the possibility of self-fertilization), the formula (3) is an exact one and applies to any value of N, whether large or small. For example, when $N = 4$, H will decrease by $\frac{1}{8} =$ 12.5 per cent generation if the individuals mate completely at random (including selfing) in contrast to the 8 per cent decrease per generation when all matings are confined to double first cousins (Chap. 14, § 5). It is interesting to note that formula (3) applies even to the most extreme case of continued selfing in which $N = 1$; then it gives a value of $\frac{1}{2}$ for loss of heterozygosis per generation, which is obviously correct. The rate $1/2N$ per generation for loss of heterozygosis also occurs in several other cases as approximations.

§ 3. *Group of* N_0 *Females and* N_1 *Males*

Now we pass on to the general case in which a group consists of N_0 female and N_1 male breeding individuals. (Memorization of these symbols is easier if one regards the subscript 0 as an abbreviation for the female sign, ♀, and the subscript 1 as an abbreviation for the male sign, ♂.) As before, we assume random mating among the $N_0 + N_1$ individuals; but selfing is clearly out of the question for dioecious organisms. Now, the probability that two random individuals should belong to the same sibship is $1/N_0 N_1$, and for mating between sibs $m = 2a'^2 b'^2 (1 + m')$. Similarly, the probability for half-sib matings is $(N_0 + N_1 - 2)/N_0 N_1$, with $m = a'^2 b'^2 (1 + 3m')$ according to (15) of the preceding chapter. The rest of the matings are between remote relatives with probability $(N_0 - 1)(N_1 - 1)/N_0 N_1$, and $m = 4a'^2 b'^2 m'$, from (30) of Chapter 14. Hence, the *average* value of m for the whole group is

$$m = a'^2 b'^2 \left\{ \frac{2 + 2m' + (N_0 + N_1 - 2)(1 + 3m') + (N_0 - 1)(N_1 - 1) 4m'}{N_0 N_1} \right\}$$

$$= a'^2 b'^2 \left\{ \frac{4 N_0 N_1 m' - (N_0 + N_1) m' + (N_0 + N_1)}{N_0 N_1} \right\}. \tag{4}$$

This is the key formula for m under random mating in a group of $N_0 + N_1$ individuals. The recurrence relation of F may be obtained in the usual manner, remembering that $b^2 a'^2 = \frac{1}{4}$, whatever the mating system, and that $b'^2 m' = F'$. Thus,

$$F = b^2 m = \frac{1}{4 N_0 N_1} \{ 4 N_0 N_1 F' - (N_0 + N_1) F' + (N_0 + N_1) b'^2 \}.$$

Substituting $b'^2 = \frac{1}{2}(1 + F'')$, we obtain

$$F = F' + \frac{N_0 + N_1}{8 N_0 N_1} (1 - 2F' + F''), \tag{5}$$

from which the recurrence relation of H may be found in the usual manner.

Since $H = H_0(1 - F)$, we have

$$H = H_0 \left\{ 1 - F' - \frac{N_0 + N_1}{8 N_0 N_1} (2 - 2F' - 1 + F'') \right\} ;$$

$$\therefore H = H' - \frac{N_0 + N_1}{8 N_0 N_1} (2H' - H'') , \tag{6}$$

indicating that H is decreasing in every generation.

After a sufficiently large number of generations, the value of H will be decreasing at approximately a constant proportion per generation. To find the constant ratio $H/H' = H'/H'' = \lambda$, we solve for the largest positive root of the equation

$$\lambda^2 - \left(1 - \frac{N_0 + N_1}{4 N_0 N_1} \right) \lambda - \frac{N_0 + N_1}{8 N_0 N_1} = 0 ;$$

$$\therefore \lambda = \frac{1}{2} \left(1 - \frac{N_0 + N_1}{4 N_0 N_1} \right) + \frac{1}{2} \sqrt{\left[1 + \left(\frac{N_0 + N_1}{4 N_0 N_1} \right)^2 \right]} . \tag{7}$$

Hence, H eventually will be decreasing at the rate of

$$1 - \lambda = \frac{1}{2} \left(1 + \frac{N_0 + N_1}{4 N_0 N_1} \right) - \frac{1}{2} \sqrt{\left[1 + \left(\frac{N_0 + N_1}{4 N_0 N_1} \right)^2 \right]} \tag{8}$$

per generation. The expressions (5), (6), (7), and (8) are exact and do not involve approximations; they apply to any values of N_0 and N_1, whether large or small. For example, brother-sister mating may be considered as random mating among a group of two individuals of whom one is female and one is male. Substituting $N_0 = N_1 = 1$, (5) reduces to $F = \frac{1}{4}(1 + 2F' + F'')$; (6) gives $H = \frac{1}{2}H' + \frac{1}{4}H''$; (7) becomes $\lambda = \frac{1}{4}(1 + \sqrt{5}) = 0.809$; and (8) shows that H decreases by $\frac{1}{4}(3 - \sqrt{5}) = 19.1$ per cent per generation after a number of generations, all agreeing with the results established previously.

§ 4. *Approximate Rate of Decrease in* H

The expression (8) is not convenient for general use. Even for moderate values of N_0 and N_1, the fraction $(N_0 + N_1)/4N_0N_1$ will be so small that we may write

$$\sqrt{\left[1 + \left(\frac{N_0 + N_1}{4 N_0 N_1} \right)^2 \right]} = 1 + \frac{1}{2} \left(\frac{N_0 + N_1}{4 N_0 N_1} \right)^2 , \quad \text{approx.}$$

Hence, the ultimate rate of decrease in H is approximately

$$1 - \lambda = \frac{N_0 + N_1}{8 N_0 N_1} - \frac{1}{4} \left(\frac{N_0 + N_1}{4 N_0 N_1} \right)^2 = \frac{N_0 + N_1}{8 N_0 N_1} - \left(\frac{N_0 + N_1}{8 N_0 N_1} \right)^2$$

$$= \frac{N_0 + N_1}{8 N_0 N_1} \left(1 - \frac{N_0 + N_1}{8 N_0 N_1} \right) = \left(\frac{1}{8 N_0} + \frac{1}{8 N_1} \right) \left(1 - \frac{1}{8 N_0} - \frac{1}{8 N_1} \right) . \tag{9}$$

To show how good this approximation is, consider the case in which $N_0 = 25$

and $N_1 = 10$, so that $(N_0 + N_1)/4N_0N_1 = 35/1000$. The exact formula (8) gives

$$\tfrac{1}{2}(1.035) - \tfrac{1}{2}\sqrt{[1 + (0.035)^2]} = 0.0172 ;$$

while, from (9), it is $0.0175(1 - 0.0175) = 0.0172$. The approximation formula (9) may also be applied when the number of individuals in one sex is much larger than that in the other sex. For example, in the system of mating in which one male is mated with an indefinite number of his half-sisters, we have $N_1 = 1$, $N_0 = \infty$. Substituting in (9), we find that the rate of decrease in H is

$$\tfrac{1}{8}(1 - \tfrac{1}{8}) = \tfrac{7}{64} = 11 \text{ per cent per generation },$$

in agreement with the result given in Chapter 14. Thus, we see that (9) is a very good approximation formula. For reasonably large populations the fraction $(N_0 + N_1)/4N_0N_1$ is so small in comparison to unity that (9) may be further simplified to

$$1 - \lambda = \frac{N_0 + N_1}{8 N_0 N_1} = \frac{1}{8 N_0} + \frac{1}{8 N_1}. \qquad (10)$$

Even for the small group in which $N_0 = 25$ and $N_1 = 10$, this approximation gives the decreasing rate as $1 - \lambda = 0.0175$, differing very little from its exact value.

It is also clear from the previous example and from (10) that, when one of the sexes is limited in number, while the other sex is very numerous, the final rate of decrease in H is largely determined by the lesser number of individuals, approximating $1/8N_0$ or $1/8N_1$, according to which sex is limited.

An approximate relation between λ and F, after a sufficiently large number of generations, should be pointed out here. Let F_n be the value of F in the nth generation. The proportion of heterozygosis is then $H_n = H_0(1 - F_n)$. But, when n is large, $H_n = H_0\lambda^n$, approximately. Hence, we obtain the relation

$$1 - F_n = \lambda^n .$$

As a numerical illustration we may turn to the results of continued sib mating tabulated on page 190 with $\lambda = 0.809$. Thus:

n	F_n	Approximation: $F_n = 1 - \lambda^n$
15......	0.9606	$1 - (0.809)^{15} = 0.9585$
20......	0.9863	$1 - (0.809)^{20} = 0.9856$

Also, when n is large,

$$\frac{H}{H'} = \frac{1 - F}{1 - F'} = \lambda .$$

Finally, it should be pointed out that the proportionate rate of decrease per generation in H, such as that given by (10), is not the same as the rate of increase in F. Let $\Delta H = H - H'$ and $\Delta F = F - F'$. Since H is proportional to $1 - F$ in any generation, we see that the *actual amount* of change per generation in these two quantities is proportional, viz., $-\Delta H \propto \Delta F$, but the *percentage change* per generation in H is

$$\frac{H' - H}{H} = \frac{-\Delta H}{H'} = \frac{\Delta F}{1 - F'},$$

which is a different ratio from $\Delta F/F'$, the percentage change in F.

§ 5. *An Important Special Case:* $N_0 = N_1$

The most important special case concerning heterozygosis in finite groups is that in which a group of N dioecious individuals is composed of females and males in equal number: $N_0 = N_1 = \frac{1}{2}N$. The results of random mating within such a group may be easily obtained from those of the previous case; but, because of their special importance and interest, they are given explicitly in the following. Note that the fraction $(N_0 + N_1)/8N_0N_1$ becomes $N/8(\frac{1}{2}N)(\frac{1}{2}N) = N/2N^2 = 1/2N$ in this case; thus,

$$F = F' + \frac{1}{2N}(1 - 2F' + F''); \tag{5'}$$

$$H = H' - \frac{1}{2N}(2H' - H''); \tag{6'}$$

$$\lambda = \frac{H}{H'} = \frac{1}{2}\left(1 - \frac{1}{N}\right) + \frac{1}{2}\sqrt{\left[1 + \left(\frac{1}{N}\right)^2\right]}; \tag{7'}$$

$$1 - \lambda = \frac{1}{2}\left(1 + \frac{1}{N}\right) - \frac{1}{2}\sqrt{\left[1 + \left(\frac{1}{N}\right)^2\right]}, \quad \text{exactly}, \tag{8'}$$

$$= \frac{1}{2N} - \frac{1}{4N^2}, \quad \text{approx. even for small } N, \tag{9'}$$

$$= \frac{1}{2N+1} \doteq \frac{1}{2N} \quad \text{for moderately large } N. \tag{10'}$$

This is a most important result in population genetics. The analysis shows that, under random mating within a group of N individuals, heterozygosis will fall off in each generation by approximately $1/2N$ of its previous value. The important conclusion is that eventually the group will reach complete homozygosis if there are no mutations, immigrants, etc. All the above results are due to Wright (1931). Recently, the result (10') has also been reached by Malécot (1944) and by Feller (1950) on a purely probabilistic basis.

If we write (10') in the form of a differential equation, when N is moderately large, we have

$$\frac{dH}{dt} = \frac{-1}{2N}H, \quad \text{or} \quad \frac{dH}{H} = \frac{-1}{2N}dt,$$

where t denotes time measured in units of generations. Integrating, we obtain

$$\log H = \frac{-t}{2N} + \text{const. or } H_t = H_0 e^{-t/2N},$$

where H_0 is the initial proportion of heterozygosis and H_t is that after t generations of random mating within the group. This formula enables us to calculate the value of H at any given time. When $t \to \infty$, $H_t \to 0$, as stated before.

§ 6. *Some Other Cases*

The results of continued random mating within a finite group have also been worked out for many other cases by Wright (summary in 1951). Full details for each case cannot be given here; but the following are a few examples of the type of results obtained.

1. When a group consists of N monoecious individuals mating at random *except for self-fertilization* (unlike the case of § 2), it should be intuitively clear that the situation is equivalent to that of a group of N dioecious individuals with equal numbers of males and females mating at random (case of § 5). A demonstration showing that this is actually the case is given in Exercise 5.

2. In all the previous cases it has been assumed, for the sake of simplicity, that each locus consists of only two alleles. When multiple alleles are present, the complete loss of a gene no longer implies homozygosis of the locus. But the number of alleles in a locus will decrease as time goes on (owing to the process of random extinction of genes); and in time the number of alleles will be reduced to two. From then on, H will decrease at the rate given in the previous sections, until finally only one allele is present for each locus (complete homozygosis).

3. Another important special case is that for sex-linked genes. The recurrence relation and the ultimate rate of decrease in H among the homogametic sex (which we take as female here) within a finite group has been given by Wright (1933a):

$$H = H' - \frac{N_0 + 1}{8 N_0} (2H' - H'') + \frac{(N_0 - 1)(N_1 - 1)}{8 N_0 N_1} (2H'' - H'''), \quad (11)$$

where N_0 is the number of breeding females and N_1 the number of males. Putting $H/H' = H'/H'' = H''/H'''$, or solving the λ-equation, we obtain the percentage decrease per generation as approximately

$$\frac{H' - H}{H'} = \frac{N_0 + 2 N_1}{9 N_0 N_1} = \frac{2}{9 N_0} + \frac{1}{9 N_1}. \quad (12)$$

In particular, when the numbers of females and males are equal ($N_0 = N_1 = \frac{1}{2}N$), this rate reduces to $2/3N$, which is always greater than $1/2N$ for autosomal genes.

4. The effects of inbreeding on autopolyploids (or on autopolysomic loci) are usually more mathematically involved; and so far we have considered only the

results of selfing tetraploids (Chap. 9). The following results by Wright (1938b, 1951) show the type of generalization obtained by the method of path coefficients. The general formula for a group of N individuals is omitted, and only the simplest cases are cited. Now, when $N = 1$, corresponding to exclusive self-fertilization, the ultimate ratio between two successive values of H after a sufficiently large number of generations is, for $2k$-somic loci,

$$H = \frac{4k-3}{4k-2} H';$$

thus:

Diploid $(k=1)$, $H = \frac{1}{2}H'$	Tetraploid $(k=2)$, $H = \frac{5}{6}H'$
Hexaploid $(k=3)$, $H = \frac{9}{10}H'$	Octoploid $(k=4)$, $H = \frac{13}{14}H'$

When $N = 2$ and self-fertilization is excluded, a situation corresponding to continued sib mating,

$$H = H' - \frac{1}{4(2k-1)} (2H' - H'').$$

Thus:

	$H =$ (Exactly)	$H = \lambda H'$, Approx.
Diploid............	$\frac{1}{2}H' + \frac{1}{4}H''$	$\frac{1}{4}(1 + \sqrt{5})H' = 0.80902H'$
Tetraploid........	$\frac{5}{6}H' + \frac{1}{12}H''$	$\frac{1}{12}(5 + \sqrt{37})H' = .92356H'$
Hexaploid........	$\frac{9}{10}H' + \frac{1}{20}H''$	$\frac{1}{20}(9 + \sqrt{101})H' = .95249H'$
Octoploid.........	$\frac{13}{14}H' + \frac{1}{28}H''$	$\frac{1}{28}(13 + \sqrt{197})H' = 0.96556H'$

The above results for tetraploids and hexaploids in cases of selfing agree with those arrived at by Haldane (1930); and the result for tetraploid sib mating is the same as that given by Bartlett and Haldane (1934) and by Fisher (1949).

In closing this chapter, it may be well to reiterate one point about which the reader should be very clear. From the above analysis it might be thought that the loss of heterozygosis in a finite breeding group is due to the occasional close inbreeding that occurs by chance in random mating. This, however, is not the case. As was shown in the first section, even with maximum avoidance of inbreeding within each generation, H continues to decrease, though at a slower rate (approximately half the rate of that for random mating). The decrease of H is a property of the *limited size* of the breeding group. Another approach to the problems of finite breeding groups will be discussed later (Chap. 22).

Notes and Exercises

1. In a group of $N = 2^k$ individuals with maximum avoidance of inbreeding, the ultimate ratio of two successive values of H will be given by the largest

positive root (close to unity) of the equation

$$\lambda^{k+1} - (\tfrac{1}{2})\lambda^k - (\tfrac{1}{2})^2\lambda^{k-1} - \ldots - (\tfrac{1}{2})^k\lambda - (\tfrac{1}{2})^{k+1} = 0 .$$

The terms, except the first, form a geometric series. This fact simplifies the equation to the form

$$\lambda^{k+2} - \lambda^{k+1} + (\tfrac{1}{2})^{k+2} = 0 ,$$

which is also evident from the new recurrence form listed in Table 59. Now, we write

$$\lambda^{k+1} (1 - \lambda) = (\tfrac{1}{2})^{k+2} = \frac{1}{4N} .$$

A rough solution is to take λ^{k+1} as unity, yielding $1 - \lambda = 1/4N$ as the percentage decrease in H per generation. If N is not large, a better approximation may be obtained by putting $\lambda = 1 - \epsilon$, where ϵ is a small positive fraction; thus, we have approximately

$$(1 - \epsilon)^{k+1}\epsilon = [1 - (k + 1)\epsilon]\epsilon = (\tfrac{1}{2})^{k+2} .$$

Solving the quadratic equation in ϵ, we obtain

$$\epsilon = \frac{2^k - \sqrt{[2^{2k} - 2^k (k+1)]}}{2^{k+1} (k + 1)} = \frac{N - N\sqrt{[1 - (k+1)/N]}}{2N (k + 1)} .$$

For example, when $N = 16$, $k = 4$; the above solution gives

$$\epsilon = \frac{4 - \sqrt{11}}{40} = 0.017 , \qquad \text{so that} \qquad \lambda = 0.983 ,$$

in agreement with the value given on page 198. When N is large, and the fraction $(k + 1)/N$ is so small that $\sqrt{[1 - (k + 1)/N]}$ may be written as $1 - (k + 1)/2N$, the above expression yields $\epsilon = 1/4N$, as before.

2. Find the recurrence relation of H and its ultimate rate of decrease in a random-mating group consisting of (i) 60 females and 20 males; (ii) 50 females and 30 males; (iii) 40 of each sex.

3. If the number of females is three times that of males in a finite random-mating group, show that

$$\frac{1}{8 N_0} + \frac{1}{8 N_1} = \frac{1}{2 N_0} .$$

This indicates that this group is equivalent to one of size N_0 in which half are females and half males as far as the effect on H is concerned. What are the corresponding values when $N_0 = 7N_1$?

4. In a group of size N, equally divided between males and females, the λ-equation derived from (6') may be written as

$$2N\lambda^2 - 2(N - 1)\lambda - 1 = 0 .$$

Show that

$$\lambda = \frac{H}{H'} = \frac{(N-1) + \sqrt{(N^2+1)}}{2N}, \qquad \text{exactly.} \quad (7')$$

Find a corresponding expression for $1 - \lambda = (H' - H)/H'$.

5. In a group of N monoecious individuals mating at random, but with self-fertilization prevented, the possibilities of different types of mating and their values of m are as follows:

Mating	Full Sibs	Half-Sibs	Remote Relatives
Probability....	$\dfrac{2}{N(N-1)}$	$\dfrac{4(N-2)}{N(N-1)}$	$\dfrac{(N-2)(N-3)}{N(N-1)}$
m............	$2a'^2b'^2(1+m')$	$a'^2b'^2(1+3m')$	$a'^2b'^2 \cdot 4m'$

Therefore, the *average* value of m for the whole group is

$$m = 4a'^2b'^2 \left\{ \frac{(1+m') + (N-2)(1+3m') + (N-2)(N-3)m'}{N(N-1)} \right\}$$

$$= 4a'^2b'^2 \left\{ \frac{1}{N} + \frac{N-1}{N} m' \right\}.$$

$$F = b^2m = \frac{1}{N} b'^2 + \frac{N+1}{N} F' \qquad (5'')$$

$$= \frac{1}{2N} \{ 1 + 2(N-1)F' + F'' \}. \qquad \text{i.e.,} \quad (5')$$

Hence, its corresponding H is the same as $(6')$, etc. In other words, this group is equivalent to one of N dioecious individuals with equal numbers of each sex. Note that the only way in which $(5'')$ differs from (2) is in having b' in place of b.

6. For the simplest model of complete random union of gametes, including the possibility of self-fertilization, the recurrence relation of $F(2)$ may be obtained directly from the following considerations: Let the N monoecious individuals produce $2N$ gametes. The probability that a gamete should unite with another gamete from the same parental individual is $1/2N$, in which case $F = 1$. For the remaining $(2N - 1)/2N$ of the cases the uniting gametes are from different individuals, and therefore their correlation is F', the same as that in the previous generation. Hence,

$$F = \frac{1}{2N} + \frac{2N-1}{2N} F'. \qquad \text{i.e.,} \quad (2)$$

For dioecious organisms with equal numbers of each sex, the situation should be approximately the same, although the small chance of selfing is excluded.

Hence, we expect that the eventual rate of percentage decrease in H is also $1/2N$ per generation, as demonstrated in the text.

7. Show that for tetraploid sib mating the larger root of the equation

$$\lambda^2 - \tfrac{5}{6}\lambda - \tfrac{1}{12} = 0$$

is $(5 + \sqrt{37})/12 = 0.92356$.

8. Show that, when $N_0 = 7N_1$ in a moderately large group, the rates of decrease in H for autosomal and sex-linked genes are approximately equal.
HINT: Equate (10) to (12).

CHAPTER 16

Irregular Pedigrees of Inbreeding

THE application of the method of path coefficients to irregular pedigrees of inbreeding, such as those in livestock, will be illustrated in this chapter. To begin with, we know that, if some sort of consanguineous mating has been practiced for several generations, the resulting individuals will have accumulated a certain amount of inbreeding. To indicate this amount, we need a numerical index. And for ready use of the index we frame it in a convenient language that makes necessary a few definitions.

§ 1. *Definitions*

Coefficient of inbreeding of an individual.—Let g and g' be two gametes which will unite to produce an individual Z. So far, F has been defined as the correlation between g and g' to measure the degree of inbreeding. Wright (1922a) has conveniently defined F also as the coefficient of inbreeding *of the individual Z* that resulted from the union of g and g'. Symbolically this definition may be represented by

$$F_{gg'} = F_Z, \quad \text{where } g + g' = Z. \tag{1}$$

As a matter of fact, this was the symbol adopted in Figure 34. Thus, we speak of F_X as the inbreeding coefficient of the individual X instead of as the correlation between the two uniting gametes that produced the zygote X. This change in definition is a matter of convenience of language, not an invention of a new measurement of inbreeding.

Coefficient of relationship between two individuals.—Two individuals are correlated only when they have one or more common ancestors. In the language of the theory of path coefficients, common ancestors are the "common causes" of two effects which, in the present case, are two related individuals. To measure the closeness between two individuals (say, B and C), Wright (1922a) defined the "coefficient of relationship" between two individuals as the correlation coefficient between them. The latter is the sum of the coefficients of all paths connecting them; that is,

$$R_{BC} = \sum_i [p_{B \cdot A_i} p_{C \cdot A_i}], \tag{2}$$

219

where A_i is a common ancestor through whom B and C are connected, $p_{B \cdot A_i}$ is the (compound) path coefficient from the common ancestor A_i to individual B, and the summation is over all independent connecting chains for all common ancestors. There may be more than one connecting chain through one common ancestor. When A_i is a remote ancestor of B and C, the paths from A_i to B and C will each consist of several "links" (generations). Note that the correlation (2) exists whether B and C are mates or not, so long as they have at least one common ancestor.

§ 2. *Path from an Ancestor to Offspring*

In order to find general expressions for (i) coefficient of inbreeding of an individual and (ii) coefficient of relationship between two relatives, we must find the compound path from an ancestor to his descendant. Figure 54 is such

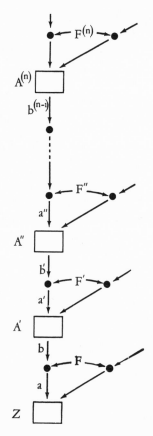

FIG. 54.—Path from an ancestor to his nth-generation descendant. By definition, $F = F_Z$, $F' = F_{A'}, \ldots, F^n = F_{A^{(n)}}$.

a path. According to definition (1), $F = F_Z$, $F' = F_{A'}$, $F'' = F_{A''}$, etc., where A' is the parent of the individual Z, A'' the grandparent, etc. In general, $F^{(n)} = F_{A^{(n)}}$, where $A^{(n)}$ is the nth-generation ancestor of Z, the individual under consideration. If the ancestor $A^{(n)}$ has not been inbred (i.e., his parents are two uncorrelated individuals), $F^{(n)} = 0$. The values of F, F', F'', etc., in the various generations depend upon what relationship the parents have in each generation.

Now, the path coefficient from parent A' to Z is (Fig. 54)

$$p_{Z \cdot A'} = b\,a = \frac{1}{2} \sqrt{\frac{1+F'}{1+F}} = \frac{1}{2} \sqrt{\frac{1+F_{A'}}{1+F_Z}}.$$

From the theorem on chain of factors, the path from grandparent A'' to Z is

$$p_{Z \cdot A''} = p_{Z \cdot A'} p_{A' \cdot A''} = \frac{1}{2} \sqrt{\frac{1+F_{A'}}{1+F_Z}} \cdot \frac{1}{2} \sqrt{\frac{1+F_{A''}}{1+F_{A'}}} = \left(\frac{1}{2}\right)^2 \sqrt{\frac{1+F_{A''}}{1+F_Z}}.$$

In general, the path coefficient pertaining to a given line of descent from an nth-generation ancestor $A^{(n)}$ to Z is

$$p_{Z \cdot A^{(n)}} = \left(\frac{1}{2}\right)^n \sqrt{\frac{1+F_{A^{(n)}}}{1+F_Z}}. \tag{3}$$

If the individual $A^{(n)}$ has not been inbred, $F_{A^{(n)}} = 0$, as mentioned before. If all the parents along the line of descent in Figure 54 are random individuals, all $F = 0$; and, in particular, $F_Z = 0$, in which case the expression (3) reduces simply to $(\frac{1}{2})^n$.

§ 3. General Formulas

Suppose that the two individuals B and C (upper part of Fig. 55) are all descendants of an ancestor A and that A and B are n generations apart and A and C are n' generations apart. Then the connecting chain between B and C, through their common ancestor A, is $p_{B \cdot A} p_{C \cdot A}$, assuming that there is only one independent path through A. The values of $p_{B \cdot A}$ and $p_{C \cdot A}$ may be found from (3); thus, this connecting chain has a value of

$$\left(\frac{1}{2}\right)^n \sqrt{\frac{1+F_A}{1+F_B}} \cdot \left(\frac{1}{2}\right)^{n'} \sqrt{\frac{1+F_A}{1+F_C}} = \left(\frac{1}{2}\right)^{n+n'} \frac{(1+F_A)}{\sqrt{[(1+F_B)(1+F_C)]}}.$$

If B and C have other common ancestors, and thus other connecting chains, the total correlation between B and C, defined as the coefficient of relationship here, is the sum of all connecting chains through all common ancestors; thus

$$R_{BC} = \frac{\Sigma \left[(\frac{1}{2})^{n+n'} (1+F_A)\right]}{\sqrt{[(1+F_B)(1+F_C)]}}, \tag{4}$$

where the summation is over all connecting chains for all A's. This is a general formula for *relationship* between any two individuals having common ancestors. The values of F_B and F_C are constants for these two individuals, and they need not be equal. Also, as remarked before, B and C need not be mates to have this relationship, although we are frequently interested in the relationship of two mates.

Now we are in a position to find the coefficient of inbreeding of any individual with a given pedigree. Consider an individual Z whose parents are related by R_{BC} (lower portion of Fig. 55). It will be recalled (Chap. 13, § 9) that, if two parents have different inbreeding backgrounds or belong to different generations, the path coefficients from these parents to their gametes will not be equal for both parents. By the general relation $b = \sqrt{[\frac{1}{2}(1 + F')]}$, we see that

$$b_B = \sqrt{[\tfrac{1}{2}(1 + F_B)]}, \quad b_C = \sqrt{[\tfrac{1}{2}(1 + F_C)]}.$$

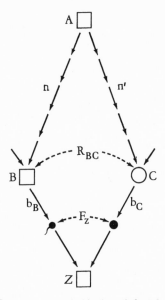

FIG. 55.—Relationship between two individuals and the inbreeding of their offspring

And the correlation between the uniting gametes that form the individual Z is the required inbreeding coefficient of Z:

$$F_Z = b_B R_{BC} b_C = \tfrac{1}{2} R_{BC} \sqrt{[(1 + F_B)(1 + F_C)]}. \tag{5}$$

This form expresses the inbreeding coefficient of an individual in terms of those of his parents. It is, however, usually more convenient to express F_Z directly in terms of common ancestors of his parents in a given pedigree. Substituting (4) in (5), we obtain immediately

$$F_Z = \tfrac{1}{2} \Sigma [(\tfrac{1}{2})^{n+n'}(1 + F_A)], \tag{6}$$

which is the most convenient form for numerical calculation. If A has been inbred himself, his F_A must be calculated from his pedigree separately. If all common ancestors are random individuals, (6) reduces to $F_Z = \frac{1}{2}\Sigma(\frac{1}{2})^{n+n'}$. Note that F_Z is equal to half the numerator of R_{BC}.

§ 4. *An Illustration of a Simple Pedigree*

Before we take up the more complicated pedigrees in the next section, it might be well first to examine a very simple pedigree with only one common an-

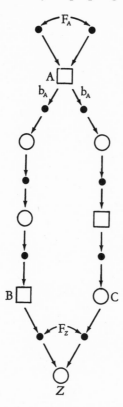

FIG. 56.—Simple pedigree with one common ancestor and one connecting chain

cestor and one connecting chain (Fig. 56). Since B and C are each three generations removed from the common ancestor A, the inbreeding coefficient of Z is thus, from (6),

$$F_Z = \frac{1}{2}\cdot(\frac{1}{2})^{3+3}(1 + F_A) = (\frac{1}{2})^7(1 + F_A).$$

Note that $n + n' + 1 = N$ is the number of zygotes in a connecting path, including both parents of Z. Thus, there are seven zygotes along the connecting path in Figure 56. For this reason the expression (6) is sometimes also written as

$$F_Z = \Sigma[(\frac{1}{2})^N(1 + F_A)], \tag{6'}$$

where $N = n + n' + 1$. It is important to recognize the various forms of the same formula given on different occasions and to remember the meaning of the symbols in each case. In review, we should recall again that N stands for the *number of zygotes* along a given chain of connection (both parents included), while n and n' are the *numbers of generations* between the common ancestor and the *two parents*. The simple pedigree of Figure 56 will help in clarifying and memorizing these meanings and relations.

The expressions for the inbreeding coefficient may also be directly derived from a consideration of "gametic generations." Again, we shall use Figure 56 for this purpose. Since F_Z is the correlation between the two gametes that unite to produce Z, we may start tracing the connecting chain from these two gametes. Since each gametic generation has a path value $ba' = b'a'' = \frac{1}{2}$, the compound path from each of them to a gamete produced by the common ancestor A is $(\frac{1}{2})^3$. Now, let b_A be the path coefficient from A to his gametes, then $b_A^2 = \frac{1}{2}(1 + F_A)$. Hence, the total chain linking the two gametes that produce Z is

$$F_Z = (\tfrac{1}{2})^3 \cdot b_A^2 \cdot (\tfrac{1}{2})^3 = (\tfrac{1}{2})^7 (1 + F_A) ,$$

as before. The expressions (6) or (6') may be deduced in exactly the same manner without obtaining the expression (4) for R_{BC}.

§ 5. *Two Examples of Livestock Pedigrees*

1. Let us consider the pedigree of Roan Gauntlet, a famous Shorthorn sire (individual Z in Fig. 57). This bull traces back in every line to a mating of Champion of England (A_2) with a daughter or granddaughter of Lord Raglan (A_1). Hence, A_1 and A_2 are the two common ancestors of the parents of Z. For the present purpose we will assume that the common ancestors themselves had not been inbred and that they are not related to each other; that is, $F_{A_1} = F_{A_2} = 0$, and $R_{A_1 A_2} = 0$. There are two connecting chains through each common parent so that there are four independent chains linking the two parents B and C. They are as shown in Table 60. The inbreeding coefficient of an individual thus obtained from an actual pedigree may be compared with that of any regular system of inbreeding. For example, the value of $F_Z = 0.14$ here is much lower than that of brother-sister mating, where $F = 0.25, 0.375, 0.50,$ $\ldots$, or parent-offspring mating, where $F = 0.25, 0.375, 0.4375, \ldots$, for the first, second, third, $\ldots$, generations, respectively (Chap. 14, Table 57 and § 3, 1).

2. As a second example, let us consider the pedigree of the Shorthorn bull Comet as given in Figure 58. The individuals B and C, as parents of Z, are connected by three chains, one through each common ancestor (A_1, A_2, A_3). But the sire B of Comet (Z) is also the sire of the dam C, so that B and C are also connected by the direct path BC, in addition to the three paths through their common ancestors. We shall evaluate the latter three first, assuming that the

A's have not been inbred before ($F_{A_i} = 0$ for all i):

$$A_1: (\tfrac{1}{2})^{1+1} ; \qquad A_2: (\tfrac{1}{2})^{2+2} ; \qquad A_3: (\tfrac{1}{2})^{3+2} .$$

But the direct path BC is not merely $(\tfrac{1}{2})^{0+1}$, because the sire B (as a common ancestor) was himself inbred to a certain extent; thus it is necessary to know the inbreeding coefficient of B to evaluate the path BC.

Regarding Figure 58 as the pedigree of B (ignoring the individuals C and Z), we see that *his* two parents, K and A_1, are connected by two chains, one through

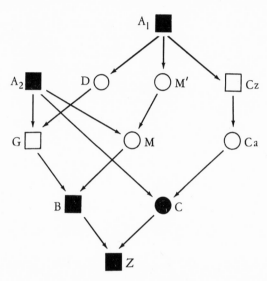

FIG. 57.—Pedigree of Roan Gauntlet (Z). Sire and Dam: B (bull) = Royal Duke of Gloster, C (cow) = Princess Royal. Common ancestors: A_1 = Lord Raglan, A_2 = Champion of England. Other individuals: G = Grand Duke of Gloster, D = Duchess of Gloster IX; M' = Mistletoe; M = Mimulus; Cz = The Czar; Ca = Carmine.

TABLE 60

CALCULATION OF INBREEDING COEFFICIENT OF Z IN FIG. 57

Common Ancestor	Connecting Individuals	Chain between B and C $(\tfrac{1}{2})^{n+n'}$
A_1.........	$\begin{cases} M, M' \text{ and } Cz, Ca \\ G, D \text{ and } Cz, Ca \end{cases}$	$(\tfrac{1}{2})^{3+3} = 0.015625$ $(\tfrac{1}{2})^{3+3} = 0.015625$
A_2.........	$\begin{cases} \quad G \\ \quad M \end{cases}$	$(\tfrac{1}{2})^{2+1} = 0.125000$ $(\tfrac{1}{2})^{2+1} = 0.125000$
$F_A = 0$ in (6),		$\Sigma(\tfrac{1}{2})^{n+n'} = 0.281250$ $F_Z = \tfrac{1}{2}\Sigma(\tfrac{1}{2})^{n+n'} = 0.140625$

A_2 and one through A_3. Hence, his inbreeding coefficient is

$$F_B = \tfrac{1}{2}[(\tfrac{1}{2})^{1+1} + (\tfrac{1}{2})^{2+1}] = 0.1875 \,,$$

and the value of the direct path BC is

$$(\tfrac{1}{2})^{0+1}(1 + F_B) = \tfrac{1}{2}(1.1875) \,.$$

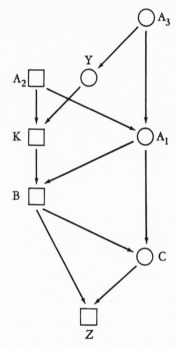

FIG. 58.—Pedigree of Shorthorn bull Comet (Z). Sire and Dam: B = Favorite-252, C = Young Phoenix. Common ancestors: A_1 = Phoenix, A_2 = Foljambe, A_3 = Favorite Cow. Others: Y = Young Strawberry, K = Bolingbroke.

The inbreeding coefficient of Comet Z is, from (6),

$$F_Z = \tfrac{1}{2}[(\tfrac{1}{2})^2 + (\tfrac{1}{2})^4 + (\tfrac{1}{2})^5 + \tfrac{1}{2}(1.1875)] = 0.4687 \,.$$

The inbreeding pedigree of Comet is thus equal to four generations of parent-offspring mating ($F = \tfrac{15}{32}$, p. 192) or nearly equal to three generations of brother-sister mating ($F = 0.50$).

When a pedigree is too large and complicated, the amount of work in tracing all connecting chains may be prohibitive. Wright and McPhee (1925) have suggested a method of taking a single random line back of sire and dam. The lines either show a common ancestor or do not. The inbreeding coefficient may be estimated from the proportion of lines that lead to a common ancestor. Some systematic procedures for calculating inbreeding coefficients have been given by Emik and Terrill (1949).

§ 6. *Inbreeding Coefficient for Sex-linked Genes*

All the above formulas apply only to diploid autosomal loci. For sex-linked genes several modifications are necessary. First of all, since males are haploids, there is no inbreeding coefficient for males. Therefore, if a common ancestor A is a male, we always take $F_A = 0$, whatever his pedigree.

Second, since the constitution of males is completely determined by that of their mothers' eggs, and completely determines that of their own gametes, it follows that the sex-linked genes of a male's sperm are the same as those of his mother's egg. Therefore, in tracing any given path, one may omit a male individual from a connecting chain as if he were not there and only count the number of females (n_0). Hence,

$$F = \Sigma[(\tfrac{1}{2})^{n_0}(1 + F_A)].$$

In applying the above formula, a third rule is necessary: When there are two (or more) males in succession along a line of descent, it is no longer a connecting chain, because the constitution of the male offspring, being determined by his mother, has nothing to do with his male parent. The father-son correlation is zero for sex-linked inheritance, as noted before. Hence, a chain "breaks" when two males appear in succession. The application of these three modifications for sex-linked genes is illustrated in Figure 59. The extension of this method to polysomic loci may be found in Wright (1951).

§ 7. *Consanguineous Matings and Rare Traits*

In a random-mating population the coefficient of relationship between two relatives is simply, from (4),

$$R = \Sigma(\tfrac{1}{2})^{n+n'},$$

and this is the value we reached in Chapter 13. In consanguineous mating, if the parents are relatives with a coefficient of relationship R_{PP}, and they have not been inbred before (that is, they have no common ancestor), the resulting child O will have an inbreeding coefficient (from [5] or [6])

$$F_O = \tfrac{1}{2}R_{PP} = \tfrac{1}{2}\Sigma(\tfrac{1}{2})^{n+n'}. \tag{7}$$

For example, the coefficient of relationship for single first cousins (in a random-mating population) is $R = (\tfrac{1}{2})^4 + (\tfrac{1}{2})^4 = \tfrac{1}{8}$. Hence, the inbreeding coefficient of the child from first-cousin marriages is $F = \tfrac{1}{16}$ (Table 61).

Rare recessive traits.—We recall that this F is the correlation between uniting gametes which produced the child. Therefore, among the offspring of a given type of consanguineous mating (F fixed), the proportion of recessives will be

$$q^2 + Fpq = Fq + (1 - F)q^2, \tag{8}$$

where q is the frequency of the recessive gene in the population. When q is small, the value of the expression (8) is much higher than q^2 (see Table 38). Thus, when $q = 0.01$, $q^2 = 0.0001$ recessives among the offspring of unrelated individuals; but among first-cousin marriages there will be $\frac{1}{16}(0.01) + \frac{15}{16}(0.01)^2 = 0.0007$ recessive children (Chap. 11).

Single-first-cousin marriages are the only important class of close consanguineous matings in human communities. If their incidence in a population

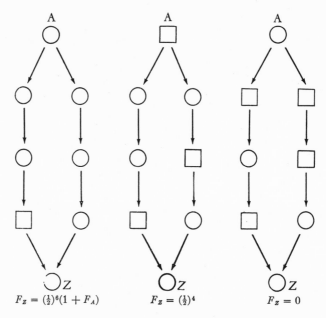

$$F_Z = (\tfrac{1}{2})^6(1 + F_A) \qquad\qquad F_Z = (\tfrac{1}{2})^4 \qquad\qquad F_Z = 0$$

FIG. 59.—Inbreeding coefficient for sex-linked genes. (Wright, 1951.) The corresponding value for autosomal genes is $F_Z = (\tfrac{1}{2})^7(1 + F_A)$ in all three cases (see Fig. 56).

TABLE 61

INBREEDING COEFFICIENTS AND THE PROPORTION OF RECESSIVES
OF THE OFFSPRING OF SOME CLOSE CONSANGUINEOUS MATINGS

Relationship of Parents		F of Resulting Child	Proportion of Recessives among Offspring
Unrelated individuals	$R=0$	$F=0$	q^2
Brother-sister (or parent-child)	$R=\frac{1}{2}$	$F=\frac{1}{4}$	$\frac{1}{4}q+\frac{3}{4}q^2$
Uncle-niece Half-sibs Double first cousins	$R=\frac{1}{4}$	$F=\frac{1}{8}$	$\frac{1}{8}q+\frac{7}{8}q^2$
Single first cousins	$R=\frac{1}{8}$	$F=\frac{1}{16}$	$\frac{1}{16}q+\frac{15}{16}q^2$
Second cousins	$R=\frac{1}{32}$	$F=\frac{1}{64}$	$\frac{1}{64}q+\frac{63}{64}q^2$

is c, the rest $(1 - c)$ being random mating, the proportion of recessives born to first-cousin marriages among the total recessives in the general population is (Dahlberg, 1948a, p. 61)

$$k = \frac{c\left(\frac{1}{16}q + \frac{15}{16}q^2\right)}{(1 - c)\,q^2 + c\left(\frac{1}{16}q + \frac{15}{16}q^2\right)} = \frac{c\,(1 + 15\,q)}{16\,q + c\,(1 - q)}. \tag{9}$$

For instance, if $q = 0.01$ as before, and $c = 0.02$ of all matings in the population, the fraction (9) comes out 0.128; in other words, 12.8 per cent of the recessives of the entire population are derived from first-cousin marriages.

Since we have used $F = \frac{1}{16}$ for first-cousin marriages, we shall use another symbol, Φ, to denote the inbreeding coefficient of the population as a whole with c first-cousin matings. Equating

$$(1 - \Phi)\,q^2 + \Phi q = (1 - c)\,q^2 + c\left(\frac{1}{16}q + \frac{15}{16}q^2\right),$$

we obtain

$$\Phi = \frac{c}{16}, \tag{10}$$

which is independent of the gene frequencies. Thus, if there are 2 per cent first-cousin marriages in a population, the inbreeding coefficient of the entire population is 0.00125.

In any set of observed data (a random collection of recessive individuals) the value of k, the proportion of recessives born to first-cousin marriages among all the recessives, may be directly estimated. If the percentage of first-cousin marriages in the whole population has been estimated from a general survey, then the expression (9) may be rewritten as

$$q = \frac{c\,(1 - k)}{16\,k - 15\,c - ck}, \tag{9Q}$$

expressing the recessive gene frequency in terms of the two proportions, c and k.

Rare dominant traits.—In the foregoing we have seen that the incidence of rare recessive traits is much higher among consanguineous matings. For rare dominant traits, however, this is not the case. They will not appear in greater frequency through consanguineous matings. Since only a single gene is required to produce a dominant trait, the probability of any relative (unilineal or bilineal) being affected is equal to the coefficient of relationship between that relative and the affected individual. Thus, examining the relatives of affected individuals, we expect the dominant trait to appear in $\frac{1}{2}$ of their parents, children, and sibs; $\frac{1}{4}$ of their grandparents, grandchildren, aunts, nephews, etc.; $\frac{1}{8}$ of their first cousins; and so on. It should be emphasized that this is true only if the dominant gene is very rare in the population and the gene always expresses itself when present. In actuality, however, many of the known dominant pathological genes of man are "provisional," "irregular," or incomplete in their penetrance or expression.

Notes and Exercises

1. The path coefficient from an nth-generation ancestor to an individual (expression [3]) need not be obtained from the zygotic generations. It may be more directly obtained by using the fact that for each gametic generation $a'b = a''b' = \ldots = \frac{1}{2}$, whatever the mating. Along the line of n generations from $A^{(n)}$ to Z (Fig. 54), there are $(n-1)$ gametic generations, plus the two paths a and $b^{(n-1)}$, at each end of the line. Hence,

$$p_{Z \cdot A^{(n)}} = a \cdot (\tfrac{1}{2})^{n-1} \cdot b^{(n-1)}$$

$$= \sqrt{\frac{1}{2(1+F_Z)}} \cdot (\tfrac{1}{2})^{n-1} \cdot \sqrt{[\tfrac{1}{2}(1+F_{A^{(n)}})]} ,$$

which reduces to (3) immediately.

2. Find the inbreeding coefficients of B and C in Figures 57 and 58 and then calculate the coefficients of relationship between B and C, using formula (4) and assuming $F_A = 0$ for all A's in the pedigree.

3. Having obtained the values of F_B, F_C, and R_{BC} for the pedigrees shown in Figures 57 and 58, show that formulas (5) and (6) give the same value of F_Z.

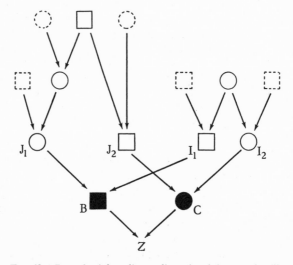

FIG. 60.—Irregular inbreeding pedigree involving two families

4. Find the inbreeding coefficient of the offspring of B and C in the pedigree in Figure 60 (in which the dotted individuals are unnecessary for the calculation).

ANS.: B and C are connected by two chains: one through the J-family with five links, and another through the I-family with four links. Therefore, $F_Z = \frac{1}{2}\{(\tfrac{1}{2})^5 + (\tfrac{1}{2})^4\} = \frac{3}{64} = 0.047$.

5. Find the inbreeding coefficient of Z in the pedigree in Figure 61, assuming that the two common ancestors A_1 and A_2 had not been inbred before.

ANS.: B and C are connected by four chains: through J_1A_1, J_1A_2, J_2A_1, J_2A_2, each with six links. Therefore, $F_Z = \frac{1}{2}r_{BC} = \frac{1}{2}\{4(\frac{1}{2})^6\} = \frac{1}{32} = 0.03125$.

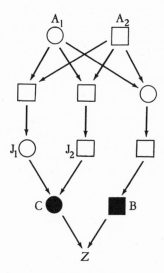

FIG. 61.—Inbreeding pedigree originated from one family

6. *Inbreeding coefficient of a breed.*—If we take random lines of ancestry back of the sires and dams of a number of animals chosen at random from a breed, and I is the proportion of cases in which the pairs of lines lead to a common ancestor, we may take $F = \frac{1}{2}I(1 + \overline{F}_A)$ as the inbreeding coefficient of the breed as a whole, where $\overline{F}_A$ is the average inbreeding coefficient of common ancestors.

7. In modern human societies matings between close relatives are fairly rare. Certain types of close inbreeding are forbidden by law. The children of full brothers, being first cousins but bearing the same family name, are referred to also as "brothers and sisters" in the Chinese language and are accepted as such in Chinese society. Marriage between them is of course out of the question. But the children of full sisters or of a brother and a sister, bearing different family names, may marry each other. Even *paternal second* cousins with the same surname are not allowed to marry in China.

In England the marriage of double first cousins is perfectly legal, that of uncle and niece illegal but not criminal, and that of half-brother and half-sister criminal. Genetically speaking, however, these three kinds of relationships are equally close, each with a coefficient of relationship of $R = \frac{1}{4}$.

CHAPTER 17

Phenotypic Assortative Mating

WE HAVE already examined the results of inbreeding based on the relationship of mates. Now we shall consider briefly the results of mating based on phenotypic resemblance of the mating individuals. Before we proceed with the analysis, it may be helpful to review some of the properties of a harmonic series.

§ 1. *Harmonic Series*

A harmonic series is one whose successive terms are the reciprocals of those of an arithmetic series. Thus,

$$u_0 = \frac{C}{b}, \qquad u_1 = \frac{C}{b+K}, \qquad u_2 = \frac{C}{b+2K}, \ldots, u_n = \frac{C}{b+nK} \qquad (1)$$

is a harmonic series, where C, b, and K are all constants and $n = 0, 1, 2, 3, \ldots$. Writing bu_0 for C, the general term of (1) may be expressed in terms of u_0. Thus, on multiplying both numerator and denominator of u_n by u_0, we obtain

$$u_n = \frac{Cu_0}{bu_0 + nKu_0} = \frac{Cu_0}{C+nKu_0}, \qquad (2)$$

by which the nth term of a harmonic series may be written down when its first term is given and the constants C and K are specified. Noting that $b + nK = C/u_n$ and that

$$u_{n+1} = \frac{C}{b+(n+1)K} = \frac{C}{b+nK+K} = \frac{C}{C/u_n + K},$$

we immediately obtain the recurrence relation between two successive terms of the series (1):

$$u_{n+1} = \frac{Cu_n}{C+Ku_n}. \qquad (3)$$

This is also known as the "sequence equation" of a harmonic series.

§ 2. *Complete Positive Assortative Mating*

Suppose that the given population is $(r, 2s, t)$, where $r + 2s + t = 1$, and that the gene A is completely dominant over a. If all matings are between individuals of the same phenotype; that is, if dominants mate only with dominants and recessives mate only with recessives, the total frequency of the former kind of mating will be $r + 2s = 1 - t$, while that of the latter is simply t among all matings. The frequencies of matings and their corresponding offspring are given in Table 62. The frequencies of the three genotypic matings of the type Dom $\times$ Dom are proportional to the terms of $(r + 2s)^2 = r^2 + 4rs + 4s^2$.

The first thing to be noticed in Table 62 is that there is no change in gene frequency under positive phenotypic assortative mating. In the parental popu-

TABLE 62

COMPLETE POSITIVE ASSORTATIVE MATING

MATING	FREQUENCY	OFFSPRING		
		AA	Aa	aa
$AA \times AA$	$\dfrac{r^2}{1-t}$	$\dfrac{r^2}{1-t}$	....	....
$AA \times Aa$	$\dfrac{4rs}{1-t}$	$\dfrac{2rs}{1-t}$	$\dfrac{2rs}{1-t}$	....
$Aa \times Aa$	$\dfrac{4s^2}{1-t}$	$\dfrac{s^2}{1-t}$	$\dfrac{2s^2}{1-t}$	$\dfrac{s^2}{1-t}$
$aa \times aa$	t	....	....	t
Total.......	1.00	$\dfrac{(r+s)^2}{1-t}$	$\dfrac{2s(r+s)}{1-t}$	$\dfrac{s^2}{1-t} + t$

lation the frequency of the gene A is $p_n = r + s$, while in the offspring population it is

$$p_{n+1} = \frac{(r + s)^2}{1 - t} + \frac{s(r + s)}{1 - t} = \frac{(r + s)(r + 2s)}{1 - t} = r + s = p_n.$$

The genotypic proportions in the population have, however, changed considerably. As usual, let H denote the proportion of heterozygotes in a population. Then, $H_n = 2s$, and

$$H_{n+1} = \frac{2s(r + s)}{1 - t} = \frac{(r + s) H_n}{r + s + s}.$$

Multiplying both numerator and denominator by 2, and remembering that $r + s = p$ and $2s = H_n$, we obtain

$$H_{n+1} = \frac{2p H_n}{2p + H_n}, \tag{4}$$

which is the recurrence relation of H under complete positive phenotypic assortative mating. The expression (4) is of the same form as the sequence equation (3) of a harmonic series for which $K = 1$ and $C = 2p$. Here the recurrence relation of H is *not* independent of gene frequencies. In this respect it is unlike the linear recurrence relation of H for inbreeding based on relationship. Being a harmonic series, the general expression for H_n after n generations of continued assortative mating is thus, from (2),

$$H_n = \frac{2pH_0}{2p + nH_0}. \tag{5}$$

Since p and H_0 are constants, the limiting value of H_n is clearly zero, as n increases indefinitely. But, generally speaking, the rate of decrease in H is much slower here than in close inbreeding, especially after the first few generations.

If the initial population is panmictic, we have $H_0 = 2pq$; the sequence equation (4) remains unchanged, but the expression for its general term (5) becomes

$$H_n = \frac{H_0}{1 + nq}. \tag{6}$$

The value of H decreases more rapidly when q is large than when it is small.

§ 3. *Complete Negative Assortative Mating*

If individuals of the same phenotype do not mate, and all matings are between dominants and recessives, there will be only two kinds of initial crosses, namely,

$$aa \times AA \quad \text{and} \quad aa \times Aa .$$

It is clear that there will be no homozygous dominants in the next generation. Therefore all matings in subsequent generations will necessarily be $aa \times Aa$ and will yield equal numbers of aa and Aa offspring. Hence, the equilibrium condition

$$(0, \tfrac{1}{2}, \tfrac{1}{2})$$

is reached immediately, whatever the original composition of the population. This result appears to furnish a satisfactory explanation of distylic hetero-

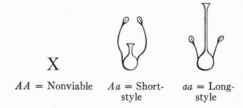

X

AA = Nonviable Aa = Short- aa = Long-
                                     style   style

FIG. 62.—Distylic heteromorphism in flowering plants

morphism in many flowering plants (Linaceae, Primulaceae, Plumbaginaceae, Boraginaceae, Scrophulariaceae, Rubiaceae, etc.). The length of style appears to be controlled by one pair of genes, short-styles being dominant over long ones, while the homozygous short-styles are probably nonviable (Fig. 62). Short-styles receive the pollen of long-styled flowers, and long-styles receive the pollen of short-styled flowers, under natural conditions. There is hardly any self-fertilization or crossing between flowers of the same phenotype. Hence, the two kinds of plants are equally numerous in natural populations.

Negative phenotypic assortative mating is what actually occurs in all bisexual populations as far as sex determination is concerned. If we identify the gene a with the X-chromosome and the gene A with the Y-chromosome in the above discussion, we see that all crosses in the population are of the type $XX \times XY$; hence, the equilibrium condition of the population consists of equal proportions of XX and XY individuals. Sex dimorphism may thus be regarded as a form of complete negative phenotypic assortative mating in equilibrium condition.

§ 4. *Incomplete Negative Assortative Mating*

In the discussion of complete negative assortative mating it was shown that the equilibrium conditions are independent of the initial composition of the population. It can be shown also that this is a general property of *negative* assortative mating—complete or incomplete. In respect to this property negative assortative mating is somewhat similar to the case of self-sterility alleles described in Chapter 7.

Consider an arbitrary population consisting of D dominants and R recessives $(D + R = 1)$. If mating were at random, the frequencies of Dom $\times$ Dom, Dom $\times$ Rec, and Rec $\times$ Rec matings would be D^2, $2DR$, R^2, respectively. Using these as the "standard" values, let w be the proportion of deficiency in matings of the same phenotype, as compared with random-mating frequencies. Then the mating frequencies in the population will be

Dom$\times$Dom	Dom$\times$Rec	Rec$\times$Rec	
$D^2(1 - w)$	$2DR(1 - w) + w$	$R^2(1 - w)$.	(7)

In order to calculate the offspring generation under this mating system, we further suppose that among the dominants there are d homozygotes and h heterozygotes $(d + h = D)$ and that the matings within the dominant group are at random. That is to say, the genotypic mating frequencies within the dominant group are in the proportions d^2, $2dh$, h^2. The offspring of the $(1 - w)(D^2 + 2DR + R^2)$ matings may be obtained immediately from the law of random mating (see Table 3). The offspring of the extra w matings of unlike phenotypes are as follows:

$$\frac{d}{D} w (AA \times aa) \to \frac{d}{D} w \{ Aa \}$$

$$\frac{h}{D} w (Aa \times aa) \to \frac{h}{2D} w \{ Aa \} + \frac{h}{2D} w \{ aa \} .$$

Since $p = d + \frac{1}{2}h$ and $q = \frac{1}{2}h + R$, the offspring generation will consist of

AA	Aa	aa	
$p^2 (1 - w)$	$2pq (1 - w) + \dfrac{p}{D} w$	$q^2 (1 - w) + \dfrac{h}{2D} w$;	(8)

so that the new frequency of the gene A becomes

$$p' = p^2 (1-w) + pq (1-w) + \frac{pw}{2D} = p \left\{ 1 - w + \frac{w}{2D} \right\}. \qquad (9)$$

The last two expressions show that under negative assortative mating genotypic proportions as well as gene frequencies change from generation to generation. However, we note from (9) that, when $D = \frac{1}{2}$, $p' = p$, *whatever the value of w*. That this is a stable equilibrium condition may be seen from the fact that, when $D > \frac{1}{2}$, p decreases and that, when $D < \frac{1}{2}$, p increases. The equilibrium values of d and h may be found from the further condition that

$$R = q^2 (1-w) + \frac{hw}{2D} = (\tfrac{1}{2}h + R)^2 (1-w) + \frac{hw}{2D}.$$

TABLE 63

EQUILIBRIUM CONDITIONS OF A POPULATION PRACTICING
NEGATIVE ASSORTATIVE MATING

The first column lists the values of w, the proportion of deficiency in matings of like pheno-types (in comparison with random-mating frequencies). At equilibrium $-w$ is the correlation coefficient between mating phenotypes. These equilibrium conditions are independent of the initial composition of the population.

w	GENOTYPIC PROPORTIONS			MATING FREQUENCIES		
	AA	Aa	aa	Dom×Dom	Dom×Rec	Rec×Rec
0.10........	0.0742	0.4258	0.5000	0.225	0.550	0.225
0.30........	.0536	.4464	.5000	.175	.650	.175
0.50........	.0359	.4641	.5000	.125	.750	.125
0.70........	.0203	.4797	.5000	.075	.850	.075
0.90........	0.0064	.4936	.5000	0.025	0.950	0.025
1.00*.......	0	0.5000	0.5000	0	1.000	0

* See Exercise 6.

Substituting $D = R = \frac{1}{2}$, the equation becomes

$$\tfrac{1}{2} = (\tfrac{1}{2}h + \tfrac{1}{2})^2 (1-w) + hw.$$

Solving, we obtain

$$h = \frac{-(1+w) + \sqrt{[2(1+w)]}}{1-w} \qquad (10)$$

and $d = \frac{1}{2} - h$. The genotypic proportions of the equilibrium population for various values of w are given in Table 63. The most significant conclusion from the preceding analysis is that dominants and recessives will occur in equal proportions even when the negative assortative mating is far from complete.

The phenotypic mating frequencies at equilibrium are

Dom×Dom	Dom×Rec	Rec×Rec	
$\frac{1}{4}(1-w)$	$\frac{1}{2}(1+w)$	$\frac{1}{4}(1-w)$.	(7e)

The values of (7e) are also given in Table 63. The two types of mating between individuals of the same phenotype are equal in frequency for all degrees of negative assortativeness. The correlation coefficient between mating phenotypes is $-w$ in an equilibrium population (Ex. 7).

§ 5. *Some General Remarks*

A general treatment of the properties of assortative mating based on phenotypic resemblance is too involved to be given here, and the student must consult Wright (1921*b*) for details. The following general conclusions, however, should be intuitively clear.

1. Complete positive assortative mating should lead to complete homozygosis of a population, though very slowly. But under natural conditions it is seldom complete. With imperfect assortative mating, the population will eventually reach an equilibrium condition with a certain proportion of heterozygosis. In fact, the degree of fixation of types is usually rather small, even with a moderate degree of assortativeness (see also Ex. 9).

2. Assortative mating based on external resemblance may lead to a population with a genetic composition very different from that reached by inbreeding based on relationship. For example, for a metric character dependent on two pairs of genes with additive and equal effects (Chap. 8, Ex. 5), complete assortative mating within each of the five phenotypes would ultimately lead to a population consisting only of the two extreme types: *AABB* and *aabb;* while continued close inbreeding would lead to fixation of all four homozygous types: *AABB, AAbb, aaBB, aabb.*

3. If a system of close inbreeding is combined with the additional restriction of phenotypic assortative mating, the rate at which characters can be fixed in a population will be much increased. As a matter of fact, in many animal-breeding practices, the breeder does use, for one reason or another, a combination of several systems of inbreeding and phenotypic assortative mating (plus selection).

Notes and Exercises

1. Show that under complete positive assortative mating

$$\Delta H_n = H_{n+1} - H_n = \frac{-H_n^2}{2p + H_n},$$

indicating that H is decreasing every generation.

2. Find the sequence equation and the general expression for H_n for populations in which $p = q = \frac{1}{2}$, all matings being between individuals of the same phenotype. Calculate the first six values of H for the initial population (.30, .40, .30). Check your answers with (4) and (5).

3. If an initial population consists of only heterozygous dominant individuals and if perfect positive phenotypic assortative mating is practiced, what will be the zygotic proportions in the subsequent generations?

HINT: $H_0 = 1$; $\therefore$ $p = \frac{1}{2}$ and $H_n = 1/(1 + n)$.

ANS.: H: $1, \frac{1}{2}, \frac{1}{3}, \frac{1}{4}, \frac{1}{5}, \ldots, 1/n$. The decrease is very slow after the first few generations.

4. Given the two initial populations, (.10, .40, .50) and (.50, .40, .10), calculate their values of H for the next six generations, assuming all matings are between individuals of the same phenotype. Which series of H is decreasing faster?

n	0	1	2	3	4	5	6
$H_n = \dfrac{0.24}{0.6 + 0.4n}$	0.4000	0.2400	0.1714	0.1333	0.1091	0.0923	0.0800
$H_n = \dfrac{0.56}{1.4 + 0.4n}$	0.4000	0.3111	0.2545	0.2154	0.1867	0.1647	0.1474

5. Perform the same calculations as in Exercise 4 with the initial populations (.09, .42, .49) and (.49, .42, .09).

HINT: Use (6).

6. On substituting $w = 1$ in (10), we obtain $h = 0/0$, which, known as an "indeterminate form" of a ratio, tells us nothing about the limiting value of h as $w \to 1$. To obtain the limiting value of h, we take the derivatives (with respect to w) of the numerator and denominator of (10) separately and then substitute $w = 1$ in the new ratio of derivatives. Thus,

$$d_1 = \frac{d}{dw} \text{ (numerator)} = -1 + \frac{\sqrt{2}}{2\sqrt{(1 + w)}} = -1 + \tfrac{1}{2},$$

$$d_2 = \frac{d}{dw} \text{ (denominator)} = -1;$$

$$\therefore \text{ Lim. } h \text{ (as } w \to 1) = \frac{d_1}{d_2} = 1 - \tfrac{1}{2} = 0.5000.$$

7. The correlation coefficient (m) between mating phenotypes may be calculated from the following table, in which the value 1 stands for dominants and 0 for recessives. Show that $m = -w$.

Mates	1	0	Total
1..........	$\frac{1}{4}(1 - w)$	$\frac{1}{4}(1 + w)$	$\frac{1}{2}$
0..........	$\frac{1}{4}(1 + w)$	$\frac{1}{4}(1 - w)$	$\frac{1}{2}$
Total...	$\frac{1}{2}$	$\frac{1}{2}$	1

8. The approach to equilibrium is rapid, even with only a moderate degree of negative assortative mating. Of course, the greater the value of w, the greater the rate of approach to equilibrium. The accompanying tabulation is a numerical illustration of the process for an arbitrary initial population (.10, .60, .30), taking $w = 0.90$ for the sake of brevity. The genotypic proportions of the successive generations (n) are obtained by repeated application of formula (8). The student should make a similar calculation, employing a different value of w (e.g., $w = .70$) and/or using a different initial population.

n	d	h	R	D	p	q
0.	0.1000	0.6000	0.3000	0.7000	0.4000	0.6000
1.	.0160	.5623	.4217	.5783	.2971	.7029
2.	.0088	.5042	.4870	.5130	.2609	.7391
3.	.0068	.4963	.4969	.5031	.2550	.7450
4.	.0065	.4941	.4994	.5006	.2535	.7465
5.	.0064	.4937	.4999	.5001	.2533	.7467
6.	0.0064	0.4936	0.5000	0.5000	0.2532	0.7468

9. If the phenotypes of AA, Aa, aa are all different, and the mating is incompletely positive assortative, but the degree of correlation between mates (m) remains the same in each generation, the population will soon reach an equilibrium state. Let the mating frequencies and offspring proportions be as follows, where k is a positive fraction, $p = D + \frac{1}{2}H$, $q = R + \frac{1}{2}H$, and $D + H + R = 1$.

OFFSPRING

Mates	AA	Aa	aa		Parent	AA	Aa	aa	
AA	D^2+k	DH	$DR-k$	D	AA	$Dp+k$	$Dq-k$	0	D
Aa	DH	H^2	HR	H	Aa	$\frac{1}{2}Hp$	$\frac{1}{2}H$	$\frac{1}{2}Hq$	H
aa	$DR-k$	HR	R^2+k	R	aa	0	$Rp-k$	$Rq+k$	R
	D	H	R	1		p^2+k	$2pq-2k$	q^2+k	1

Hence, at equilibrium,

$$D = p^2 + k, \quad H = 2pq - 2k, \quad R = q^2 + k.$$

Thus we see that the results of this type of incomplete positive assortative mating are equivalent to those of inbreeding, with $k = Fpq$. Verify:

$$m = \frac{2k}{pq+k} = \frac{2F}{1+F};$$

$$r_{PO} = \frac{pq+3k}{2pq+2k} = \frac{1}{2}(1+m).$$

Stanton (1946) gives the values of m and r_{PO} in successive generations, assuming an initial panmictic population.

CHAPTER 18

Gene Mutations

GENE mutations, the naturally occurring sudden and spontaneous changes that take place in genes from time to time, are the ultimate source of new alleles and thus of genetic variability. The "new" mutations we observe today must have occurred in nature many, many times before, since we have good reasons to believe that the same gene mutations are constantly arising anew. Any change that occurs consistently in every generation over a long period of time should gradually change the gene frequencies in a population. The effects of such changes in gene frequency are independent of the mating system (though the proportions of mutant genotypes is not, as will be pointed out later).

Mutations tend to increase the hereditary variation of a population, but there is no evidence of *direct* adaptation in the mutation process. The direction of mutation seems at random and is unpredictable. Mutations and new gene combinations merely provide the raw material for natural selection to work upon. The origin of hereditary variations is a part, and only a part, of the mechanism of evolution. The "origin of species" is a different and a much more complicated problem. For a full discussion of this subject the reader should consult Dobzhansky's *Genetics and the Origin of Species* (1951).

What will be said here about gene mutations applies as well to the various kinds of chromosomal aberrations which also arise spontaneously at a finite rate in nature. If multiple alleles are present at a locus, we may still apply the same approach by concentrating our attention on a particular mutant allele and regarding the rest as one allele.

§ 1. *A Single Mutation*

Let us first investigate the fate of a single mutation in a population consisting wholly of AA individuals. Suppose that one of the A genes mutates to a new allele a; then there will be one Aa individual—and only one—in the whole population. This heterozygote must mate with an AA individual, assuming bisexual reproduction. If this mating leaves no offspring, the new allele a will be lost in the next generation; and the characteristics of aa, beneficial or deleterious, will remain unknown. If the mating yields just one offspring, the probability that this offspring will be AA is $\frac{1}{2}$, which is thus also the probability that the new allele will be lost from the population. Even if the offspring is Aa, there will still be only one a allele in the next generation. If the mating yields *two* offspring, the probability of a's being lost is $\frac{1}{4}$, because the probability of having two AA offspring is $\frac{1}{4}$. On the other hand, the chance that the number of a's should be increased from one to two is also $\frac{1}{4}$. This consideration extends to any number of offspring they may have. The important point is that the new allele may increase or decrease in frequency or be lost from the population by pure chance.

Let k be the number of offspring produced by the mating $AA \times Aa$. The probability that the new allele a will be absent among their k offspring is $(\frac{1}{2})^k$.

TABLE 64

PROBABILITY OF LOSING A NEW MUTATION IN ONE GENERA-
TION AFTER ITS OCCURRENCE

	No. of Offspring in Family, k						
	0	1	2	3	...	k	...
Frequency of family with k offspring, p_k.......	e^{-2}	$2e^{-2}$	$\frac{2^2}{2!}e^{-2}$	$\frac{2^3}{3!}e^{-2}$	...	$\frac{2^k}{k!}e^{-2}$	...
Probability of losing a, L_k	1	$\frac{1}{2}$	$(\frac{1}{2})^2$	$(\frac{1}{2})^3$	...	$(\frac{1}{2})^k$	...

To calculate the total probability that a will be lost in the next generation, we need to know the distribution of k (i.e., the frequencies with which the mating would produce $k = 0, 1, 2, 3, \ldots$, offspring). In the absence of other assumptions, it is convenient and approximately correct to take the distribution of k as a Poisson series (Fisher, 1930a, 1939). Ignoring the problem of increase in the absolute size of a population, we further assume that the average number of offspring per family is $\bar{k} = 2$; so that the population size remains constant. The frequency of families having k offspring is then $p_k = e^{-2}2^k/k!$ (Table 64).

The total probability that the mutant gene a will be lost in the first generation after its occurrence is thus (Table 64)

$$l_1 = \sum_k p_k L_k$$

$$= e^{-2}\left\{1 + 1 + \frac{1}{2!} + \frac{1}{3!} + \ldots + \frac{1}{k!} + \ldots\right\}$$

$$= e^{-2}\{e\} = e^{-1} = 0.3679 , \tag{1}$$

which is roughly $\frac{3}{8}$. If it is not lost in the first generation, it will again be exposed to the same kind of risk of being lost in the second generation. Now, in the first generation, there is only $1 - 0.3679 = 0.6321$ of the new allele left, so to speak. Hence, the probability that it will be lost in two generations after its occurrence is

$$l_2 = e^{-(1-0.3679)} = e^{-0.6321} = 0.5315 .$$

(A proof of this method of calculation is given in Ex. 3.) We see that if there are 100 new mutations in a generation, more than half of them, or 53 per cent, will be lost among their descendants in just two generations after their occurrence.

Similarly, if a new mutant gene survives the first two generations, it will again be exposed to the same kind of risk of being lost in the third generation.

TABLE 65

PROBABILITIES OF EXTINCTION (l) OF A
SINGLE MUTANT GENE
(Based on Fisher, 1930a)

GENERATION n	No SELECTIVE ADVANTAGE		1 PER CENT ADVANTAGE	
	l_n	$1-l_n$	l_n	$1-l_n$
1..........	0.3679	0.6321	0.3642	0.6358
2..........	.5315	.4685	.5262	.4738
3..........	.6259	.3741	.6197	.3803
4..........	.6879	.3121	.6811	.3189
5..........	.7319	.2681	.7246	.2754
6..........	.7649	.2351	.7572	.2428
7..........	.7905	.2095	.7825	.2175
.				
15..........	.8873	.1127	.8783	.1217
31..........	.9411	.0589	.9313	.0687
63..........	.9698	.0302	.9591	.0409
127..........	0.9847	.0153	.9729	.0271
.				
Limit.........	1.0000	0.0000	0.9803	0.0197

The probability that it should be lost within three generations after its occurrence is

$$l_3 = e^{-(1-0.5315)} = e^{-0.4685} = 0.6259 .$$

By this process of calculation, Fisher (1930a) tabulated the probabilities of extinction (l_n) and survival ($1 - l_n$) of a single mutant gene for up to 127 generations (Table 65). Examination of the table will show that, in 15 generations, 88.7 per cent, or nearly $\frac{8}{9}$, will have failed to survive the fate of chance extinction. The limiting value of the extinction probability l_n is unity. We are here concerned only with "neutral" genes which are neither beneficial nor harmful to the individual carrying them. A discussion of advantageous mutations (right-hand half of Table 65) is postponed until we are ready to examine the effects of selection (Chap. 20, § 6).

Since the loss of a new mutation is an irreversible process, most mutant genes never become established in a population. The great majority of them are lost within a few generations after their occurrence, even though some of them may be favorable to individuals either in heterozygous or in homozygous conditions. Only a few "lucky" ones become established in natural populations.

§ 2. *Recurrent Mutation Pressure*

It is true that most mutations are lost, due to chance, within a few generations after their occurrence; but mutations arise anew in every generation. This is the main reason why so many mutations have established themselves in populations. The rate of mutation per generation varies with different loci, some mutating more frequently than others. For a particular locus, however, the rate seems to remain reasonably constant from generation to generation under constant environmental conditions. Since mutation rates can be greatly accelerated by high temperatures, X-rays and other short rays, various kinds of chemicals, etc., we have reason to believe that the rates vary with environmental conditions. Throughout the following passages, however, we shall assume that the environment is uniform and that mutation rates remain constant from generation to generation.

Let the "type gene" be A and the mutant a; and let μ be the mutation rate from A to a per generation. If the frequency of gene A in a population is p_n in one generation, and μ of them mutate to a, then the frequency of a in the next generation will be increased by the amount μp_n. Thus,

$$q_{n+1} = q_n + \mu p_n = q_n + \mu(1 - q_n)$$
$$= \mu + (1 - \mu)q_n . \tag{2}$$

This may be regarded as the sequence equation of the q_n series. The expression for its general term is readily found by repeated substitutions of the values of $q_{n-1}, q_{n-2}, \ldots$. Thus, from (2),

$$q_n = \mu + (1 - \mu)\{\mu + (1 - \mu)q_{n-2}\}$$
$$= \mu + (1 - \mu)\mu + (1 - \mu)^2 q_{n-2}$$
$$= \ldots$$
$$= \mu + (1 - \mu)\mu + (1 - \mu)^2\mu + \ldots + (1 - \mu)^n q_0 .$$

The n terms of the above expression (excluding the last term) form a geometric progression with common ratio $(1 - \mu)$. The sum of these n terms is $1 - (1 - \mu)^n$. Hence, the general expression for q_n may be written

$$q_n = 1 - (1 - \mu)^n + (1 - \mu)^n q_0 = 1 - (1 - \mu)^n (1 - q_0)$$

or

$$(1 - \mu)^n = \frac{1 - q_n}{1 - q_0} = \frac{p_n}{p_0} . \tag{3}$$

When the initial gene frequency q_0 and the mutation rate μ are specified, we may calculate the gene frequency after a given number of generations or, conversely, calculate the number of generations required for the gene frequency to rise to a given level.

Since μ is a small quantity, usually of the order of 10^{-5} or 10^{-6}, the expression (3) for large n may be written, for all practical purposes, as

$$q_n = 1 - (1 - q_0) e^{-n\mu}$$

or

$$e^{-n\mu} = \frac{1 - q_n}{1 - q_0}.$$

$$(3')$$

When q_0 and q_n are given, the number of generations needed to effect such a change is easily calculated from the last expression by using (natural) logarithms. For example, the number of generations needed for $q_0 = 0.10$ to increase to $q_n = 0.20$ will be given by

$$- n\mu = \log_e \left(\tfrac{8}{9}\right)$$

or

$$n\mu = \log_e \left(\tfrac{9}{8}\right) = \log_e 1.125 = 0.1178 .$$

The number n is inversely proportional to the rate μ. If $\mu = 10^{-4}$, it would take 1178 generations to effect such a change in gene frequency; if $\mu = 10^{-5}$, it would take 11,780 generations.

The limiting value of q_n is clearly unity, as $e^{-n\mu} \rightarrow 0$ when n increases indefinitely. So we must conclude that, if the mutation from A to a is not opposed by some countermeasure, all the genes in the population will eventually be a, although it may take a great number of generations to effect such a complete change.

The amount of increment in q per generation is

$$\Delta q_n = q_{n+1} - q_n = \mu(1 - q_n) . \tag{4}$$

This increment is larger when A genes are abundant (q small) than when they are rare (q large) in the population. Thus, if $q_0 = 0.80$ is increased to $q_n = 0.90$, $n\mu = \log_e 2 = 0.69315$ instead of 0.1178, although the absolute amount of change in q is the same in both cases.

§ 3. Compensation by Reverse Mutation

All alleles mutate. But, when an allele is rare, its mutation to other alleles is hardly detectable because of the generally low rate of mutation. As an allele becomes fairly common in a population, the mutations both to and from it have to be taken into consideration. Let μ be the mutation rate from A to a and ν be the reverse rate (from a to A). Then the *net* amount of change in the frequency of a per generation is

$$\Delta q = \mu p \text{ (gain)} - \nu q \text{ (loss)} . \tag{5}$$

The increase or decrease of q depends upon the relative magnitude of its gain or loss per generation. Suppose that at a given stage its gain is greater than its loss, so that q increases. As q increases, however, its loss, vq, will also increase, so that eventually the amount of loss per generation will balance the gain. When this equilibrium point is reached, there will be no further change in q in subsequent generations. Putting $\Delta q = 0$ or $\mu p = vq$ in (5), and solving for values of p and q, we have

$$\hat{q} = \frac{\mu}{\mu + v}, \qquad \hat{p} = \frac{v}{\mu + v}, \qquad (6)$$

where the "hat" ($\wedge$) denotes the equilibrium value. A graphic representation of this situation is given in Figure 63. For example, if $\mu = 0.00003$ and $v =$

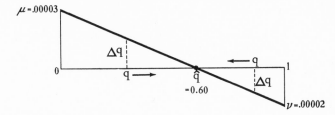

Fig. 63.—Equilibrium between opposing mutations. The vertical scales of μ and v are greatly exaggerated to show their effects. Note that Δq is positive when $q < \hat{q}$, and negative when $q > \hat{q}$. (Wright, 1940a, in Huxley.)

0.00002, then $\hat{q} = \frac{3}{5} = 0.60$ and $\hat{p} = \frac{2}{5} = 0.40$; and the gain or loss through opposing mutations is each equal to $0.0003 \times 0.40 = 0.00002 \times 0.60 = 12 \times 10^{-6}$, so that there will be no change in q in the next generation.

Since μ and v are constants, this equilibrium (6) is a stable one. The equilibrium value of q is independent of the initial gene frequencies of the population and is entirely determined by the relative magnitudes of the two opposing rates of mutation. If q of any generation is higher than $\hat{q}$, it will decrease from generation to generation until the point $\hat{q}$ is reached. Conversely, if it is lower than $\hat{q}$, it will gradually increase up to the equilibrium point. Should the value of q depart from $\hat{q}$ for any reason, it will come back gradually to $\hat{q}$ when the cause for departure ceases to operate. The rate of approach to equilibrium is of course very slow, depending only upon the excess of mutation in one direction over that in the opposite direction.

When the actual q is different from $\hat{q}$, the amount of change in q per generation, as given by (5), may be expressed in terms of the deviation $(q - \hat{q})$. Thus, writing $\mu = (\mu + v)\hat{q}$ according to (6), we have

$$\Delta q = \mu(1 - q) - vq = \mu - \mu q - vq$$

$$= (\mu + v)\hat{q} - (\mu + v)q = -(\mu + v)(q - \hat{q}). \qquad (7)$$

This expression brings out the fact that the rate of approach to equilibrium is proportional to the deviation of the actual q from its equilibrium value.

At this stage it may be well to introduce a method, widely used in population genetics, for calculating the number of generations required to effect a specified change in gene frequency. Since Δq is a small quantity, we may treat (7) as a differential equation by replacing Δq by dq/dt, where t denotes time in units of generations. Thus, (7) becomes

$$\frac{dq}{dt} = - (\mu + \nu)(q - \hat{q}) ; \qquad \frac{dq}{q - \hat{q}} = - (\mu + \nu) \, dt .$$

Integrating both sides over a period of n generations,

$$\int_{q_0}^{q_n} \frac{dq}{q - \hat{q}} = - (\mu + \nu) \int_0^n dt$$

$$\log_e \left(\frac{q_n - \hat{q}}{q_0 - \hat{q}} \right) = - (\mu + \nu) \, n$$

or

$$(\mu + \nu) \, n = \log_e \left(\frac{q_0 - \hat{q}}{q_n - \hat{q}} \right). \tag{8}$$

For example, when $\mu = 0.00003$, $\nu = 0.00002$, and $\hat{q} = 0.60$, the number of generations needed to raise $q_0 = 0.10$ to $q_n = 0.20$ will be given by

$$(0.00005) \, n = \log_e \frac{0.1 - 0.6}{0.2 - 0.6} = \log_e 1.25 = 0.22314 .$$

$$\therefore n = 4463 \text{ generations} .$$

Note the similarity of (8) to the logarithmic form of (3'). The method of integrating a differential equation will again be employed in connection with selection problems in the next chapter.

§ 4. *Mutant Genotype in a Population*

The above analysis of gene frequencies is independent of the mating systems, but the proportion of mutant genotypes is not. Let a be the mutant gene with a frequency q in the population. In the initial stages, when q is very small, a random-mating population consists of $2pq \doteq 2q$ heterozygotes; and the proportion of aa genotypes is negligible, so that nearly all the mutant genes are in heterozygous combinations. Even when q becomes as large as 0.001, the ratio of heterozygous to homozygous mutants is still approximately 2000:1 in the population. Only when q is much larger does the proportion of mutant genotypes become appreciable at all.

In a self-fertilizing pure line (all AA, say), a new mutation would give rise to a heterozygous individual. The mutation rate, μ $(A \rightarrow a)$, is the probability that in any given generation a given gamete of a homozygote will carry a mutated gene. Hence, the probability that a homozygous diploid individual will become a heterozygote through the mutation of one of the two alleles is 2μ in any generation. Since the proportion of heterozygotes in a selfing population is halved in each generation, and at the same time μ new mutations arise in every generation, the proportion of heterozygotes due to mutation pressure in such a "pure line" is (Haldane, 1936)

$$2\mu\{1 + \tfrac{1}{2} + (\tfrac{1}{2})^2 + (\tfrac{1}{2})^3 + \ldots\} = 4\mu .$$

If a diploid population practices brother-sister mating, there will be two individuals (4 genes) involved in each mating; and the probability that a cross will involve one heterozygous individual is thus 4μ. Therefore the proportion of heterozygotes in a sib-mating population is

$$4\mu\{\tfrac{1}{2} + \tfrac{2}{4} + \tfrac{3}{8} + \tfrac{5}{16} + \tfrac{8}{32} + \ldots\} = 12\mu .$$

If the mutant gene is lethal in homozygous condition, a heterozygote, on selfing, will produce $\tfrac{1}{3}AA + \tfrac{2}{3}Aa$. Therefore the proportion of heterozygotes due to recurrent mutations in a selfing population is

$$2\mu\{1 + \tfrac{2}{3} + (\tfrac{2}{3})^2 + (\tfrac{2}{3})^3 + \ldots\} = 6\mu .$$

Similar expressions for some other mating systems have also been given by Haldane (1936).

Notes and Exercises

1. In many biological and genetical problems we assume that the numbers of offspring left by a mating, $k = 0, 1, 2, 3, \ldots$, form a Poisson series. The number k here refers to the number of offspring that actually survive to maturity and are therefore capable of mating and producing offspring. In other words, k is the number of offspring that attain the same maturity as their parents. Thus, the number of parents and of offspring are counted at the same stage of development.

   Many organisms, however, produce at one time a vast number (K) of eggs, of which only a very small fraction reach maturity. We shall see in the following that, if the elimination of eggs and larvas is at random, the resulting numbers of mature offspring still form a Poisson series.

   Let us assume that $\bar{k} = 2$ and that the probability of leaving k mature offspring is $e^{-2}2^k/k!$ Now, let the number of eggs laid by a parent be K, of which only $1/n$ survive to maturity. The average value of K must be $2n$. If K forms a Poisson series with mean $\overline{K} = 2n$, the probability of producing K eggs will be $e^{-2n}(2n)^K/K!$ The probability that there should be k reaching maturity from any given set of K eggs is given by the binomial term

$$\frac{K!}{k!\,(K-k)!}\left(\frac{1}{n}\right)^k\left(\frac{n-1}{n}\right)^{K-k} ,$$

assuming that the survival is a random process. Therefore, the total probability of having k mature offspring (k fixed) from the various possible values of K is (Fisher, 1939)

$$\sum_{K=k}^{K=\infty} \left\{ e^{-2n} \frac{(2n)^K}{K!} \times \frac{K!}{k!\,(K-k)!} \left(\frac{1}{n}\right)^k \left(\frac{n-1}{n}\right)^{K-k} \right\}$$

$$= e^{-2n} \frac{2^k}{k!} \sum_{K=k}^{K=\infty} \frac{2^{K-k}\,(n-1)^{K-k}}{(K-k)!}$$

$$= e^{-2n} \frac{2^k}{k!} \left\{ e^{2(n-1)} \right\} = e^{-2} \frac{2^k}{k!},$$

which is the probability of a Poisson series for k offspring with mean $\bar{k} = 2$. It is this property which gives the Poisson series its special significance; and the choice of the stage of sexual maturity at which to count the number of offspring is thus something more than a matter of convenience.

2. Calculate the terms $p(k) = e^{-2}2^k/k!$ for $k = 0, 1, 2, \ldots$, taking $e^{-2} = 0.13534$. Check your answer with those tabulated in Karl Pearson's *Tables for Statisticians and Biometricians*, Part I. Show that $\bar{k} = 2$ and that $\sigma_k^2 = 2$. Prove that, in general, $\sigma_k^2 = \bar{k}$ for any Poisson series. (This proof may be found in most elementary textbooks of mathematical statistics.)

3. *The chance of survival of an individual gene* (Fisher, 1930a; Haldane, 1932, Appendix). Let the single mutant gene be a, so that all crosses involving its carrier are of the type $AA \times Aa$, and consequently their offspring are either AA or Aa. Then the number of Aa offspring is also the number of mutant genes left by the original Aa parent. Our previous assumption that the average number of offspring per mating is $\bar{k} = 2$ (one AA and one Aa) is equivalent to saying that the average number of mutant genes in the next generation from an Aa parent is unity. In the following we shall deal with the number of Aa offspring or the number of mutant genes among offspring.

(i) Let $p_0, p_1, p_2, \ldots, p_r, \ldots$, be the probabilities of producing 0, 1, 2, $\ldots, r, \ldots Aa$ offspring from an Aa parent, where $\Sigma_r\, p_r = 1$ and p_0 is the probability of losing the mutant gene in the next generation from one Aa parent. Further, let us define the function

$$f(x) = p_0 + p_1 x + p_2 x^2 + \ldots + p_r x^r + \ldots.$$

Note that $f(0) = p_0$ is the probability of extinction of a single mutant gene in one generation.

(ii) Suppose that the mutant gene is already present in r individuals. The chance of its extinction in the next generation will be p_0^r, assuming the r individuals to be reproducing independently. The chance of having only one mutant gene in the next generation will be $rp_0^{r-1}p_1$; and so on. In general, the chance of leaving s mutant genes in the next generation will be the coefficient of x^s in the expansion of

$$[f(x)]^r = [p_0 + p_1x + p_2x^2 + \ldots]^r .$$

(iii) Now, let us start with a single mutant gene. The chance of its leaving r in the next generation is p_r, and the chance that these leave s in the third generation will be the coefficient of x^s in $p_r[f(x)]^r$. Therefore the total probability of leaving s mutant genes in the third generation from the various possible values of r in the second is the coefficient of x^s in

$$\sum_r p_r[f(x)]^r = p_0[f(x)]^0 + p_1[f(x)]^1 + p_2[f(x)]^2 + \cdots$$

$$= f(f(x)),$$

which is the same function of $f(x)$ as $f(x)$ is of x. Proceeding as before, we see that the total probability of having t mutant genes in still another generation will be the coefficient of x^t in the function $f(f(f(x)))$, and so on for as many generations as required.

(iv) Just as putting $x = 0$ in $f(x)$ to obtain the probability of extinction of the mutant gene in one generation after its occurrence, putting $x = 0$ ($s = 0$) in the function $f(f(x))$ will give us the probability of extinction in two generations after its occurrence. If we let $l_1 = p_0$, then $l_2 = f(l_1)$; and, in general,

$$l_{n+1} = f(l_n) .$$

(v) If the number of Aa offspring or mutant genes is distributed according to the Poisson series with mean equal to unity, the values of $p_0, p_1, p_2, \ldots$ are

$$e^{-1} \left\{ 1, \quad 1, \quad \frac{1}{2!}, \quad \frac{1}{3!}, \quad \frac{1}{4!}, \cdots \right\}$$

and

$$f(x) = e^{-1} \left\{ 1 + x + \frac{x^2}{2!} + \frac{x^3}{3!} + \cdots \right\}$$

$$= e^{-1} \{ e^x \} = e^{x-1} .$$

Hence,

$$l_1 = f(0) = e^{-1} = 0.3679 ;$$

$$l_2 = f(f(0)) = f(l_1) = e^{0.3679-1} = e^{-0.6321} = 0.5315 ,$$

and so on. Verify the values of l_n for the first seven generations as shown in Table 65.

4. From Table 65 it can be seen that the chance of survival $(1 - l_n)$ for neutral mutations is approximately halved when the number of generations is doubled. In fact, when n is large, the chance of survival is very nearly $2/n$. Thus after 255 generations, this chance will be approximately 0.0078.

5. If the opposing rates of mutation are equal, $\mu = \nu$, what are the equilibrium values of the gene frequencies? (See [6].)

6. Show that, using (3'),

$$\log_e \frac{1 - q_0}{1 - q_n} = n\mu .$$

7. If $q_0 = 0$ in the initial population, (3') becomes

$$1 - q_n = p_n = e^{-n\mu} .$$

Verify the following values of q_n for various values of n and μ, assuming no reverse mutations.

	$n = 1000$	$n = 5000$	$n = 10,000$	$n = 50,000$
$\mu = 10^{-4}$......	0.095	0.393	0.632	0.993
$\mu = 10^{-5}$......	.010	.049	.095	.393
$\mu = 10^{-6}$......	0.001	0.005	0.010	0.049

8. The equilibrium values of gene frequencies (6) due to opposing mutation pressures may be derived by first finding the general expression for q_n. Now, (5) may be written as

$$q_{n+1} = q_n + \mu(1 - q_n) - \nu q_n$$
$$= \mu + (1 - \mu - \nu)q_n .$$

By repeated substitution of this sequence relation, we find that

$$q_n = \mu + \mu (1 - \mu - \nu) + \mu (1 - \mu - \nu)^2 + \ldots + (1 - \mu - \nu)^n q_0$$

$$= \frac{\mu}{\mu + \nu} - \left(\frac{\mu}{\mu + \nu} - q_0\right)(1 - \mu - \nu)^n$$

$$= \frac{\mu}{\mu + \nu} - \left(\frac{\mu}{\mu + \nu} - q_0\right) e^{-n(\mu + \nu)} .$$

The limiting value of q_n is thus $\mu/(\mu + \nu)$ as $n \to \infty$ and $e^{-n(\mu + \nu)} \to 0$.

9. If $\mu = 0.0005$ and $\nu = 0.0015$ per generation in a population with $p = 0.80$ and $q = 0.20$, what will be the equilibrium values of the gene frequencies? Calculate the values of q for the next three generations. Calculate the number of generations required for q to increase from 0.20 to 0.21.

ANS.: Substituting the known values in the general expression for q_n given in the previous problem, we have

$$0.21 = 0.25 - (0.25 - 0.20)e^{-n(0.002)}$$

or

$$0.80 = e^{-0.002n} .$$

Therefore, $n = 111$ generations.

CHAPTER 19

Selection

NATURAL selection is the most plausible explanation for the many adaptive characters of organisms. The molding of hereditary variation, produced by mutation, into varieties and species is due to the action of environments through the mechanism of natural selection. The mathematical treatment of this subject has been developed largely by Haldane, Fisher, Wright, and other geneticists.

The main assumption inherent in the theory of natural selection is that some hereditary types in a population have a certain advantage over others in survival and reproduction. The number of gene combinations on which selection may act is staggeringly large. For each locus with three alleles there are, for diploids, six genotypes. If there are only 200 loci to each zygote, there will be 6^{200} possible genotypes! If there are 5000 loci in a zygote, the number of possible genotypes is beyond calculation. So there are almost unlimited possibilities for gene combinations, and it is hardly surprising that no two individuals (except identical twins) should ever be alike in all genes, however large the random-mating population. Therefore, large populations possess at all times a great store of potential variability. This property may conveniently be called the "plasticity" of a population.

When environmental conditions change, existing genotypes may no longer be fit for survival; but a plastic population may be able to go through a genotypical recombination so that new and more fitting types are produced. Thus we see that adaptability is *a response of populations rather than of the individual,* who cannot react to the needs of the changing environment by purposefully and immediately producing beneficial mutations where and when they are needed.

The action of selection may operate at any stage of the life-cycle of an organism, and the means of selection may vary widely for different cases. In the employing of mathematical methods, however, biological facts must be reduced to a mere abstract of their real complexity. It is important to understand that this simplification is recognized for what it is: a working method. It does not mean to ignore the complexity and totality of biological relationships. These clearly remain the foundation upon which any mathematical model may be built.

The primary consequence of selection is a change in the frequencies of genes involved in the trait upon which the selection force is acting. In a large population, selection is probably the most important force responsible for changing gene frequencies. This change is *an elementary step* in evolution. In most of the following sections we shall be concerned with the simplest model: a single pair of alleles whose effects on adaptation of the organism are assumed to be independent of all other loci.

§ 1. *Complete Elimination of Recessives*

Suppose that the recessive individuals (*aa*) of a large random-mating population are entirely eliminated from the population and that only the dominants are allowed to mate and reproduce. The proportions of the various genotypes in the population before and after such selection will be as shown in Table 66.

TABLE 66

COMPLETE ELIMINATION OF RECESSIVES

	ZYGOTIC PROPORTIONS			FREQUENCY OF a
	AA	Aa	aa	
Before selection........	p^2	$2pq$	q^2	q
After selection.........	$\dfrac{p^2}{p^2+2pq}$	$\dfrac{2pq}{p^2+2pq}$	0	$\dfrac{q}{1+q}$
	This is the mating population that produces the next generation			
Next generation, before selection...........	$\dfrac{1}{(1+q)^2}$	$\dfrac{2q}{(1+q)^2}$	$\dfrac{q^2}{(1+q)^2}$	$\dfrac{q}{1+q}$

Thus we see that the relation between two consecutive q's is

$$q_{n+1} = \frac{q_n}{1+q_n},\tag{1}$$

which is the sequence equation of a harmonic series (Chap. 17). Therefore, the general expression of q_n after n generations of complete elimination of recessives is

$$q_n = \frac{q_0}{1+nq_0},\tag{2}$$

where q_0 is the initial frequency of gene a before the selection operates. The amount of change in q per generation is

$$\Delta q = \frac{q}{1+q} - q = \frac{-q^2}{1+q}.\tag{3}$$

Familiar examples of complete elimination of a certain homozygous genotype in nature are the cases involving lethal and sterility genes. The value of q decreases very rapidly when q is large; its rate of decrease lessens as q becomes small. Also, from (2) we see that $q_n = \frac{1}{2}q_0$ when $nq_0 = 1$. In other words, the gene frequency is halved in a period of $n = 1/q_0$ generations.

Complete elimination of a certain genotype every generation is the severest type of selection against that type of organism. It is a very rapid method of diminishing the gene frequencies from the evolutionary point of view, in which a period of time usually involves hundreds of thousands of generations. It should be pointed out, however, that this type of elimination is not very practical when applied to human populations. For example, let $q_0 = 1/50 = 0.02$, so that the proportion of the recessive (presumably defective) genotype in the population is 0.0004. If *every* one of the recessives is subject to compulsory sterilization every generation, and this process of elimination continues for fifty generations (so that $nq_0 = 1$), the final frequency of a will be decreased only by half: q_n will be 0.01, and the proportion of aa, 0.0001. Taking thirty years as one generation, we see that it will require fifteen hundred years of compulsory sterilization of all individuals with a simple defective recessive trait to reduce the frequency of that recessive gene by half. If q is smaller, it would take even longer to reduce it by the same amount. This shows that the results of even the most vigorous sterilization measure are far short of what is expected by some eugenicists. Furthermore, if the trait is due to two pairs of recessive genes (*aabb*), it may be shown that the recessive-gene frequencies would decrease much more slowly than in the unit-factor case. Also, if sterilization is on a voluntary basis, so that the elimination is only partial in each generation, the rate at which q decreases will be considerably less. These facts are not presented in order to raise any objection to the sterilization idea. They do serve, however, to point out that the elimination of a *recessive* defect by sterilization is, in terms of human life, a very slow process in a random-mating population and probably of no immediate value in a practical eugenic program.

§ 2. *Partial Selection against Recessives*

Let us suppose, for the purpose of discussion, that the dominants are favored by selection. Whatever the real causes of their advantages over the recessives, the final effect is their higher fertility or lower mortality. In other words, for every *one* offspring produced by the dominants, the recessives on the average have only $(1 - s)$ offspring, where s is a positive number between 0 and 1 and is usually known as the "coefficient of selection" against the recessives (or other types). It is a measure of the *intensity* of selection.

The value of s varies greatly with different characters. As we saw in the last section, $s = 1$ for lethal recessives. For many semilethals in *Drosophila*, $s \leq 0.90$, while for other unfavorable traits, s may vary from 0.50 to 0.10. On the other hand, $s = 0$ for "neutral" characters which are neither of any advantage nor of any disadvantage to the individuals. In many cases the value of s may be so small (e.g., 0.01 or 0.001) that it is hardly detectable under ordinary laboratory conditions. Even so, it may be of significance over a long period of time under natural conditions.

The ratio of the number of offspring produced by dominants and recessives, $1:(1 - s)$, has been called the relative "fitness," "survival value," "adaptive value," "reproductive rate," etc., of the two types of individuals. The effect of partial selection on gene frequencies of a large random-mating population may be derived from Table 67. The frequency of the recessive gene in the next gen-

TABLE 67

PARTIAL SELECTION AGAINST RECESSIVES

	AA	Aa	aa	Total
Initial proportion......	p^2	$2pq$	q^2	1
Relative fitness........	1	1	$1-s$	....
After selection.........	p^2	$2pq$	$q^2(1-s)$	$1-sq^2$

eration becomes

$$q_1 = \frac{p\,q + q^2\,(1 - s)}{1 - s\,q^2} = \frac{q\,(1 - s\,q)}{1 - s\,q^2}.$$

In general, the relations between any two consecutive gene frequencies are

$$p_{n+1} = \frac{p_n}{1 - s\,q_n^2} \quad \text{and} \quad q_{n+1} = \frac{q_n\,(1 - s\,q_n)}{1 - s\,q_n^2}, \tag{4}$$

where $p_n + q_n = p_{n+1} + q_{n+1} = 1$. Unfortunately, there seems to be no general solution to this sequence, except when $s = 1$, in which case (4) reduces to (1). The value of q decreases because of the selection against aa individuals. The amount of change per generation is

$$\Delta q = q_1 - q = \frac{-\,s\,q^2\,(1 - q)}{1 - s\,q^2}. \tag{5}$$

The magnitude of Δq is appreciable when the value of q is intermediate. But, when either p or q is small, Δq is very small. It follows that selection of a given intensity (s fixed) is most effective for common traits in a population and ineffective for rare characters. For example, if $s = 0.20$ against aa individuals, the values of Δq will be as follows:

$q=0.99$	$q=0.50$	$q=0.01$
$\Delta q = -0.00244$	$\Delta q = -0.0263$	$\Delta q = -0.0000198$

When q is very small, (5) becomes $\Delta q = -sq^2$, approximately. If selection favors the recessives, the foregoing formulas still hold except for changing the sign of s or replacing $(1 - s)$ by $(1 + s)$ for the "fitness" of recessives.

§ 3. *Slow Selection against Recessives*

If the coefficient of selection against the recessives is small, the change in gene frequencies will be a slow process even in the evolutionary scale. Then the quantity sq^2 will be so small in comparison with unity that the denominator of (5) may be regarded, for all practical purposes, as being unity. Thus the amount of change in q per generation due to selection pressure may be written as

$$\Delta q = -sq^2(1 - q) , \qquad (6)$$

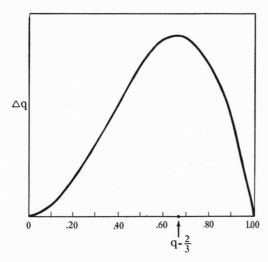

FIG. 64.—Equation (6): $\Delta q = -sq^2(1 - q)$, where s is a constant

approximately. It is easy to see that the maximum value of Δq is attained when $q = \frac{2}{3}$. The shape of the curve (6) is shown in Figure 64.

To calculate the amount of change in q over a number of generations, we may put (6) into the form of a differential equation by replacing Δq by dq/dt, where t denotes time as measured in units of generations. Thus,

$$\frac{dq}{dt} = -sq^2(1 - q) ; \qquad \frac{dq}{q^2(1 - q)} = -sdt .$$

Integrating both sides over n generations, we have (see also Ex. 5)

$$\int_{q_0}^{q_n} \frac{dq}{q^2(1 - q)} = -s \int_0^n dt = -sn .$$

$$\therefore sn = \left[\frac{1}{q} + \log_e \frac{1 - q}{q}\right]_{q_0}^{q_n}$$

$$= \frac{1}{q_n} - \frac{1}{q_0} + \log_e \frac{1 - q_n}{q_n} - \log_e \frac{1 - q_0}{q_0} \tag{7}$$

$$= \frac{q_0 - q_n}{q_0 q_n} + \log_e \frac{q_0 (1 - q_n)}{q_n (1 - q_0)} . \tag{7'}$$

For example, let $s = 0.001$ be the coefficient of selection against the recessives. The number of generations required to reduce the proportion of recessives from 50 per cent to 1 per cent, that is, to reduce $q_0 = \sqrt{0.50} = 0.7071$ to $q_n = \sqrt{0.01} = 0.100$, will be, from (7') and with natural logarithms replaced by common ones,

$$0.001 n = \frac{0.6071}{0.0707} + 2.303 \log_{10} \left(\frac{0.707 \times 0.90}{0.293 \times 0.10} \right) = 11.665 .$$

$\therefore n = 11,665$ generations .

As was pointed out before, selection is only effective for intermediate values of gene frequencies. The decrease of q becomes appallingly slow when q is small. Thus, with $s = 0.001$ as before, it will take 309,783 generations to reduce the proportion of recessives from 1 per cent to 0.001 per cent in a large random-mating population. This is shown in the following calculation, where $q_0 = 0.10$ and $q_n = \sqrt{0.00001} = 0.00316228$; and (7') gives

$$0.001 n = \frac{0.09683772}{0.00031623} + 2.303 \log_{10} \left(\frac{0.10 \times 0.9968377}{0.90 \times 0.0031623} \right) = 309.783 .$$

Several tables are available giving the number of generations required for a specific amount of change in various arguments (e.g., p or q, $u = p/q$, $R = q^2$, etc.) and for various intensities of selection. Table 68, cited for its brevity,

TABLE 68

NUMBER OF GENERATIONS (n) REQUIRED TO
EFFECT A SPECIFIED CHANGE IN q WITH
$s = 0.01$ AGAINST THE RECESSIVES

(Pätau, 1938)

Reduction in q	n
0.9999 to 0.9990	230
0.9990 to 0.9900	232
0.9900 to 0.5000	559
0.5000 to 0.0200	5,189
0.0200 to 0.0100	5,070
0.0100 to 0.0010	90,231
0.0010 to 0.0001	900,230

gives the calculations of Pätau (1938), assuming $s = 0.01$ against the recessives.

Note that Δq, as given by (3), (5), and (6), will not vanish unless $q = 0$. This means that the selection against aa will eventually eliminate the recessive gene entirely from the population, if not opposed by some countermeasure, but it may take thousands (or even millions) of generations.

Calculations such as those in Table 68 are purely schematic. The proviso that environment remain constant throughout millions of years seems scarcely credible. Environmental conditions can and do change gradually or suddenly. The selection intensity with respect to a certain character will vary accordingly, and the value of s cannot remain constant for a long period of time. A disadvantageous character under one set of conditions may become advantageous under a wholly different set of conditions. The important point brought out by such calculations is that the selection pressure *can* slowly change an entire population even when the selective disadvantage of a particular genotype is minute ($s = 0.01$ or 0.001). Comparatively slight changes in environment could continually alter the relative fitnesses of different genotypes and enable more rapid evolution to take place than has sometimes been thought possible.

§ 4. *Gametic Selection and Intermediate Heterozygotes*

Selection might act in the gametic stage rather than in the zygotic stage. It is conceivable that one type of gametes is of advantage over others in fertilization. If the relative contribution to the next generation of the A and a gametes is $1: (1 - s)$, and their frequencies in a population are p and q, respectively, in one generation, then their frequencies will be p and $q(1 - s)$, respectively, in the next generation. Consequently, the amount of change in q, noting that $p + q(1 - s) = 1 - sq$, will be

$$\Delta q = \frac{q(1 - s)}{1 - sq} - q = \frac{-sq(1 - q)}{1 - sq}. \tag{8}$$

Now, let us turn to a case of zygotic selection in which the fitness of heterozygotes is exactly intermediate between that of two homozygous types; that is,

TABLE 69

ZYGOTIC SELECTION WHEN THERE IS NO DOMINANCE

	AA	Aa	aa	Total
Initial proportion......	p^2	$2pq$	q^2	1
Relative fitness........	1	$1-s$	$1-2s$	....
After selection.........	p^2	$2pq(1-s)$	$q^2(1-2s)$	$1-2sq$

there is no dominance. The effect of selection on genotypes in such a case is shown in Table 69. Proceeding as before, by first finding the new gene frequency in the next generation and simplifying, we obtain

$$\Delta q = \frac{q - sq(1 + q)}{1 - 2sq} - q = \frac{-sq(1 - q)}{1 - 2sq}. \tag{9}$$

If s is small (slow selection), the rate of decrease of q in both (8) and (9) is practically

$$\Delta q = -sq(1 - q) . \qquad (8 \cdot 9)$$

In other words, selection against zygotes without dominance is equivalent to selection directly against the gametes. Obviously, the above formulas also apply when there are only two types of individuals in a closely inbred population and the selection is against one of them.

As before, to calculate the number of generations required to effect a specific amount of change in q by slow genic selection, we write (8·9) in the form of a differential equation by replacing Δq by dq/dt, where t denotes time in units of generations. Separating the variables and integrating both sides over n generations, we have

$$\int_{q_0}^{q_n} \frac{dq}{q(1 - q)} = -s \int_0^n dt .$$

Therefore

$$sn = \left[\log_e \frac{1 - q}{q} \right]_{q_0}^{q_n} = \log_e \frac{q_0(1 - q_n)}{q_n(1 - q_0)} . \qquad (10)$$

As an example, let $s = 0.01$ against the gene a (or 0.01 against Aa and 0.02 against aa). The number of generations required to reduce $q_0 = 0.40$ to $q_n = 0.04$ will be given by

$$n = 100 \times 2.303 \, \log_{10} \left(\frac{0.40 \times 0.96}{0.04 \times 0.60} \right) = 277 .$$

For a fixed intensity of selection the decrease in q is more rapid for gametic selection than for zygotic. If selection operates only against the gametes of one sex (pollen, say), the results will remain the same except for replacing s by $\frac{1}{2}s$ in a random-mating population in which the sex ratio is unity, as in maize (Ex. 7).

§ 5. Equilibrium When Selection Favors Heterozygotes

If the adaptive value of heterozygotes is superior to that of both homozygous types, the situation will be different from that described in the previous four sections in that the gene frequencies will eventually reach a stable equilibrium value instead of approaching zero or unity as a limit (Fisher, 1922, 1930a; Haldane, 1926; Wright, 1931). The change in gene frequencies per generation may be derived from Table 70. Having found the new gene frequency in the next generation, and simplifying by the fact that $pq + q^2 = q$, we obtain (Fig. 65)

$$\Delta q = \frac{q - s_2 q^2}{1 - s_1 p^2 - s_2 q^2} - q = \frac{pq(s_1 p - s_2 q)}{1 - s_1 p^2 - s_2 q^2} . \qquad (11)$$

Thus, we see that q increases or decreases according to whether $s_1 p$ is greater or less than $s_2 q$. There will be no change in gene frequency ($\Delta q = 0$) when

$s_1 p = s_2 q$. Solving this equation, we obtain the equilibrium values

$$\hat{p} = \frac{s_2}{s_1 + s_2}, \qquad \hat{q} = \frac{s_1}{s_1 + s_2}. \tag{12}$$

These equilibrium values are independent of the initial gene frequencies of the population and entirely determined by the selection coefficients against the homozygotes. Since s_1 and s_2 are constants, this equilibrium condition is a

TABLE 70

SELECTION FAVORING HETEROZYGOTES

	AA	Aa	aa	Total
Initial proportion........	p^2	$2pq$	q^2	1.00
Relative fitness..........	$1-s_1$	1	$1-s_2$	....
After selection...........	$p^2(1-s_1)$	$2pq$	$q^2(1-s_2)$	$1-s_1 p^2 - s_2 q^2$

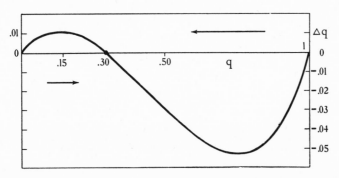

Fig. 65.—Selection favoring heterozygotes. The curve shown is equation (11) with $s_1 = 0.15$ and $s_2 = 0.35$ against AA and aa, respectively, so that the equilibrium value is $\hat{q} = 0.30$ according to (12). (Modified from J. F. Crow, unpublished notes.)

stable one. When it is disturbed in any direction for any reason, the gene frequencies gradually come back to the same equilibrium values specified by (12). An example of this kind in *Drosophila* is given in Exercise 8. Another property of (12) is given in Exercise 9.

Note that the deviation $(q - \hat{q})$ in any generation is $q - s_1/(s_1 + s_2)$. Therefore, $(s_1 + s_2)(q - \hat{q}) = (s_1 + s_2)q - s_1$. On the other hand, the factor $(s_1 p - s_2 q)$ in the numerator of (11) may be written as $s_1 - (s_1 + s_2)q$. If s_1 and s_2 are both small, so that the denominator of (11) is nearly unity, the change per generation takes the form

$$\Delta q = -(s_1 + s_2)pq(q - \hat{q}), \tag{13}$$

approximately. It is clear that, when q is below its equilibrium point, it will increase from generation to generation; when it is greater than $\hat{q}$, it decreases until the equilibrium point is reached.

The above result (12) may be generalized to the case of multiple alleles (Wright, 1949a). Let us assume that all heterozygotes (A_iA_j) have the *same* fitness, which we take as unity, and that the fitness of the homozygote A_iA_i is $1 - s_i$. Let the frequencies of the alleles A_1, A_2, A_3, . . . , be q_1, q_2, q_3, . . . , where $\Sigma q = 1$. Proceeding exactly as before, it will be found that the increment in q_1 for A_1 in the next generation is

$$\Delta q_1 = \frac{(1 - s_1)\, q_1^2 + q_1 q_2 + q_1 q_3 + \ldots}{1 - s_1 q_1^2 - s_2 q_2^2 - s_3 q_3^2 - \ldots} - q_1$$

$$= \frac{q_1\{\,(1 - s_1 q_1) - (1 - \Sigma s_i q_i^2)\,\}}{1 - \Sigma s_i q_i^2}$$

$$= \frac{q_1\{\Sigma s_i q_i^2 - s_1 q_1\}}{1 - \Sigma s_i q_i^2}.$$

The corresponding expressions for Δq_2, Δq_3, . . . , are similar except for replacing subscript 1 by 2, 3, . . . , etc. At equilibrium all $\Delta q_i = 0$; hence, $s_i q_i = \Sigma s_i q_i^2$, or

$$s_1 q_1 = s_2 q_2 = s_3 q_3 = \ldots ;$$

that is,

$$q_1 \;:\; q_2 \;:\; q_3 \;:\; \ldots = \frac{1}{s_1} \;:\; \frac{1}{s_2} \;:\; \frac{1}{s_3} \;:\; \ldots .$$

$$\therefore \; \hat{q}_i = \frac{1}{s_i} \Big/ \Sigma \Big(\frac{1}{s_i}\Big). \tag{14}$$

When there are only two alleles, (14) reduces to (12).

In the above we assumed that all types of heterozygotes were of the same fitness, while the homozygotes were of various degrees of inferiority. It may be shown, however, that if one type of heterozygote $(A_1A_2$, say) is extraordinarily superior to others, then all alleles other than A_1 and A_2 tend to be eliminated from the population (Wright, 1949a). An algebraic demonstration of this, based on a simplified model, is given in Exercise 15.

Various equilibrium conditions are also possible for lethal genes (or chromosomal abnormalities) which are of advantage in heterozygous conditions. For example, if the survival values of AA, Aa, aa are $1 - s$, 1, 0, respectively, it is easy to show that the equilibrium value of the lethal gene is $\hat{q} = s/(1 + s)$.

The condition in which selection favors heterozygotes is the only one in which the alleles of a locus can remain in stable equilibrium *and* retain substantial frequencies within a single environment. This results in what is known as "balanced polymorphism," which furnishes plasticity to a species and thus may be of great evolutionary significance.

§ 6. *Selection against Heterozygotes*

If selection is against heterozygotes, the consequences will be entirely different from those of Section 5. Let 1, $1 - s$, 1 be the fitness of AA, Aa, aa in a random-mating population. Proceeding as before, we find that, after the operation of selection, the new frequency of a will be

$$q' = \frac{pq\,(1 - s) + q^2}{1 - 2spq} = \frac{q - spq}{1 - 2spq},$$

so that (Fig. 66)

$$\Delta q = \frac{spq\,(2q - 1)}{1 - 2spq} \doteq 2spq\,(q - \tfrac{1}{2}) \tag{15}$$

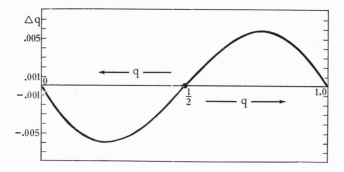

Fig. 66.—Selection against heterozygotes. The unstable equilibrium value $q = \tfrac{1}{2}$ acts as a "repulsive" point to q, which moves away from it toward the ends. The curve shown is that of (15) with $s = 0.50$ and with exaggerated Δq scales. (Modified from J. F. Crow, unpublished notes.)

when s is small. When $q = \tfrac{1}{2}$, $\Delta q = 0$; but this is an *unstable* equilibrium point, because, if q exceeds $\tfrac{1}{2}$, Δq will be positive, and thus q will increase; and, if q is less than $\tfrac{1}{2}$, Δq will be negative, and q will diminish. In other words, the smaller (larger) the value of q, the smaller (larger) it will become in later generations. This situation is obvious even without the explicit expression (15). When $q = \tfrac{1}{2}$, the proportions of the two homozygous types are equal ($p^2 = q^2 = \tfrac{1}{4}$) in a random-mating population, and therefore complete or partial elimination of heterozygotes will not change the gene frequency. The population will restore its original zygotic proportions in the next generation on random mating. But if p and q are not equal ($p > q$, say), the heterozygotes will bear a relatively higher proportion of the rare allele; and hence selection against heterozygotes will act more against the rare allele than against the common one. The result will be to diminish the rare allele still further.

The number of generations required to effect a specified amount of change in q may be calculated by the usual method of integrating the differential equation (15), writing dq/dt for Δq; thus (Haldane, 1942),

$$s n = \left[\log_e \frac{(q - \frac{1}{2})^2}{pq} \right]_{q_0}^{q_n} . \tag{16}$$

The Rh factor.—The above analysis assumes that *all* heterozygotes of a population are of fitness $1 - s$. A different type of selection against heterozygotes in man has been discovered with the Rh factor. When the mother is recessive (*rh rh*, said to be Rh-negative), and her baby is heterozygous (*Rh rh*, said to be Rh-positive), there often results a hemolytic disease (*Erythroblastosis fetalis*), which may cause the death of the child. The selection here is not against the heterozygotes per se but only against those heterozygotes born to recessive mothers. Since *rh rh* mother $\times$ *Rh Rh* father gives *Rh rh* babies; and since *rh rh* mother $\times$ *Rh rh* father gives 50 per cent *Rh rh* babies, the proportion of hetero-

TABLE 71

SELECTION AGAINST HETEROZYGOTES BORN TO RECESSIVE MOTHERS
(Li, 1953c)

MOTHER$\times$FATHER	FREQUENCY	CHILD			TOTAL
		AA	Aa	aa	
$AA\times$—.........	p^2	p^3	p^2q	0	p^2
$Aa\times$—.........	$2pq$	p^2q	pq	pq^2	$2pq$
$aa \times AA$........	p^2q^2	0	$p^2q^2(1-s)$	0	
$aa \times Aa$........	$2pq^3$	0	$pq^3(1-s)$	pq^3	q^2-spq^2
$aa \times aa$........	q^4	0	0	q^4	
Total........	1.00	p^2	$2pq-spq^2$	q^2	$1-spq^2$

zygotes born to recessive mothers is $p^2q^2 + pq^3 = pq^2$ among all births in the population. Let the fitness of *these* heterozygotes be $1 - s$; the remaining heterozygotes are normal. This situation is shown in Table 71, in which we write A for *Rh* and a for *rh*, since we are considering only the two major alleles in the Rh series. The frequency of the recessive gene in the next generation becomes

$$q' = \frac{pq - \frac{1}{2}spq^2 + q^2}{1 - spq^2} = \frac{q - \frac{1}{2}spq^2}{1 - spq^2} ,$$

so that

$$\Delta q = q' - q = \frac{spq^2(q - \frac{1}{2})}{1 - spq^2} \doteq spq^2(q - \frac{1}{2}) \tag{17}$$

when s is small (Haldane, 1942). This quantity is usually much smaller than that given by (15). Here, $q = \frac{1}{2}$ is also an unstable equilibrium point, as q increases when it exceeds $\frac{1}{2}$ and diminishes if it is less than $\frac{1}{2}$. The formula for the number of generations required to effect a specified amount of change in q has also been given by Haldane (1942).

If *Erythroblastosis fetalis* reduces the survival rate of a portion of the hetero-zygotes, the recessive *rh* gene should be reduced to a very low frequency in a few hundred generations, assuming its initial frequency below 0.50. And we do find that the *rh* gene is very rare in the Chinese population. But the relatively high frequency of this gene in the United States ($q = \sqrt{0.145} = 0.38$, approximate-ly) requires some consideration. One hypothesis is that it is of recent origin and due to the intermarriage of different races, some having higher *Rh* fre-quencies, the others higher *rh* frequencies. Such a situation would imply that the present American population is not in equilibrium and that its frequency of *rh* is decreasing. Another possibility is that the loss of *rh* may be counterbalanced by a superior survival rate of heterozygotes in general and that a *stable* equilibri-um is therefore being maintained. If the fitness of heterozygotes is $1 + h$ in comparison with the homozygotes, then at equilibrium we should have

$$(2pq - spq^2)(1 + h) = 2pq \; ;$$

that is,

$$h = \frac{sq}{2 - sp} \doteq \tfrac{1}{2}sq, \qquad \text{or} \qquad \hat{q} = \frac{2h}{s}. \tag{18}$$

Thus, if $s = 0.05$ and $q = 0.38$, h will be approximately 0.009. That is to say, a small advantage (hardly detectable in ordinary genetic data) of heterozygotes in general will be sufficient to counterbalance the loss of those born to recessive mothers.

Recently, it has been suggested that a compensation effect may be responsible for maintaining the high *rh* frequency. Glass (1950) has shown that the Rh-negative mothers tend not only to have more recessive births to replace their lost (heterozygous) children but to "overcompensate" by continuing to pro-duce living (*rh rh*) babies in excess of the number of living children produced by the average family. Consequently, the frequency of *rh* may be actually on the increase! This mechanism of compensation, however, does not lead to stable equilibrium values of q. For more detailed discussions see Spencer (1947), Glass (1950), and Li (1953c).

Finally, there is the hypothesis that there may be a very high mutation rate from *Rh* to *rh*, which compensates for the loss of the latter. Recurrent mutations usually can hold the frequency of a "deleterious" gene at a low level in the popu-lation, as will be shown in the next chapter; but it is extremely doubtful if we should assume an extraordinarily high mutation rate to *rh* without any direct evidence.

§ 7. *Some Other Types of Selection*

Many other types of selection have been investigated by Haldane (1932 and later) and others. Only a few of them will be mentioned in the following:

1. If selection is against the dominants, obviously it is more effective for the same intensity of selection and the same gene frequency than when it is against

recessives. If $s = 1$ against the dominants, they will be completely eliminated in one generation. Sterilization in man against dominant abnormalities should thus be more successful than with recessive defects. However, if the dominant gene is rare, a substantial proportion of the affected individuals are the result of new mutations; and therefore, population-wise, failure of affected persons to reproduce would make relatively little difference in the incidence of the trait in the next generation.

2. The selection intensities for females and males may be different. Indeed, this is probably the case for many characters under natural conditions. If the selection coefficients against the female and male recessives are s_0 and s_1, respectively, then the proportion of recessives in the whole population will be reduced from q^2 to

$$q^2\{1 - \tfrac{1}{2}(s_0 + s_1)\}$$

in the next generation, assuming both sexes are equally numerous in a random-mating population. This leads to changes in gene frequencies at the same rate as though there were a selection of intensity $s = \tfrac{1}{2}(s_0 + s_1)$ against the recessives of both sexes equally.

3. Selection for sex-linked genes is equivalent to gametic selection in males (XY) and zygotic selection in females (XX). Therefore, for a fixed value of s, selection against both male and female sex-linked recessives is more effective than against autosomal ones.

4. Selection against recessive autopolyploids is less effective than against diploids. For example, if the selective value of autotetraploid recessives, $aaaa$, is $1 - s$, its proportion will be reduced from q^4 to $q^4(1 - s)$ because of the selection, so that

$$\Delta q = \frac{-sp\,q^4}{1 - s\,q^4} \cdot = - sp\,q^4,$$

which is considerably smaller than the corresponding Δq for diploids ([5] and [6]).

5. If the gene a is of advantage in gametes, but aa individuals are at a disadvantage, a stable equilibrium point exists at which the loss of a in the zygotic stage will be compensated by its gain in the gametic stage. This balanced condition may be obtained approximately by equating (6) to (8·9); thus,

$$s_{aa}p\,q^2 = s_a p\,q ; \qquad \therefore \; \hat{q} = \frac{s_a}{s_{aa}},$$

where s_{aa} is the selection coefficient against genotype aa and s_a represents the advantage of a gametes over A, both assumed to be small, and $s_a \leq s_{aa}$. If the recessive gene affects only the gametes of one sex (e.g., faster growth of pollen tubes), s_a should be replaced by $\tfrac{1}{2}s_a$, as mentioned before.

§ 8. *Different Local Environments*

In all the preceding sections we have assumed a single environment for the entire population. If there are several different local environments (ecological niches), with one allele favored in one niche and the other allele favored in another, it is possible to attain a stable equilibrium with both alleles present in substantial proportions, resulting in balanced polymorphism. The effect is similar to the case in which the heterozygote is favored by selection in a single environment (§ 5). But the equilibrium due to differential local selection pressures is maintained without the heterozygote being superior to both homozygotes in any single niche. The sufficient (not necessary) condition for equilibrium of this kind is simply that the (weighted) mean of the survival rate of both homozygotes of the various niches be lower than that of the heterozygote, as shown by Levene (1953). The model considered by him is as follows.

Let the initial zygotic proportions be p^2, $2pq$, q^2. The zygotes then settle down at random in large numbers into each of the niches and are subjected to the local selection pressure. The gene frequency of a local group occupying a niche increases or decreases, depending on whether the gene is favorable or unfavorable in that niche; and therefore we need not consider the absolute fitness in the different niches. After selection, let c_i denote the proportion of the total survivors to be found in the ith niche, and $\Sigma c_i = 1$. At the time of reproduction the survivors leave the niches and mate at random in the entire population. Hence, the new gene frequency of this mating population is then $q' = \Sigma c_i q_i'$, where q_i' is the gene frequency in the ith niche after selection. And the $\Delta q = q' - q$ is the weighted mean of the Δq's for the individual niches. In brief, the model requires that selection act differently in the various niches but that mating be at random throughout the entire population. The effect of differential selection *and* isolation in mating will be discussed in Chapter 21.

The following is a numerical illustration of a stable equilibrium for which the selection is of three different types in the three different niches. Suppose that the initial population is $(p^2, 2pq, q^2)$ and that the fitness of the genotypes in the three niches is as shown below:

	Niche I			Niche II			Niche III		
Genotype........	AA	Aa	aa	AA	Aa	aa	AA	Aa	aa
Fitness..........	1.2	1.0	0.9	0.6	1.0	0.8	0.7	1.0	1.1
Proportion among total survivors..	$c_1=0.20$			$c_2=0.30$			$c_3=0.50$		

The problem now is to find the equilibrium values of gene frequencies under these conditions. By trial and error, it has been found that $p = 0.158$ and $q = 0.842$ are the equilibrium values (for which $\Delta q = 0$). Hence, the initial (before selection) population is (.025, .266, .709), and the final (after selection) mating population is (.0199, .2762, .7039). Note that there is no change in gene frequencies; therefore, this mating population will give rise to (.025, .266, .709) again in the next generation. The final mating population is obtained according to the fitness values postulated above, and the arithmetic detail is given in Table 72 to illustrate the method.

Since we take the fitness of the heterozygote as unity in each niche, the situation is the same as that shown in Table 70 for each niche; and thus formula (11) gives the amount of change in gene frequency in a particular niche. Only here

TABLE 72

DIFFERENTIAL SELECTION IN VARIOUS ECOLOGICAL NICHES FOR
THE EQUILIBRIUM POPULATION (.025, .266, .709)

The fitness values of the genotypes in different niches and
the proportion of total survivors are shown on
the preceding page.

Niche	Relative Frequency after Selection	Adjusted to Proportions	Survivors in Entire Population (Weighted by c_i)	Final Mating Population
I $\begin{cases} AA\ldots \\ Aa\ldots \\ aa\ldots \end{cases}$	0.0300 .2660 0.6381	0.0321 .2848 0.6831	0.0064 .0570 0.1366	0.0199 AA
Total...	0.9341	1.0000	0.2000	
II $\begin{cases} AA\ldots \\ Aa\ldots \\ aa\ldots \end{cases}$	0.0150 .2660 0.5672	0.0177 .3136 0.6687	0.0053 .0941 0.2006	0.2762 Aa
Total...	0.8482	1.0000	0.3000	
III $\begin{cases} AA\ldots \\ Aa\ldots \\ aa\ldots \end{cases}$	0.0175 .2660 0.7799	0.0164 .2502 0.7334	0.0082 .1251 0.3667	0.7039 aa
Total...	1.0634	1.0000	0.5000	

the value of s_1 or s_2 may be negative, so that the fitness value $1 - s_1$ or $1 - s_2$ may be greater than unity. To avoid possible confusion as to the signs, it may be more convenient to use the fitness values directly. Writing W for the fitness of AA, and V for the fitness of aa, we may rewrite formula (11) for the ith niche (indicated by the subscript i) as follows:

$$\Delta q_i = p\,q\,\frac{(1 - W_i)\,p - (1 - V_i)\,q}{W_i p^2 + 2 p q + V_i q^2}. \tag{11'}$$

The amount of change in q in the entire population is the weighted mean of these individual changes in each niche; thus,

$$\Delta q = \sum_i c_i \Delta q_i = p\,q \sum_i c_i\,\frac{(1 - W_i)\,p - (1 - V_i)\,q}{W_i p^2 + 2 p q + V_i q^2}. \tag{11T}$$

This expression is equivalent to that given by Levene (1953). The equilibrium gene frequency ($p = 0.158$ and $q = 0.842$) in the numerical example was found by making the sum on the right of the last expression zero.

§ 9. *Stability of an Equilibrium*

We have already considered some examples of stable as well as unstable equilibrium. Now it may be helpful to examine the problem of stability in a somewhat general manner. Suppose that, under a certain selection scheme, the change in gene frequency between two successive generations takes the form

$$\Delta q = q(1 - q) \cdot f(q) ,$$

where $f(q)$ is a function of q. The factor $q(1 - q)$ gives two trivial equilibrium points at $q = 0$ and $q = 1$. These values are of little interest and will be ex-

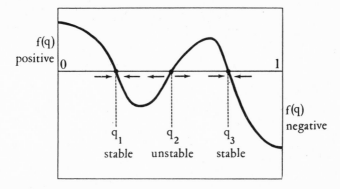

Fig. 67A.—Hypothetical forms of the function $f(q)$, which has the same sign as Δq. The left-hand form gives two stable equilibrium values with an unstable point (q_2) between them. The point q_2 thus divides the q scale into two regions: when $q < q_2$, it goes to q_1 as the stable goal; when $q > q_2$, it goes to q_3 as the stable goal.

cluded from further consideration. The nontrivial equilibrium values of q, stable or unstable, are given by the roots of the equation $f(q) = 0$.

Assume that $f(q)$ is a continuous function, as it is in the usual problems. The function $f(q)$ will have the same sign as Δq for $0 < q < 1$. Hence, if $f(q)$ is negative, q decreases; and, if $f(q)$ is positive, q increases. For a given function $f(q)$, if $f(0)$ is positive and $f(1)$ is negative, there will be at least one value of q between 0 and 1 for which $f(q) = 0$. And there will be at least one stable equilibrium point for such an $f(q)$.

The number and the stability of equilibrium points depend upon the function $f(q)$. As an example, suppose that $f(q) = 0$ has three roots (viz., q_1, q_2, q_3) and that $f(q)$ is of the form shown in Figure 67A. In the neighborhood of q_1 and q_3, the situation is similar to that shown in Figure 65; and the two points, q_1 and q_3, are stable. In the neighborhood of q_2, the situation is similar to that shown in Figure 66, and the point q_2 is unstable. Conversely, if the function $f(q)$ is of the form shown in Figure 67B, there will be only one stable equilibrium point at q_2, while the other two points, q_1 and q_3, are unstable. In the latter case, we see that, as long as the existing q is between q_1 and q_3, it will eventually reach the point q_2. But, if it is outside the range from q_1 to q_3, it will approach 0 or 1 ultimately.

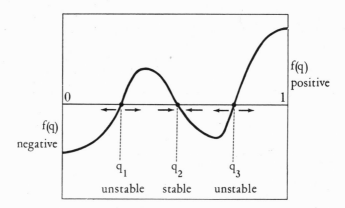

Fig. 67B.—The right-hand form gives two unstable points with a stable one between them. When the gene frequency is within the range of the two unstable values ($q_1 < q < q_3$), it approaches the stable point q_2. If q is outside that range, it goes to the nearest end point, 0 or 1.

Now a numerical example will be given in which there are two distinct nontrivial stable equilibrium values in a random-mating population. When the males and females differ in both direction and degree in their fitness values, it is possible to have three equilibriums, of which the two side ones are stable and the middle one unstable (corresponding to the situation shown in Fig. 67A). Thus, if the fitness values of the females are 0.50, 1.00, 0.50, and those of the males, 2.15, 1.00, 2.15 (as shown in Table 73), the three equilibrium values of gene frequencies are as follows (Owen, 1952, 1953):

EQUILIBRIUM STATE	IN FEMALES		IN MALES		CHARACTER
	p	q	p	q	
I.........	0.368	0.632	0.253	0.747	Stable
II........	.500	.500	.500	.500	Unstable
III.......	0.632	0.368	0.747	0.253	Stable

Table 73 gives a numerical verification of Equilibrium State I. Random union of the female and male gametes gives rise to the initial population (.0931, .4348, .4721), whose members will then be subjected to different selection pressures according to their sex. Therefore, it should be noted that the equilibrium gene frequencies of the two sexes are not equal. Random mating, however, will give the same initial female and male population in the next generation *before* selection.

TABLE 73

EQUILIBRIUM UNDER DIFFERENTIAL SELECTION OF THE TWO SEXES

	FEMALES				MALES			
	AA	Aa	aa	Total	AA	Aa	aa	Total
Before selection..	0.0931	0.4348	0.4721	1.00	0.0931	0.4348	0.4721	1.00
Fitness value....	0.50	1.00	0.50	....	2.15	1.00	2.15	......
After selection...	0.04655	0.4348	0.23605	0.7174	0.2002	0.4348	1.0150	1.650
Proportions.....	0.0649	0.6061	0.3290	1.00	0.1213	0.2635	0.6152	1.00
Gene frequencies	A 0.368		a 0.632	1.00	A 0.253		a 0.747	1.00

Random union of these female and male gametes gives rise to the initial population in the next generation:

$$
\begin{array}{cc}
 & 0.253 \quad\ \ 0.747 \\
\begin{array}{c} 0.368 \\ 0.632 \end{array} &
\boxed{\begin{array}{cc} 0.0931 & 0.2749 \\ 0.1599 & 0.4721 \end{array}}
\end{array}
\rightarrow
\left(\begin{array}{ccc} AA & Aa & aa \\ 0.0931, & 0.4348, & 0.4721 \end{array}\right)
$$

Differential selection of sexes provides still another mechanism by which balanced polymorphism may be maintained.

§ 10. *General Expressions for Selection Pressure*

Consider the general case in which the fitness of AA, Aa, aa are all different, and let W denote the fitness of a genotype (Table 74). The *average* fitness for the population as a whole is

$$\bar{W} = \Sigma fW = 1 - 2s_1 pq - s_2 q^2 \ .$$

TABLE 74

GENERAL SELECTION PRESSURE

Genotype	Proportion f	Fitness W	fW
AA.............	p^2	1	p^2
Aa.............	$2pq$	$1-s_1$	$2pq(1-s_1)$
aa.............	q^2	$1-s_2$	$q^2(1-s_2)$
Total........	1.00	....	$\bar{W}$

And

$$\frac{d\bar{W}}{dq} = 2\{-s_1 + (2s_1 - s_2)q\}.$$

The change in recessive-gene frequency per generation is

$$\Delta q = \frac{pq(1-s_1) + q^2(1-s_2)}{\bar{W}} - q = \frac{pq}{\bar{W}}\{-s_1 + (2s_1 - s_2)q\};$$

$$\therefore \Delta q = \frac{q(1-q)}{2\bar{W}}\frac{d\bar{W}}{dq}. \tag{19}$$

This is a very general expression for the effect of selection on gene frequency. All the particular cases studied in the foregoing sections may be summarized by this one formula (19). For instance, putting $s_1 = 0$, it reduces to (5), and so on. If s_1 and s_2 are both small, so that the average fitness of the whole population is close to unity ($\bar{W} = 1$), $\Delta q = \frac{1}{2}q(1-q)d\bar{W}/dq$, approximately. In explicit form it is

$$\Delta q = pq\{-s_1 + (2s_1 - s_2)q\} = pq(-s + tq), \tag{20}$$

where $2s_1 - s_2 = t$, a constant. When heterozygotes are exactly intermediate between homozygotes, $2s_1 = s_2$, and (20) reduces to (8·9).

The expression (19) may be written in a still more generalized form to include polyploids and sex-linked genes. When the selection coefficients are small, Wright (1942, 1945) gives it as

$$\Delta q = \frac{q(1-q)}{k\bar{W}}\frac{d\bar{W}}{dq} \tag{21}$$

for k-ploids. When $k = 1$, this expression applies to haploids, and the case is thus equivalent to gametic selection, and (21) reduces to (8). For $k = 4$, it applies to autotetraploids, etc. For sex-linked genes, (21) is also approximately true by taking $k = \frac{2}{3}$ and $\bar{W} = \sqrt{(\bar{W}_{\female}\bar{W}_{\male})}$, where $\bar{W}_{\female}$ and $\bar{W}_{\male}$ are the mean fitness of females and males, respectively.

The expressions (19) and (21) are general only for constant selection coefficients and do not apply to the cases to be discussed in Section 13.

§ 11. *Selection in Populations with Inbreeding*

It will be recalled that equilibrium populations with inbreeding may be thought of as consisting of two components: one inbred and one random. For the sake of simplicity we shall derive the general expression for Δq when the selection is against the recessives (Table 75), although the final formula (22) is perfectly general.

Let $\bar{W}_I$ and $\bar{W}_{II}$ be the average fitness of the inbred and random components, respectively, and $\bar{W}$ be that of the entire population. Proceeding as before (with each component *separately*), it is easy to see that

$$\bar{W}_I = 1 - sq , \qquad \bar{W}_{II} = 1 - sq^2 ,$$

$$\frac{d\bar{W}_I}{dq} = -s , \qquad \frac{d\bar{W}_{II}}{dq} = -2sq ,$$

and

$$\bar{W} = F\bar{W}_I + (1-F)\bar{W}_{II} = F(1-sq) + (1-F)(1-sq^2) ;$$

$$\frac{d\bar{W}}{dq} = F\frac{d\bar{W}_I}{dq} + (1-F)\frac{d\bar{W}_{II}}{dq} = -sF - 2sq(1-F) .$$

TABLE 75

SELECTION IN POPULATIONS WITH INBREEDING

Genotype	Inbred I	Random II	Fitness W
AA.............	Fp	$(1-F)p^2$	1
Aa.............	0	$2(1-F)pq$	1
aa.............	Fq	$(1-F)q^2$	$1-s$
Total........	F	$1-F$	........../......

The new frequency of the recessive gene in the next generation is (Wright, 1942)

$$q' = \frac{1}{\bar{W}}\{pq(1-F) + q^2(1-F)(1-s) + qF(1-s)\} ;$$

$$\therefore \Delta q = \frac{q(1-q)}{\bar{W}}\{-sF - sq(1-F)\}$$

$$= \frac{q(1-q)}{\bar{W}}\left\{F\frac{d\bar{W}_I}{dq} + \tfrac{1}{2}(1-F)\frac{d\bar{W}_{II}}{dq}\right\}$$

$$= \frac{q(1-q)}{2\bar{W}}\left\{\frac{d\bar{W}}{dq} + F\frac{d\bar{W}_I}{dq}\right\} . \tag{22}$$

It is clear from the above expressions that selection is more effective in populations with inbreeding than in panmictic populations because of the relative increase of recessive homozygotes. The selection effect is equivalent to a combination of gametic selection and zygotic selection in the proportion $F:(1-F)$. Therefore, the relaxing of inbreeding in a population would lessen the effectiveness of selection, even though the intensity of the latter were to remain the same. (See discussion in Chap. 20, § 4.)

§ 12. *Improvement of Average Fitness*

The scheme of assigning $1, 1-s_1, 1-s_2$ as the fitness values of the various genotypes is a device used only for algebraic convenience, and what matters is the *relative* magnitude of the values. This scheme always gives the average fitness of a population smaller than unity. If we are not considering the growth of one species in relation to others, or if we assume that the population under consideration is approximately in a stationary state in nature, it is sometimes desirable to take the average fitness of the population as unity. This can always be done by taking three numbers

$$W_{AA} : W_{Aa} : W_{aa} = 1 : 1 - s_1 : 1 - s_2$$

so that

$$\bar{W} = p^2 W_{AA} + 2pq W_{Aa} + q^2 W_{aa} = 1 \,.$$

Since the relative magnitude of fitness of the various genotypes is the same in both notations, any change in gene frequency also is the same in both notations. Table 76 gives a numerical illustration of this point; in the example, $q = 0.40$; and Aa is 25 per cent less viable, aa only half as viable, as AA. The frequency of the recessive gene will be decreased by the amount 0.075 in the next generation.

In the new notation, the average fitness of a population can always be taken as unity whether the selection intensities are severe or mild.

All the preceding sections have dealt with the effect of selection on gene frequencies. This problem, however, may be viewed from a different angle. As the individuals with low viability will be relatively less numerous after the operation of selection than before it, so the *average* fitness of the selected population will be higher than that of the preceding generation. The following theorem on the "gain" in average fitness due to selection is a very general one, and we do not have to limit ourselves to one pair of alleles with three genotypes, nor do we have to assume equilibrium. Suppose there are many genotypes in a population:

Genotypes, G	G_1 G_2 ... G_i	
Proportions, f	f_1 f_2 ... f_i	$\Sigma f = 1$
Fitness, W	W_1 W_2 ... W_i	

The mean and variance of *fitness* in this population are

$$\bar{W} = \Sigma fW \,, \qquad \sigma_W^2 = \Sigma f(W - \bar{W})^2 = \Sigma fW^2 - \bar{W}^2 \,.$$

After selection has taken place, the new proportions (f') of the various genotypes in the resultant population will be

$$f' : f_1 W_1 , \qquad f_2 W_2 , \dots , f_i W_i , \dots ,$$

with fitness

$$W_1 , \qquad W_2 , \dots W_i , \dots .$$

Hence, the new average fitness of the selected population becomes

$$\bar{W}' = \frac{\Sigma f'W}{\Sigma f'} = \frac{\Sigma fW^2}{\bar{W}},$$

and the "gain" or improvement in the average fitness on account of the selection is

$$\Delta \bar{W} = \bar{W}' - \bar{W} = \frac{\Sigma fW^2}{\bar{W}} - \bar{W} = \frac{\sigma_W^2}{\bar{W}}. \tag{23}$$

This is a fundamental formula in population genetics, applicable to any set of W's. Now, if we choose the W's such that $\bar{W} = 1$, it reduces to

$$\Delta \bar{W} = \sigma_W^2, \tag{24}$$

TABLE 76

TWO METHODS OF ASSIGNING FITNESS

	SCHEME I				SCHEME II		
	A A	*A a*	*aa*		*A A*	*A a*	*aa*
f...........	0.36	0.48	0.16	f..........	0.36	0.48	0.16
W..........	1.00	0.75	0.50	W........	1.250	0.9375	0.625
fW.........	0.36	0.36	0.08	fW........	0.450	0.450	0.100

$\bar{W} = 0.80$	$\bar{W} = 1.00$
$\Delta q = \dfrac{0.26}{0.80} - 0.40 = -0.075$	$\Delta q = 0.325 - 0.400 = -0.075$

which is a simplified version of Fisher's (1930a) *fundamental theorem of natural selection:* "The rate of increase in fitness of any organism at any time is equal to its genetic variance in fitness at that time."

The improvement in average fitness of a population by selection is of course due to the changes in gene frequencies. Therefore, $\Delta \bar{W}$ and Δq are merely two different ways of describing the same effect of selection. One form may be more convenient than the other, depending on the nature of the problem. The use of $\Delta \bar{W}$ as a measure of the effect of selection is usually practical for polygenic characters.

The average fitness of any natural population over a period of time must be very near unity, because, otherwise, the population would either multiply without limit or become extinct.

§ 13. *Variable Selection Coefficients*

It has been assumed in the preceding sections that the value of W for a genotype is a constant, being independent of gene frequencies in the population.

This may not be the case at all for many characters in nature. The territory occupied by a population may contain diverse ecological niches, for each of which one genotype is better adapted than the others. Therefore, each genotype is favored when it is rare (competition for niches low) but selected against when abundant (competition for niches high), assuming that the individuals are capable of exercising some choice. In other words, the selective values may be functions of gene frequencies themselves. We shall consider the simplest model of this kind in the following. Let the fitnesses of the genotypes be (Wright, 1948)

$$W: \quad \overset{AA}{1 - s + tq}, \quad \overset{Aa}{1}, \quad \overset{aa}{1 + s - tq} \tag{25W}$$

so that the heterozygote is always exactly intermediate between the two homozygous types (s and t are constants). We see that, when q is small, individuals aa will be favored and AA will be selected against. When q is large, their fitnesses will be reversed. For example, if $s = 0.08$ and $t = 0.20$, then

	AA	Aa	aa
When $q = 0.10$	$W = 0.94$	1	1.06
When $q = 0.80$	$W = 1.08$	1	0.92

For random-mating populations it will be found that

$$\bar{W} = 1 - (s - tq)(p - q)$$

and

$$\Delta q = \frac{q(1 - q)(s - tq)}{\bar{W}}, \tag{25}$$

yielding an equilibrium value of $\hat{q} = s/t$. Taking $s = 0.08$ and $t = 0.20$ as before, we have $\hat{q} = 0.40$. Therefore, the population $(.36, .48, .16)$ is in an equilibrium condition for which the fitness of all genotypes is the same ($W = 1 - s + tq = 1$, etc.). This situation is similar to the case in which heterozygotes are favored by selection, in that the equilibrium point is stable and independent of the initial gene frequencies of the population. If the actual q is higher or lower than $\hat{q}$, it will gradually come back to the point s/t. Needless to say, when $s > t$, individuals aa will be favored by selection at all times, whatever the value of q; and thus no stable equilibrium value is possible except when q reaches unity.

§ 14. *Selection in a Two-Factor Case*

Let p_1, q_1 and p_2, q_2 be the frequencies of A, a and B, b, respectively, in a random-mating population. Each of the nine genotypes may have a different adaptive value. We assume dominance and additive selection intensities as shown in the following scheme:

Phenotype	A-B-	A-bb	aaB-	$aabb$
Proportion.........	$(1-q_1^2)(1-q_2^2)$	$(1-q_1^2)q_2^2$	$q_1^2(1-q_2^2)$	$q_1^2 q_2^2$
W...............	1	$1-t_2$	$1-t_1$	$1-t_1-t_2$

Thus, it is easy to see that

$$\bar{W} = 1 - t_1 q_1^2 - t_2 q_2^2 ; \qquad \frac{\partial \bar{W}}{\partial q_1} = -2t_1 q_1 .$$

The new value of q_1 in the next generation may be found by the formulas given in Chapter 8, writing out the nine genotypic proportions first. Upon simplification it will be found that

$$q_1' = \frac{1}{\bar{W}} \{ q_1 - t_1 q_1^2 - t_2 q_1 q_2^2 \} ,$$

so that

$$\Delta q_1 = \frac{q_1 (1 - q_1)}{\bar{W}} \{ -t_1 q_1 \} .$$

This conforms to expression (19), except that $d\bar{W}/dq$ is replaced by $\partial \bar{W}/\partial q_1$. In general, for selection of multiple-factor characters,

$$\Delta q_i = \frac{q_i (1 - q_i)}{2\bar{W}} \frac{\partial \bar{W}}{\partial q_i} . \qquad (26)$$

It should be pointed out here that, in addition to the conditions attached to (19), the present formula is valid only when the selection coefficients are so small that the proportions of genotypes are not seriously disturbed (from equilibrium proportions) by selection in any generation.

If a gene is advantageous in one combination of genes but deleterious in another, there may be various possible equilibrium values for the gene frequencies. Again, for the purpose of illustration, let us consider the simplest case, where the adaptive values of the above four phenotypes are

$$1, \quad 1 - t, \quad 1 - t, \quad 1 + 2t ,$$

respectively. Proceeding exactly as before, we find

$$\bar{W} = 1 - t (q_1^2 - 4 q_1^2 q_2^2 + q_2^2) ; \qquad \frac{\partial \bar{W}}{\partial q_1} = -2t q_1 (1 - 4 q_2^2) .$$

Hence, from (26),

$$\Delta q_1 = \frac{q_1 (1 - q_1)}{\bar{W}} \{ -t q_1 (1 - 4 q_2^2) \} .$$

The expression for Δq_2 may be obtained by replacing q_1 by q_2. When $\Delta q_1 = \Delta q_2 = 0$, we have $\hat{q}_1 = \hat{q}_2 = \frac{1}{2}$. But this is an unstable equilibrium point. The stable ones are $q_i = 0$ or 1. In a more complicated scheme it is possible that there is more than one stable equilibrium point for a two-factor case and that there may be many equilibrium points for multiple-factor characters.

Notes and Exercises

1. When the recessive individuals are completely eliminated in every generation of a random-mating population, show that the proportion of heterozygotes are, using (1) and (2),

$$H_1 = \frac{2q}{(1+q)^2}, \qquad H_2 = \frac{2q(1+q)}{(1+2q)^2}, \qquad H_3 = \frac{2q(1+2q)}{(1+3q)^2},$$

$$H_4 = \frac{2q(1+3q)}{(1+4q)^2}, \cdots, \qquad H_n = \frac{2q[1+(n-1)q]}{(1+nq)^2}.$$

Calculate the genotypic proportions of the first five generations, assuming the initial population is (.25, .50, .25).

2. Let $R_n = q_n^2$ be the proportion of recessives in a random-mating population and s the selection coefficient against them. Check some of the following results, with the aid of (4), for the initial population (.25, .50, .25).

	$s=0.10$	$s=0.25$	$s=0.50$	$s=1.00$
R_1..........	0.2373	0.2178	0.1837	0.1111
R_2..........	.2253	.1901	.1374	.0625
R_3..........	.2140	.1664	.1051	.0400
R_4..........	.2033	.1461	.0822	.0278
R_5..........	0.1932	0.1287	0.0656	0.0204

3. Calculate the values of Δq, as given by (5), for the following values of q, assuming $s = 0.20$ against the recessives, and plot the curve.

q	0.01	0.10	0.30	0.50	0.60	0.70	0.90	0.99	0.995
Δq									

4. Using (7) or (7′), check the statement that it takes 5,189 generations to reduce the value of q from 0.50 to 0.02 when $s = 0.01$ against the recessives of a random-mating population (Table 68).

5. If we work with the gene-frequency ratio, $u = p/q$, a population $(u^2, 2u, 1)$ will become $(u^2, 2u, 1 - s)$ after selection against the recessive individuals. Show that

$$\Delta u = \frac{su}{u+1-s}.$$

When s is small, it may be replaced by the differential equation $du/dt = su/(u + 1)$. Integration gives (Haldane, 1924, 1932)

$$s n = u_n - u_0 + \log_e \frac{u_n}{u_0},$$

which is a simpler form of our (7).

6. For gametic selection show that (10) is equivalent to

$$\log_e \frac{u_n}{u_0} = s n ; \qquad \therefore u_n = u_0 e^{sn} .$$

Derive these formulas independently by showing that $\Delta u = su$, approximately, when s is small. If $s = 0.01$ against the recessive gene, show that it takes 230 generations to raise $u_0 = 1$ to $u_n = 10$.

7. If selection acts only on the gametes of one sex, we may still use expression (9) if we replace s by $\frac{1}{2}s$. The proof of this is indicated in the following:

		p	$q(1-s)$
p		p^2	$pq(1-s)$
q		pq	$q^2(1-s)$

The genotypic proportions in the next generation will be

$$p^2 AA + (2pq - spq)Aa + (q^2 - sq^2)aa$$

of a total of $1 - spq - sq^2 = 1 - sq$. Hence

$$\Delta q = \frac{pq - \frac{1}{2}spq + q^2 - sq^2}{1 - sq} - q = \frac{-\frac{1}{2}spq}{1 - sq} .$$

8. In Chapter 4 there was mention of the various kinds of gene arrangements in the third chromosome of *Drosophila pseudoobscura*. Dobzhansky (1943) found cyclic changes in the frequencies of certain types of chromosomes in populations collected on Mount San Jacinto, California. The "standard" type (ST) is least frequent in June, increases in frequency during summer, remains high during autumn and winter, but declines again during the next spring. The frequency of the "Chiricahua" type (CH) undergoes a cyclic change just opposite to that of ST. Similar changes have been observed in artificial population cages, where the natural conditions are nearly reproduced (Wright and Dobzhansky, 1946). These changes in chromosomal frequencies are best explained by the effect of natural selection under the varying conditions of the seasons.

   It was estimated from observed data that the adaptive values of ST/ST, ST/CH, CH/CH flies at 20° C. are approximately 0.70, 1.00, 0.30, respectively. These estimates were confirmed by later experiments. In one set of experiments, Dobzhansky (1947) introduced an initial population of 1,366 flies into an artificial cage. The frequency of ST chromosomes was $p = 0.203$ and that of CH chromosomes $q = 0.797$. Samples of eggs deposited in the cage were taken at approximately four-week intervals, and in each sample the gene arrangement was determined for 300 chromosomes (from 150 larvas). The expected and the observed frequencies of the two types of chromosomes are shown in the left half (Experiment I) of the following table:

	EXPERIMENT I				EXPERIMENT II		
Time (1945)	Observed		Expected		Time (1945)	Observed	
	ST	CH	ST	CH		ST	CH
Initial......	0.203	0.797	0.203	0.797	Initial......	0.896	0.104
Oct.........	.323	.677	.351	.649	Nov.........	.867	.133
Nov........	.427	.573	.470	.530	Dec.........	.850	.150
Dec........	0.547	0.453	.548	.452	Jan., 1946..	0.800	0.200
Limit.......	...	...	0.700	0.300			

The expected chromosomal frequencies are calculated according to (11), assuming $s_1 = 0.30$ and $s_2 = 0.70$, and taking the length of a generation to be approximately one month. Thus, the expected CH frequency in the October generation is

$$q_1 = \frac{0.797 - 0.70\,(0.797)^2}{1 - 0.3\,(0.203)^2 - 0.7\,(0.797)^2} = \frac{0.3523}{0.5430} = 0.649.$$

The agreement between the observed and expected frequencies is excellent. Unfortunately, the population cages were destroyed by mite infections in early January, 1946, and it was impossible to check the validity of the theoretical prediction that the final frequencies of ST and CH should be 0.70 and 0.30, respectively.

But, if our hypothesis is true, it follows that, if the initial frequency of CH is less than its equilibrium value, it should gradually increase toward it as a limit. To test this, Dobzhansky in another set of experiments in October, 1945, introduced into a population cage, maintained at the same temperature as before, 2,235 flies containing 89.6 per cent ST and 10.4 per cent CH chromosomes. Samples of eggs were taken at monthly intervals, and 300 III-chromosomes were examined in each sample. The frequencies are shown in the right half of the above table. The frequency of CH, this time, steadily increases. The observed rate of change is again as fast as expected on the assumption that $s_1 = 0.30$ and $s_2 = 0.70$ against the "homozygous" types. The stable equilibrium point (12) may be approached from either direction. It should be pointed out that, even if the experiment had been carried a few generations more, the value of Δq in later generations would be much smaller per generation as q approached $\hat{q}$, as indicated by (13).

No change in chromosomal frequencies was observed at 16.5° C. or below. This means that the adaptive values of the various types of flies are approximately the same at low temperatures and clearly shows that the "fitness" of an organism varies with environmental conditions. The increase in CH frequency in spring under natural conditions indicates a complete change of the values of s_1 and s_2 during that season. What physiological properties of the individuals with various gene arrangements are responsible for the differential survival is unknown. It has been shown, however, that selection acts between the larval and the adult stages of the flies.

The superiority of the inversion heterozygotes over the homozygotes may furnish a mechanism for the maintenance of heterosis. This problem will be discussed in the next chapter.

9. When the adaptive values of genotypes are constants, the equilibrium values of gene frequencies are such that the average fitness of the population is maximum. To illustrate this principle, let us consider the case in which the heterozygotes are superior to the homozygotes (Table 70). Here, we have

$$\bar{W} = 1 - s_1 p^2 - s_2 q^2 ; \qquad \frac{d\bar{W}}{dq} = 2 s_1 (1 - q) - 2 s_2 q .$$

The maximum value of $\bar{W}$ is attained when $d\bar{W}/dq = 0$, the solution of which yields (12), the same value of q which makes $\Delta q = 0$. Assuming $s_1 = 0.20$ and $s_2 = 0.10$, plot the curve $\bar{W} = 1 - 0.2(1 - q)^2 - 0.1q^2$.

10. When selection favors heterozygotes, the equilibrium condition may also be obtained by equating the gene frequency *ratio* of one generation to that of the next. Thus, at equilibrium, we have

$$\frac{p}{q} = \frac{p^2 (1 - s_1) + pq}{q^2 (1 - s_2) + pq} .$$

Show that the solution of this equation is also that given by (12). This is essentially the form given by Fisher (1930a), except that his relative selective values of genotypes are $a:b:c(= 1 - s_1:1:1 - s_2)$, so that the average fitness of the population is $\bar{W} = p^2 a + 2pqb + q^2 c = 1$.

11. Since the gene frequencies are given by (12) at equilibrium, the population will consist of

$$\frac{s_2^2}{(s_1 + s_2)^2} A A + \frac{2 s_1 s_2}{(s_1 + s_2)^2} A a + \frac{s_1^2}{(s_1 + s_2)^2} a a , \qquad (11P)$$

with fitness $1 - s_1$, 1, $1 - s_2$. Show that the mean and variance of fitness are, respectively (Crow, 1948; Haldane, 1949a),

$$\bar{W} = 1 - \frac{s_1 s_2}{s_1 + s_2}, \qquad \sigma_W^2 = \left(\frac{s_1 s_2}{s_1 + s_2}\right)^2.$$

12. Suppose that in the preceding population (11P) selection acts through differential mortality before reproductive maturity is attained rather than through differential fertility. Then, after selection has operated, the remaining effective mates in the population would consist of

$$s_2^2(1 - s_1)AA + 2s_1 s_2 Aa + s_1^2(1 - s_2)aa$$

of a total of $T = (s_1 + s_2)(s_1 + s_2 - s_1 s_2)$ individuals. Show that the offspring generation of these individuals under random mating is actually the same as that given by (11P).

HINT: Tabulate your calculations systematically as follows:

MATING	RELATIVE FREQUENCY OF MATING	OFFSPRING		
		AA	Aa	aa
$AA \times AA$	$s_2^4(1-s_1)^2$			
$AA \times Aa$	...			
...	...			
Total, T^2	$(s_1+s_2)^2(s_1+s_2-s_1 s_2)^2$			

You will find that the proportion of AA offspring is

$$\frac{1}{T^2}\{ s_2^4 (1 - s_1)^2 + 2 s_1 s_2^3 (1 - s_1) + s_1^2 s_2^2\} = \frac{s_2^2}{(s_1 + s_2)^2},$$

and so on.

13. If the selective advantages of AA, Aa, aa in a random-mating population are $1 + t$, 1, $1 - s$, respectively, show that

$$\Delta q = \frac{q(1 - q)[q(t - s) - t]}{\bar{W}},$$

which is equivalent to (19) and (20).

14. If there are three alleles, and $s_1 = 0.02$, $s_2 = 0.05$, $s_3 = 0.10$, against the homozygotes $A_1 A_1$, $A_2 A_2$, $A_3 A_3$, respectively, while all types of heterozygotes are of equal fitness, what will be the equilibrium frequencies of the alleles A_1, A_2, A_3 in a random-mating population?
ANS.: 0.625, 0.250, 0.125.

15. If one type of heterozygotes is extraordinarily superior to other heterozygotes, the situation is different. Let $W_{ii} = 1$ for all types of homozygotes

and let $W_{ij} = 1 + s$ for all heterozygotes, except that $W_{12} = 1 + t = 1 + s + (t - s)$, where t is larger than s. Then (Wright, 1949a)

$$\bar{W} = 1 + s\,(1 - \Sigma q^2) + 2\,(t - s)\,q_1 q_2\,;$$

$$\Delta q_1 = \frac{q_1}{\bar{W}}\{\,s\,(\Sigma q^2 - q_1) - (t - s)\,(2\,q_1 q_2 - q_2)\,\}\,.$$

The expression for Δq_2 is the same, except that q_1 and q_2 are interchanged. The amount of change in frequency of other alleles is $(i = 3, 4, \ldots, k)$

$$\Delta q_i = \frac{q_i}{\bar{W}}\{\,s\,(\Sigma q^2 - q_i) - 2\,(t - s)\,q_1 q_2\}\,.$$

When equilibrium is reached, all $\Delta q = 0$. Hence, we obtain the following k equations:

$$\begin{cases} s(\Sigma q^2 - q_1) = (t - s)(2q_1 q_2 - q_2) \\ s(\Sigma q^2 - q_2) = (t - s)(2q_1 q_2 - q_1) \end{cases}$$

$$\begin{cases} s(\Sigma q^2 - q_3) = (t - s)2q_1 q_2 \\ \quad \cdots \qquad\qquad \cdots \\ s(\Sigma q^2 - q_k) = (t - s)2q_1 q_2\,. \end{cases}$$

From the first two equations we conclude that $\hat{q}_1 = \hat{q}_2$; and from the last $k - 2$ equations we see that $\hat{q}_3 = \hat{q}_4 = \ldots = \hat{q}_k$ at equilibrium (on account of the simplified assumption that all heterozygotes except $A_1 A_2$ are of the same fitness, $1 + s$). Hence

$$2\hat{q}_1 + (k - 2)\hat{q}_3 = 1\,. \tag{15P}$$

Now, subtracting the third from the first of the above k equations, we obtain $sq_3 = (2s - t)q_1$ or

$$\hat{q}_3 = \frac{2s - t}{s}\,\hat{q}_1\,.$$

Substituting this in (15P), we obtain

$$\hat{q}_1 = \hat{q}_2 = \frac{s}{2s + (k - 2)\,(2s - t)}\,;$$

$$\hat{q}_3 = \ldots = \hat{q}_k = \frac{2s - t}{2s + (k - 2)\,(2s - t)}\,.$$

Thus, we see that, if $0 < t < 2s$, all $\hat{q}_i$ are stable. But, if $t > 2s$, $\hat{q}_3 = \hat{q}_4 = \ldots = 0$; all alleles will be eliminated except A_1 and A_2.

16. Let the fitness of the genotypes be 1.2500, 0.9375, 0.6250 in the population (.36, .48, .16) so that $\bar{W} = 1$. Show that in the next generation the improved average fitness of the population is 1.046875 and that $\sigma_W^2 = 0.046875$. (See [24].)

17. Suppose that a metrical character is determined by two pairs of genes with equal and additive effects (Chap. 8, Ex. 5) and that medium size is most favored by selection.

Genotypes	Proportion f	Fitness W
$AABB$	$p_1^2 p_2^2$	$1-4t$
$AaBB, AABb$	$2p_1q_1p_2^2+2p_1^2p_2q_2$	$1-t$
$AAbb, AaBb, aaBB$	$p_1^2q_2^2+4p_1q_1p_2q_2+q_1^2p_2^2$	1
$Aabb, aaBb$	$2p_1q_1q_2^2+2q_1^2p_2q_2$	$1-t$
$aabb$	$q_1^2q_2^2$	$1-4t$

$$\bar{W} = 1 - 2t\,(p_1^2 + p_2^2 + 4q_1q_2 - q_1 - q_2) \ .$$

$$\frac{\partial \bar{W}}{\partial q_1} = 6t - 4t\,(q_1 + 2q_2) \ .$$

Hence, from (26),
$$\Delta q_1 = \frac{q_1\,(1 - q_1)}{\bar{W}}\{3t - 2tq_1 - 4tq_2\}.$$

The expression for Δq_2 is similar except that q_1 and q_2 are interchanged. At equilibrium $\Delta q_1 = \Delta q_2 = 0$; therefore, $\hat{q}_1 = \hat{q}_2 = \frac{1}{2}$, and $\bar{W} = 1 - t$.

CHAPTER 20

Joint Effects of Mutation and Selection

THE effects of mutation and selection were considered separately in the preceding two chapters, and it was seen that each pressure, if unopposed, would gradually change the gene frequencies from 0 to 1 or vice versa over a sufficiently long period of time. In nature, however, these two pressures act simultaneously in a population, and, therefore, it is more realistic to examine their joint effects on gene frequencies.

Needless to say, if mutation and selection are exerting pressures in the same direction, the change in gene frequencies will be faster than that indicated in the previous chapters. But, if they oppose each other, their effects may cancel each other; and a stable equilibrium condition may result. In the following we shall deal largely with such equilibrium conditions. Since the equilibrium value of gene frequency is a function of selection intensity and mutation rate, many of the results obtained provide an indirect method of estimating the mutation rate based upon observed values of gene frequency and selection intensity.

§ 1. *Balance between Mutation and Selection*

We begin with the simplest case. Suppose that selection is against the recessive individuals with an intensity s (i.e., $W_{aa} = 1 - s$) and that mutations from A to a occur at the rate μ per generation. The selection pressure will diminish the value of q, while that of mutation will increase it. The net change in q per generation in a random-mating population is

$$\Delta q = \mu(1 - q) - sq^2(1 - q) . \tag{1}$$

The first term represents the gain through incoming mutations; the second, the amount of loss on account of selection, assuming s to be small. When these two opposing pressures cancel each other, so that there is no longer any change in gene frequencies, $\Delta q = 0$. The equilibrium value of q is thus given by

$$\mu = s\,\hat{q}^2, \qquad \hat{q}^2 = \frac{\mu}{s}, \qquad \hat{q} = \sqrt{\frac{\mu}{s}} . \tag{2}$$

A graphic representation of (1) and (2) is given in Figure 68.

284

This equilibrium state is stable, although it is approached very slowly; and it may well explain the fact that a certain proportion of unfavorable recessives usually persists in natural populations instead of being wiped out entirely. Since the existence of the recessive gene is supported only by mutation pressure, the value of $\hat{q}$ is usually kept at a very low level. For example, if $\mu = 0.000018$ to the recessive locus and $s = 0.02$ against the recessive zygotes, the equilibrium population will contain $\mu/s = 0.0009$ recessives, with $\hat{q} = \sqrt{0.0009} = 0.03$. Most of the recessive genes are in heterozygous combinations, as the proportion of heterozygotes in this population is $2(0.97)(0.03) = 0.0582$, nearly sixty-five times as high as that of recessives. Moreover, the selection is not effective when

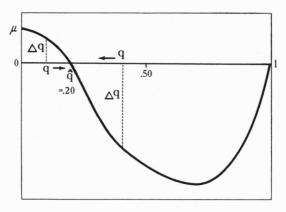

Fig. 68.—The joint effects of mutation and selection. Equation of curve is (1). In actual plotting we take $\mu = 0.04s$ or $s = 25 \mu$, so that $\hat{q} = 0.20$ from (2). When $q < \hat{q}$, Δq is positive and q increases. When $\hat{q} < q$, Δq is negative and q decreases. (From Wright, 1940a, in Huxley.)

q is small. Even when $\hat{q}$ is so small that the proportion of recessives is negligible, the recessive *gene* will still exist in the population, though hidden in heterozygous combinations. So we see that there is really no way of getting rid of a recessive gene in a large population if there is recurring mutation to it.

When the *aa* combination is nearly lethal, so that s is nearly equal to unity, the proportion of *aa* individuals in the population will be roughly equal to the mutation rate:

$$\mu = s\hat{q}^2 \doteq \hat{q}^2 ; \quad \hat{q} \doteq \sqrt{\mu} . \tag{2L}$$

If selection is against homozygous dominants, stable equilibrium may be established by mutations from the recessive to the dominant gene. This situation is identical with the previous case (2) except that q is replaced by p and μ by ν (mutation rate from a to A). Thus, $\hat{p} = \sqrt{(\nu/s)}$.

Human major brachydactyly (short-fingeredness) is a familiar example of a dominant defect. It has been shown that all individuals with brachydactyly are heterozygous, while homozygous combinations are lethal or nearly so (i.e., $s \doteq 1$). Hence, $\hat{p} = \sqrt{\nu}$ approximately. This is a small quantity, so that

$1 - \hat{p} = \hat{q}$ is nearly unity. Now, observed data give us directly the proportion of heterozygous (brachydactylous) individuals in the population. This proportion should be equal to

$$H = 2\hat{p}(1 - \hat{p}) \doteq 2\hat{p} \doteq 2\sqrt{\nu} \; ;$$

$$\therefore \; \nu = \tfrac{1}{4}H^2 \; .$$

Further, when the homozygous dominants are nonviable, but the heterozygous dominants are of a fitness value $W = 1 - s$, as in the case of achondroplasia (chondrodystrophy, a form of dwarfism), the situation may be approximately represented as follows:

Genotype.........	Aa	aa	
Before selection...	H	$R = 1 - H$	
Relative fitness....	$1-s$	1	New Mutants
After selection....	$H-sH$	$1-H$	$2\nu(1-H)$

The elimination of the heterozygous dominants must be balanced by new mutants from the recessive normal allele to the dominant deleterious allele at equilibrium state. Hence, if H is small, we obtain the equation

$$2\nu\,(1 - H) = sH \; ;$$

$$\therefore \nu = \frac{sH}{2\,(1 - H)} \doteq \tfrac{1}{2}sH = \tfrac{1}{2}\,(1 - W)\,H \; . \tag{3}$$

For an application of this formula see Haldane (1949b).

If the heterozygous dominants are also usually nonviable, as in the case of retinoblastoma, the mutation rate from the recessive normal gene to the dominant deleterious gene will be approximately equal to (as $W \rightarrow 0$, or $s \rightarrow 1$),

$$\nu = \tfrac{1}{2}H = p \; . \tag{3L}$$

That is to say, the frequency of the dominant lethal *gene*, or half the incidence of the dominant *trait*, is equal to the mutation rate to that gene. These expressions provide us with an indirect method of estimating the mutation rate from the recessive gene to the dominant gene in the human population.

When the equilibrium value of a gene frequency is small, the effect of reverse mutation is negligible and need not be considered. If q is of intermediate magnitude, then mutations in both directions should be taken into consideration, unless mutations in one direction are known to be much lower than in the other. The total effect of mutations in both directions and of selection against recessive individuals is

$$\Delta q = \mu(1 - q) - \nu q - sq^2(1 - q) \; . \tag{4}$$

Here, Δq is a cubic function of q, and therefore the equation $\Delta q = 0$ may have three roots. (If a root is smaller than 0 or greater than 1, it is of no interest in genetics.) Note that, if $q = 0$, $\Delta q = \mu$, a positive value; and if $q = 1$, $\Delta q = -\nu$, a negative value. In the light of the discussion in Section 9 of Chapter 19, we see that there is at least one stable equilibrium value of q between 0 and 1. But under certain conditions two distinct stable equilibrium values are possible. (In the latter event there will be an unstable point between them.) The number and the stability of the equilibrium values depend upon the given quantities μ, ν, and s in a specific case.

§ 2. *Balance when Selection Is against Heterozygotes*

Selection against heterozygotes, as will be recalled, leads to the unstable value $\hat{q} = \frac{1}{2}$ and to the stable values $\hat{q} = 0$ or 1, depending upon the initial condition of the population. Suppose that the initial q is less than $\frac{1}{2}$ and is thus decreasing every generation because of selection against the heterozygotes. This trend may be balanced by mutations from A to a, so that a stable equilibrium may be maintained. Since the existence of the rare gene is supported only by the mutation pressure, its equilibrium value is necessarily low.

The new value of q after selection against the heterozygotes, and also of Δq, are given by (15) of Chapter 19. From the expression for q', we obtain $p' = 1 - q' = (p - spq)/(1 - 2spq)$. Now, the gain in q through incoming mutations is $\mu p' = \mu(1 - q') = \mu(p - spq)/(1 - 2spq)$. In equilibrium condition this amount gained through mutation must be equal to that lost on account of selection. Hence, we obtain the following equation, the denominators $(1 - 2spq)$ of both sides being canceled off:

$$\mu(p - spq) = spq(1 - 2q) .$$

Simplifying, we obtain

$$\mu = \frac{sq\,(1 - 2q)}{1 - sq} \doteq sq\,(1 - 2q) \doteq sq\,, \qquad \text{or} \qquad q \doteq \frac{\mu}{s}\,, \qquad (5)$$

if both s and q are small. The equilibrium gene frequency $\hat{q} = \mu/s$ is much smaller than $\hat{q} = \sqrt{(\mu/s)}$, as given by (2), where the selection is against the recessives instead of against the heterozygotes. That this should be the case becomes clear at once if it is recalled that, when q is small, the proportion of heterozygotes in a panmictic population is much higher than that of recessives; thus the selection against heterozygotes is more effective, and consequently the equilibrium $\hat{q}$ is lower.

Now, if $q = \mu/s$ is a small quantity, then q^2 will be negligible. The equilibrium population will consist of only two genotypes in the following proportions (Haldane, 1927, 1942, 1949a):

$$(1 - 2q)\,AA + 2q\,Aa = \left(1 - \frac{2\mu}{s}\right)AA + \frac{2\mu}{s}\,Aa\,. \qquad (5Z)$$

It should be remarked that the above analysis, and the result (5) in particular, apply only to cases where *all* heterozygotes in the population have a survival value of $1 - s$. The situation in which there is selection against heterozygous babies born to recessive mothers, as in the case of the Rh factor, has also been discussed by Haldane (1942).

Also note that the *limiting* situation for selection against the heterozygote, as given in this section, becomes the same as selection against the dominant deleterious gene described in the preceding section. Thus, in (5Z), we have $H = 2\mu/s$, or $\mu = \frac{1}{2}sH$, which is equivalent to (3) except that μ is replaced by v.

§ 3. *Balance for Sex-linked Genes*

Hemophilia is a well-known recessive sex-linked trait which is semilethal for men but practically unknown in women (may be extremely rare or nonviable). Since only a minority of hemophilic men live long enough to have children, this trait should be rapidly disappearing from the population unless new genes for hemophilia are arising by mutation. This last does indeed seem to be the case for some pedigrees.

Let us assume that the population is in approximate equilibrium condition with respect to this locus and that q is the frequency of the recessive gene for hemophilia. Then q is also the proportion of hemophiliacs among men. Let their survival value be $W = 1 - s$. Then there will be sq genes for hemophilia lost among the males in one generation. The same amount must have been balanced by new mutations from normal alleles. Since every female has two X-chromosomes and every male has one, the total mutations from all sex chromosomes in the population must be approximately (Haldane, 1935)

$$3\mu = sq \quad \text{or} \quad \mu = \tfrac{1}{3}sq . \tag{6}$$

No exact estimates of the incidence of hemophilia exist, since this defective trait is so rare. From hospital records, however, it has been estimated that q is probably between 0.00004 and 0.00017. If we take the survival value of hemophiliacs as 0.25, so that $s = 0.75$, the mutation rate for this gene would be between 0.00001 and 0.00004, according to (6). Hence, Haldane (1935) reached the conclusion that $\mu = 0.00002$, or 1 in 50,000, would be a fairly good estimate.

Expression (6) refers to the case in which selection operates only against male recessives. If selection operates against the recessive of both sexes when q is not too small, appropriate expressions for $\hat{q}$ may be obtained by writing out the values of Δq due to selection for each sex and then equating the average value of Δq for both sexes to the gain through new mutations.

§ 4. *Balance in Populations with Inbreeding*

Before dealing with inbreeding populations, we shall deduce a more general expression for any equilibrium population. Let D, H, R be the proportions of AA, Aa, aa whose selective values are $1, 1, 1 - s$, respectively, so that the average fitness of the population is $1 - sR$. Then the new frequency of the recessive gene after selection is

$$q' = \frac{\frac{1}{2}H + R(1-s)}{1-sR} = \frac{q - sR}{1 - sR};$$

so that

$$\Delta q = q' - q = \frac{-s(1-q)R}{1-sR} \doteq -s(1-q)R,$$

approximately, when s is small. This amount of change due to selection must be balanced by an equal amount through new mutations from A to a at equilibrium. The latter amount is $\mu p = \mu(1-q)$. Equating these two quantities, we obtain

$$\hat{R} = \frac{\mu}{s}, \tag{7}$$

regardless of the mating system, provided that this is a small quantity. In a random-mating population it reduces to the middle expression of (2).

For an equilibrium population with inbreeding coefficient F, the values of D, H, R are given in Chapter 11. Substituting, we have (Haldane, 1940)

$$\hat{R} = q^2 + Fpq = (1-F) q^2 + Fq = \frac{\mu}{s}; \tag{8}$$

$$\therefore \hat{q} = \frac{-F + \sqrt{[F^2 + 4(1-F)\mu/s]}}{2(1-F)}, \tag{9}$$

taking the positive root of (8) as the equilibrium value of q. This $\hat{q}$ is always smaller than that given by (2) for random-mating populations because of the inbreeding which produces proportionally more recessives for selection to act upon. For example, when $\mu = 0.000018$ and $s = 0.02$ (as assumed on p. 284), but with $F = 0.05$, the proportion of recessive individuals (R) in an equilibrium population still will be 0.0009, according to (8). But the value of $\hat{q}$ will be much lower than the 0.03 value for random-mating populations. From (9) we obtain

$$\hat{q} = \frac{-0.05 + \sqrt{[0.0025 + 4(0.95)(0.0009)]}}{2(0.95)} = 0.01418.$$

It is clear that the effect of inbreeding is to diminish the equilibrium value of q rather than the recessive proportion R.

When both F and q are small, so that the term Fq^2 is negligible in comparison with the other terms of (8), the proportion of recessives at equilibrium will be approximately

$$q^2 + Fq \doteq \frac{\mu}{s}, \quad \text{and} \quad \hat{q} \doteq \frac{1}{2}\left\{\sqrt{\left(F^2 + \frac{4\mu}{s}\right)} - F\right\}. \tag{10}$$

For human populations in which F is small this approximation may be used for rare defective recessive genes. For instance, if $F = 0.005$ in the above example, (9) yields $\hat{q} = 0.0277$, while (10) gives $\hat{q} = 0.0276$.

§ 5. *Lessening of Inbreeding*

The lessening of inbreeding in a population will increase the value of q until a new equilibrium value corresponding to the new (lower) value of F is reached. Let us consider once more the population with $\mu = 0.000018$ and $s = 0.02$, so that $R = 0.0009$. If the inbreeding coefficient of this equilibrium population is $F = 0.011282$, then $\hat{q} = 0.025$ according to (9). Now, as an extreme example, suppose inbreeding is abolished entirely. The proportion of recessives in the following generation will be $(0.025)^2 = 0.000625$ on account of random mating. The *immediate* effect of relaxation of inbreeding is a sharp fall in the proportion of recessives in the population (from 900 to 625 per million in our example). This newly lowered value of R is below the equilibrium value of $\mu/s = 0.0009$,

TABLE 77

ESTABLISHMENT OF A NEW EQUILIBRIUM WITH $\mu = 0.000018$ AND
$s = 0.02$ AFTER RELAXATION OF INBREEDING

Stage I	Stage II	$\longrightarrow$	Stage III
Original Status:	Immediately after relaxation of in-breeding	. . .	*Final Result:*
Old equilibrium $F=0.0113$ $q=0.0250$	$F=0$ $q=0.0250$	(*q* increasing)	New equilibrium $F=0$ $\hat{q}=0.0300$
$D=p^2+Fpq\ =0.9509$ $H=2(1-F)pq=0.0482$ $R=q^2+Fpq\ =0.0009$	$D=p^2\ =0.950625$ $H=2pq=0.048750$ $R=q^2\ =0.000625$	. . . .	$D=\hat{p}^2\ =0.9409$ $H=2\hat{p}\hat{q}=0.0582$ $R=\hat{q}^2\ =0.0009$
Total. 1.0000	1.000000	. . .	1.0000

at which the pressures of selection and mutation balance each other. Since there are fewer recessives for selection to act upon, the recessive gene will increase gradually from 0.025 until it reaches 0.030, so that $R = 0.0009$ again (Table 77).

Since the increase of q depends solely upon the excess of new incoming mutations in each generation (over those eliminated by selection), the approach to the new equilibrium condition is a very slow process indeed. It will take several hundred or thousand generations for q to increase from 0.025 to 0.030 in the above example. Furthermore, even when it reaches the new and higher equilibrium value of 0.03, the proportion of recessive individuals in the population will be 0.0009, exactly the same as that before inbreeding was relaxed, although higher than the 0.000625 value immediately after relaxation. In other words, the relaxation of inbreeding increases the final value of q but not that of R. The value of R cannot be increased as long as μ and s remain constant. In view of the above analysis, the problem of whether or not certain human defective recessive genes may be on the increase due to recent relaxation of inbreeding is largely academic. The decrease of s against recessive individuals which results from modern medical science may have a more serious effect because it increases the final equilibrium value of R as well as that of q.

§ 6. *Hypotheses of Heterosis*

Broadly speaking, there are two principal hypotheses to explain hybrid vigor and the "deleterious" effects of inbreeding. One is based on the observation that recessive genes are usually detrimental in homozygous condition (*favorable dominance hypothesis*). Inbreeding increases homozygosis and thus results in deterioration. Hybridization brings homozygous loci of both parents into heterozygous condition, which covers up the detrimental effects of recessive loci. In other words, the vigor of hybrids is due to the presence of a larger number of dominant favorable genes in hybrids than in either parent. According to this hypothesis, the theoretical maximum vigor would be attained when there is at least one dominant allele in each locus of the organism. The difference in vigor between any two individuals would be determined by the number of homozygous recessive loci possessed by these individuals.

The other hypothesis assumes that there is something about hybridity per se that contributes to vigor. This means that there are loci for which the heterozygote is superior to either homozygote and that the increased vigor is proportional to the amount of heterozygosis (*overdominance or superdominance hypothesis*).

In the following we shall assume that "vigor" is measured by the selective values of genotypes, and we shall examine the effects in natural populations of the above two hypotheses. As before, let the selective value of recessive individuals be $W_{aa} = 1 - s$ and the mutation rate from the dominant allele to the recessive be μ per generation. Then the average adaptive value of the entire population is (Haldane, 1937*b;* Crow, 1948, 1952)

$$\bar{W} = 1 - sR = 1 - s\left(\frac{\mu}{s}\right) = 1 - \mu. \tag{11}$$

Thus, the average reduction in $\bar{W}$ due to a detrimental recessive gene is equal to the mutation rate to that gene and is independent of its selective value. Now, if there are n deleterious recessive loci in the population, the reduction in $\bar{W}$ of the population will be

$$\mu_1 + \mu_2 + \mu_3 + \ldots + \mu_n = n\bar{\mu},$$

assuming gene effects to be additive, where $\bar{\mu}$ stands for the average mutation rate of the n loci under consideration. The quantity $n\bar{\mu}$ is not likely to be large. For example, taking $\bar{\mu} = 10^{-5}$ and $n = 5000$, $n\bar{\mu} = 0.05$ (Crow, 1948). This means that, even if all the 5000 deleterious loci were replaced by their dominant alleles, we could expect only a 5 per cent increase in $\bar{W}$ (which we take as a measure of vigor). This may well explain the fact that many self-pollinating plants (e.g., wheat, barley, etc.) in nature are of normal vigor and show only slight heterosis on hybridization. In fact, the quantity $n\bar{u}$ may be much smaller than 0.05; and perhaps no more than 1 per cent improvement can be expected from this source (Fisher, 1949).

If a normally open-pollinated species with $\hat{q} = \sqrt{(\mu/s)}$ is inbred for several generations until most individuals become homozygous for a certain locus, the proportion of homozygous recessives in the inbred population is equal to $\hat{q}$ (Chap. 9). For inbred populations (see gametic selection, p. 257)

$$\bar{W} = 1 - sq = 1 - s\sqrt{\frac{\mu}{s}} = 1 - \sqrt{s\mu};$$

and the reduction in $\bar{W}$ due to n recessive loci is $n\sqrt{s\mu}$, assuming gene effects additive. This value is much larger than $n\bar{u}$. The favorable dominance hypothesis can account for the loss of vigor in inbreeding plants such as maize and for its recovery on crossing different inbred lines, but it can hardly account for any large increase (15 or 20 per cent or sometimes even more) beyond the original vigor before inbreeding.

When the vigor in crosses between inbred lines is considerably higher than that of the random-mating populations from which they were derived, the over-dominance hypothesis seems more plausible. When heterozygotes are more vigorous than either homozygote,

$$\bar{W} = 1 - s_1 p^2 - s_2 q^2 = 1 - \frac{s_1 s_2}{s_1 + s_2};$$

and the reduction in $\bar{W}$ for such a locus is much greater than μ, as pointed out by Haldane (1937b). It would not require very many such loci to account for the pronounced excess vigor of hybrids between inbred lines, because a single overdominant locus has a tremendously greater effect on the population fitness than a recessive locus.

The most reasonable conclusion that may be drawn from the above analysis is that the phenomenon "heterosis" possibly is due to two (or more) different causes. The loss of vigor in artificially inbred lines of normally cross-pollinated plants, and their recovery of the original vigor on hybridization, may well be explained by the favorable dominance hypothesis. On the other hand, any large increase in vigor beyond the level of vigor of the original equilibrium population may be due to genes which are more favorable in the heterozygous condition Crow (1948, 1952) gives a fuller discussion of this problem.

§ 7. *Favorable Mutations*

We have seen that a single neutral mutation ultimately will be lost by chance from the population (Chap. 18). This is, however, not quite the case if a new gene confers a certain selective advantage on the individuals who carry it. Let the fitness of such individuals (carrying the newly mutated gene) be $1 + s$. By the same chance mechanism described in Section 1 of Chapter 18, the great majority of the new advantageous genes will be lost in the first few generations after their occurrence, just as in the case of the neutral genes. But the difference here is that an advantageous mutation does have a chance of ultimate survival in the population. When s is small, this chance of survival is approximately equal to $2s$. We shall indicate the proof briefly in the following.

Proceeding exactly as in Exercise 3 of Chapter 18, we define a function

$$f(x) = p_0 + p_1 x + p_2 x^2 + p_3 x^3 + \ldots ,$$

where p_i is the probability that there will be i new genes left in the offspring generation from a parent that carries the new gene. By the same argument we reach the conclusion that

$$l_{n+1} = f(l_n) ,$$

where l_n is the probability of extinction of the gene after n generations of its occurrence. Let us once again assume that the number of offspring of an individual forms a Poisson series. The only difference from the case of a neutral mutation is that the *mean* number of offspring (thus the mean number of the new gene) per parent is $1 + s$ for advantageous genes, instead of unity. Therefore the values of p_i are

$$e^{-(1+s)} \left\{ 1, \quad (1+s), \quad \frac{(1+s)^2}{2!}, \quad \frac{(1+s)^3}{3!}, \quad \ldots \right\}.$$

Hence,

$$f(x) = e^{-(1+s)} \left\{ e^{(1+s)x} \right\} = e^{(1+s)\,(x-1)} ;$$

and

$$l_{n+1} = e^{(1+s)\,(l_n-1)} . \tag{12}$$

The values of l_n were given in the right-hand half of Table 65 for $s = 0.01$. Let us calculate the first few values of l_n by way of illustration. Thus, $l_1 = f(0) = e^{-1.01} = 0.3642$; $l_2 = e^{1.01(0.3642-1)} = e^{-0.6421} = 0.5262$; and so on. The probabilities of extinction for the first seven generations have been given in Table 65. We see that, even if the mutations are beneficial to the individuals from the very beginning, more than three-quarters of the new genes will be lost in the first six generations after their occurrence merely through the chance mechanism of reproduction.

The limiting value of l_n may be found from the relation $l_{n+1} = f(l_n)$. The limiting value must be such that l_{n+1} and l_n are equal when n is large. In other words, it must satisfy the equation (Königs, in Haldane, 1932, appendix)

$$l = f(l) = e^{(1+s)\,(l-1)} . \tag{12'}$$

To solve this equation, we put $l = 1 - y$, so that y is the probability of ultimate survival of an advantageous mutation:

$$1 - y = e^{-(1+s)y} ;$$

$$\therefore \ -(1+s)y = \log\,(1-y) .$$

Since y is a small quantity, $\log_e (1 - y)$ may be expanded into a power series of y. Thus,

$$- y - sy = - y - \frac{y^2}{2} - \frac{y^3}{3} - \cdots ;$$

$$\therefore s = \frac{y}{2} + \frac{y^2}{3} + \cdots . \tag{13}$$

This is the relation between selective advantage and ultimate survival probability. Putting $s = 0.01$ and neglecting any powers of y higher than its square in (13), we obtain $y = 0.0197$ and $1 - y = l = 0.9803$, which are the limiting values tabulated on page 242. When s is small, and therefore the chance of survival is also small, we have

$$y = 2s , \tag{13'}$$

approximately. The same conclusion has been reached by Wright (1931, p. 133) through a different method.

Let us assume that both s and y are so small that (13′) holds and that $l = 1 - 2s$. We may now ask how many new mutations are required, or how many times must a mutation occur, in order to insure that its chance of survival is greater than its chance of extinction? If there are N such mutations in the population in one generation, the chance that all of them should be lost eventually is $l^N = (1 - 2s)^N$. We want this probability to be less than $\frac{1}{2}$, so that the probability that some of the N mutations will survive is greater than $\frac{1}{2}$. Thus, we put

$$(1 - 2 s)^{N} < \tfrac{1}{2} \qquad \text{or} \qquad (1 - 2 s)^{-N} > 2 ;$$

$$- N \log_e (1 - 2 s) \doteq - N \{ - 2 s \} > \log_e 2 ;$$

that is,

$$N > \frac{\log_e 2}{2 s} = \frac{0.69315}{2 s} . \tag{14}$$

Therefore, when $s = 0.01$, the new mutation must occur more than $0.69315 \times 50 = 35$ times before chance is in favor of its establishment in the population. If the mutation rate is $1/10^5$ per generation, it requires a population of 3.5 million individuals in order that this mutation may occur 35 times per generation. We must conclude that new mutations, *even if beneficial, have practically no chance of survival in a small population.* The role of mutation in the evolutionary change of small natural populations must be relatively insignificant. The leading factor in such change is chance fixation of genes, which will be discussed in Chapter 22.

If a mutation is neutral in heterozygous but favorable in homozygous combination, its chance of ultimate survival is much smaller than indicated in the foregoing, because selection cannot act in its favor until two such (recessive) mutations are present in the same zygote. This could happen only when the frequency of the new gene has become appreciable. Before this stage is reached, however, it will very probably be lost by chance. So the initial increase of a recessive gene depends largely on its mutation rate and on chance. When this gene becomes so frequent that recessive individuals appear in the population, selection begins to accelerate its rate of increase.

The general implications of the joint effects of mutation and selection in human populations are too intricate to be discussed here. The reader is referred to Muller's *Our Load of Mutations* (1950) for a thorough review of this subject.

Notes and Exercises

1. The equation (1) may be represented graphically in a manner different from that shown in Figure 68. The effects of mutation and selection may be plotted separately by the following equations:

$$\Delta_1 = \mu(1 - q), \quad \text{and} \quad \Delta_2 = sq^2(1 - q).$$

Their intersection point gives us the equilibrium value of q as shown in Figure 69, because at this point $\Delta_1 = \Delta_2$, so that $\Delta q = 0$. The distance between the two curves gives the magnitude of Δq.

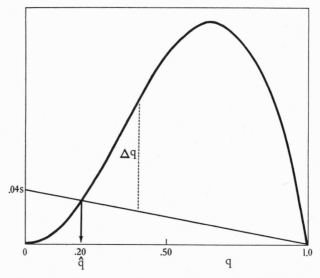

FIG. 69.—Joint effects of mutation and selection. Equation of straight line is $\Delta_1 = \mu(1 - q)$; curve is $\Delta_2 = sq^2(1 - q)$. In the figure $\mu = 0.04s$, so that $\hat{q} = 0.20$, from (2). (Modified from Wright, 1931.)

2. When selection is against aa with an intensity s, and the mutation rate from A to a is μ per generation, the equilibrium condition may also be obtained by equating the gene-frequency ratio of one generation to that of the next; thus

$$\frac{p}{q} = \frac{p^2 + pq - \mu p}{(1 - s) q^2 + pq + \mu p}.$$

Show that its solution is $q^2 = \mu/s$, the same as (2).

3. If recessive individuals are completely eliminated from a random-mating population, but incoming mutations are at the rate of μ per generation, show that the new gene frequency is

$$q' = \frac{q}{1+q} + \frac{\mu}{1+q} \quad \text{and} \quad \Delta q = \frac{\mu - q^2}{1+q}.$$

What is the equilibrium value of q? Check with (2L).

4. If the mutation rate from A to a is μ per generation, but the selective value of the a gametes is $1 - s$ in comparison with a value of unity for A gametes. show that

$$\Delta q = \mu(1 - q) - sq(1 - q) \quad \text{and} \quad \hat{q} = \frac{\mu}{s}.$$

Note that this equilibrium value is much lower than that for zygotic selection.

5. If there are two brachydactylous individuals per thousand in a large random-mating population, and we assume that homozygous brachydactyly is lethal, what would be the mutation rate from normal to brachydactyly gene in order to balance loss of the latter gene through selection? Ans.: $\nu = 10^{-6}$.

6. Suppose that the homozygous dominants all die and that the heterozygous dominants have a fitness value of $W = 1 - s$. If the mutation rate from the recessive normal gene to the deleterious dominant gene is $\nu = 0.000016$ per generation, the incidence of the dominant trait, that is, the proportion of heterozygous individuals (H) in the population, will be as follows:

W	Equilibrium State	H
1........	$\nu = 0.000016 = \frac{1}{4}H^2$	0.008000
0.75.....	$\nu = 0.000016 = \frac{1}{2}(0.25)H$	0.000128
0.50.....	$\nu = 0.000016 = \frac{1}{2}(0.50)H$	0.000064
0.25.....	$\nu = 0.000016 = \frac{1}{2}(0.75)H$	0.000043
→0......	$\nu = 0.000016 = \frac{1}{2}H$	0.000032

7. In an equilibrium population with $F = 0.05$, $s = 0.02$ against the recessives, and $\mu = 0.000018$ to the recessive gene, if inbreeding is suddenly relaxed completely, what will be the proportion of recessive individuals in the next generation? What will happen in subsequent generations? Hint: $(0.01418)^2 = 0.000201$.

8. If both types of homozygotes are equally inferior to the heterozygote (i.e., $s_1 = s_2 = s$), show that $\bar{W} = 1 - \frac{1}{2}s$.

9. Since the limiting value of l_n is 0.9803 for $s = 0.01$, verify the relation that

$$0.9803 = e^{1.01(0.9803-1)} . \qquad\qquad \text{i.e., } (12')$$

10. Farm crops and livestock may be improved by artificial selection as practiced by plant and animal breeders. Upon suspension of selection, however, the improved strain sometimes shows a retrogression to the unimproved state; and nongeneticists often wonder if the gain through breeding is permanent. Two genetic explanations may be offered to account for this phenomenon. One is that new deleterious mutations arise unopposed by any selection pressure. Another is that the trait selected for has a lower fitness under natural conditions which tends to restore the population to its original favorable type. Nothing is really "permanent" in the biological world.

CHAPTER 21

Subdivision and Migration

WHEN we examine actual populations under natural conditions, they seldom turn out to be the single breeding unit that has been used as our model in the preceding chapters. The subdivision of a large population into subpopulations or groups, each forming, more or less, a breeding unit by itself, is known as *isolation*, which may be complete or only partial. The isolation may result from a variety of physical or physiological causes. Whatever the cause, such divisions have effects which are of importance to our genetical analysis of the total population.

Many of the phenomena to be described in this chapter have long been known to naturalists and ecologists, but the formulation of the effects of isolation in *quantitative* terms is largely the work of Wright.

§ 1. *Wahlund's Formula*

The simplest case is that of a large population subdivided into K groups of equal size, within each of which matings are at random. Let q_i be the frequency of gene a in the ith group ($p_i + q_i = 1$), and $\bar{q}$ be the frequency of a in the total population ($\bar{p} + \bar{q} = 1$). We further assume that each group is of a size large enough that the zygotic proportions will be p_i^2, $2p_iq_i$, q_i^2. The mean and variance of the group gene frequencies are thus

$$\bar{q} = \frac{\Sigma q_i}{K}, \qquad \sigma_q^2 = \frac{\Sigma (q_i - \bar{q})^2}{K} = \frac{\Sigma q_i^2}{K} - \bar{q}^2, \tag{1}$$

where the summation is over all groups. Now, if we consider the total population, its zygotic proportions will be

$$
\left.
\begin{aligned}
AA &: \quad \frac{\Sigma p_i^2}{K} = \bar{p}^2 + \sigma_q^2 \\[2mm]
Aa &: \frac{2\Sigma p_i q_i}{K} = 2\bar{p}\,\bar{q} - 2\sigma_q^2 \\[2mm]
aa &: \quad \frac{\Sigma q_i^2}{K} = \bar{q}^2 + \sigma_q^2
\end{aligned}
\right\}, \tag{2}
$$

as may be readily verified (Ex. 1). This expression was first given by Wahlund (1928). Should the total population form a single random-mating unit instead of being subdivided into several groups, its zygotic proportions would be simply $\bar{p}^2$, $2\bar{p}\bar{q}$, $\bar{q}^2$. We see at once that the effect of subdivision on the total population is to increase each homozygous proportion by the amount σ_q^2, at the expense of heterozygotes. This effect is thus similar to that of inbreeding with respect to the whole population and will be discussed in the next section. A numerical illustration of (2) is given in Table 78.

TABLE 78

SUBDIVISION OF A LARGE POPULATION INTO FIVE ($K = 5$)
RANDOM-MATING GROUPS OF EQUAL SIZE

Group	p_i	q_i	p_i^2	$2p_iq_i$	q_i^2
I	0.9	0.1	0.81	0.18	0.01
II	.8	.2	.64	.32	.04
III	.7	.3	.49	.42	.09
IV	.5	.5	.25	.50	.25
V	0.1	0.9	0.01	0.18	0.81
Total population	**0.6**	**0.4**	**0.44**	**0.32**	**0.24**
Proportions if no subdivision			0.36	0.48	0.16
Difference			+0.08	−0.16	+0.08

$$\sigma_p^2 = \sigma_q^2 = 0.40/5 = 0.08$$

If the groups are not of equal size, a weight, w, proportional to group size, may be assigned to each group; and, for the sake of simplicity, we may take $\Sigma w = 1$. Then the mean and variance of q are

$$\bar{q} = \Sigma w_i q_i \quad \text{and} \quad \sigma_q^2 = \Sigma w_i q_i^2 - \bar{q}^2. \tag{1'}$$

The proportion of aa zygotes in the total population will be

$$\Sigma w_i q_i^2 = \bar{q}^2 + \sigma_q^2. \tag{2'}$$

So Wahlund's formula is of general application whether the group sizes are equal or not. The actual magnitude of σ_q^2 depends, of course, upon how the value of q_i is distributed among the various groups.

§ 2. *Subdivision and Inbreeding*

Comparing Wahlund's proportions (2) with those of an equilibrium population having an inbreeding coefficient F (Chap. 11, eq. [2]), we obtain the relation (Wright, 1943)

$$\sigma_q^2 = F\bar{q}(1 - \bar{q}) \quad \text{or} \quad F = \frac{\sigma_q^2}{\bar{q}(1 - \bar{q})}. \tag{3}$$

It should be emphasized at this point that the F here applies to the total population. By this we mean that the zygotic proportions in the entire population (e.g., those shown in Table 78) are such as would result if a certain degree (F) of inbreeding had been practiced within the whole population. As far as each group is concerned, however, the matings are still at random. To be more precise, if we let F_G be the inbreeding coefficient of a group, and F_T be the inbreeding coefficient of the total population, we have, for the numerical example in Table 78, $F_G = 0$ for all groups, and yet $F_T = 0.08/(0.6 \times 0.4) = \frac{1}{3}$ according to (3). Thus we see that the value of F depends upon the population to which it refers. With a fixed system of mating, the larger the population we consider, the higher will be the value of F.

TABLE 79

RESULTS OF TWO GENERATIONS OF SIB MATING, FOR WHICH
THE INITIAL POPULATION CONSISTS ENTIRELY
OF HETEROZYGOTES

(Taken from the Row for $n = 2$ in Table 36)

Matings	q	f	fq	fq^2
$AA \times AA$	0	9	0	0
$AA \times Aa$	0.25	12	3	0.75
$\left.\begin{array}{l} AA \times aa \\ Aa \times Aa \end{array}\right\}$	0.50	22	11	5.50
$Aa \times aa$	0.75	12	9	6.75
$aa \times aa$	1.00	9	9	9.00
Total	....	64	32	22.00

$$\bar{q} = \tfrac{32}{64} = \tfrac{1}{2}, \qquad \sigma_q^2 = \tfrac{22}{64} - (\tfrac{1}{2})^2 = \tfrac{3}{32}$$

The relation between subdivision and inbreeding may be further illustrated by the following simple example. It will be recalled that continued sib mating subdivides the total population into many small isolates, each consisting of only two individuals. Within each sibship, however, brothers and sisters mate at random. Since each "group" consists of only two individuals (four genes), the possible values of q's of the groups are 0, 0.25, 0.50, 0.75, 1.00. The results tabulated in Table 36 (Chap. 10), where $\bar{q} = \frac{1}{2}$, may be re-examined from this new angle. The frequency of $AA \times AA$ matings in the tabulation refers to the relative frequency of groups in which $q = 0$, and that of $AA \times Aa$ matings gives the relative frequency of isolates with $q = 0.25$, etc. For example, the results of two generations of sib mating may be rewritten as in Table 79.

On the other hand, later in Chapter 10 it was shown that $F = \frac{3}{8}$ for two generations of sib mating. Hence, $F\bar{p}\bar{q} = \frac{3}{8} \times \frac{1}{2} \times \frac{1}{2} = \frac{3}{32} = \sigma_q^2$, in agreement with the relation (3). Thus, we see that the subdivision of a population into separate breeding groups is equivalent to the practice of inbreeding within the total population.

§ 3. *Subdivision and Genetic Variance*

Consider a metrical character (Z) which takes the values 2, 1, 0 corresponding to genotypes AA, Aa, aa. Let $\bar{q}$ be the frequency of gene a in the entire population, which has been divided into K equal and random-mating groups with gene frequencies q_i ($i = 1, 2, \ldots, K$). If there were no subdivision, the variance of Z in the entire population would simply be $2\bar{p}\bar{q} = \sigma_0^2$. With subdivision it may be readily found that the variance of Z in the entire population (2) is

$$2\bar{p}\bar{q} + 2\sigma_q^2 = 2\bar{p}\bar{q} + 2F\bar{p}\bar{q} = 2\bar{p}\bar{q}(1 + F) = \sigma_0^2(1 + F) = \sigma_T^2 ,$$

where T stands for the total population. In each of the random-mating groups the mean and variance of character Z are $2p_i$ and $2p_iq_i$, respectively. The average variance within groups is thus

$$\frac{2\Sigma p_i q_i}{K} = 2\bar{p}\,\bar{q} - 2\sigma_q^2 = 2\bar{p}\,\bar{q}\,(1 - F) = \sigma_0^2\,(1 - F) = \sigma_W^2 ,$$

TABLE 80

ANALYSIS OF VARIANCE OF A METRICAL CHARACTER Z
IN A SUBDIVIDED POPULATION

(Wright, 1951, and Earlier)

SOURCE	VARIANCE OF Z	
	General	Unit-Factor
Within groups..........	$\sigma_W^2 = (1-F)\sigma_0^2 = 2(1-F)\bar{p}\bar{q}$	
Between groups.........	$\sigma_M^2 = 2F\sigma_0^2 = 4F\bar{p}\bar{q}$	
Total population....	$\sigma_T^2 = (1+F)\sigma_0^2 = 2(1+F)\bar{p}\bar{q}$	

where W stands for "within groups." The variance of the *means* of Z of the various groups (briefly, the variance of group means) is

$$\frac{\Sigma\,(2p_i - 2\bar{p})^2}{K} = 4\sigma_q^2 = 4F\bar{p}\,\bar{q} = 2F\sigma_0^2 = \sigma_M^2 ,$$

where M stands for group means. This quantity is usually known, for brevity, as the "variance between groups." These relationships are summarized in Table 80.

So we have the following simple theorem regarding the variance of metrical characters:

$$\sigma_T^2 = \sigma_W^2 + \sigma_M^2 . \tag{4}$$

Further, if we use $\sigma_0^2 = 2\bar{p}\bar{q}$, expected under panmixia, as the "standard" value, we see that F measures the proportional *decrease* in the variance of characters *within* random-breeding groups but gives the proportional *increase* in the variance of the *total* population. Also, Table 80 gives us the following ratios:

$$\frac{2F}{1-F} = \frac{\sigma_M^2}{\sigma_W^2}; \qquad \frac{2F}{1+F} = \frac{\sigma_M^2}{\sigma_T^2}.$$

Hence,

$$F = \frac{\sigma_M^2}{2\sigma_W^2 + \sigma_M^2} = \frac{\sigma_M^2}{2\sigma_T^2 - \sigma_M^2}. \tag{5}$$

Although the above demonstration is based on only one pair of genes with additive effects, the formulas (4) and (5) are also applicable to polygenic characters as long as *all* gene effects are additive (between as well as within loci). For one pair of genes, (3) is equivalent to (5); only the former is in terms of the variance of gene frequencies, while the latter is in terms of the variance of characters (remembering that $4\sigma_q^2 = \sigma_M^2$ for between-group means). It should also be noted that the ratio $\sigma_M^2/\sigma_T^2 = 2F/(1 + F)$ is the correlation coefficient between mates with respect to the total population (see eq. [6] of Chap. 11).

All the variance formulas in this chapter refer to the case in which the heterozygote is intermediate between the two homozygotes. The effect of inbreeding or subdivision on the genetic variance due to recessive genes has been recently investigated by Robertson (1952). The same effect in an equilibrium population was described by Wright (1952a).

§ 4. *Effects of Migration*

In the preceding sections we have assumed that the subgroups are completely isolated from each other, so that each group has its own fixed gene frequency. The group gene frequency may, however, be changed by migration of individuals between the various groups. Suppose that a large population with an average gene frequency $\bar{q}$ is subdivided into many groups, each exchanging a proportion m of its group with a random sample of the whole population every generation. Let the gene frequency of the particular group under consideration be q. Then, on account of the replacement by immigrants, its gene frequency in the next generation will be

$$q' = (1 - m)q + m\bar{q} = q - m(q - \bar{q}),$$

so that

$$\Delta q = q' - q = -m(q - \bar{q}), \tag{6}$$

being proportional to the deviation of the group gene frequency from the general average of the entire population.

The conditions postulated above are, of course, very artificial. The subgroups may actually exchange individuals more often with their neighboring groups than with distant ones, so that the immigrants do not constitute a random sample of the entire population. In such cases the magnitude of Δq would be smaller than indicated by (6), because neighboring groups tend to have more or less equal gene frequencies owing to the continuous interchange of individuals between them. It would be nearer the truth if we let $\bar{q}$ in (6) stand for the gene frequency of the immigrants to the group rather than that of the entire population. Selective migration (some genotypes migrate more than others) is another complicating factor. However, the simple form (6), which we shall adopt in the following, will suffice to illustrate the effect of migration pressure on gene frequencies.

The most obvious effect of continued intergroup migrations is to make the gene frequencies of the various groups more nearly alike and thus, in the absence of any countermeasures, render the total population more homogeneous. Now, the deviation of a local q from its average value is $(q - \bar{q})$; in the next generation after the exchange of individuals, the deviation will reduce to

$$\text{new dev.} = q' - \bar{q} = [q - m(q - \bar{q})] - \bar{q} = (1 - m)(q - \bar{q}) . \qquad (7)$$

If σ_q^2 is the variance of q among the subgroups in one generation, then this variance in the next generation will reduce to

$$(1 - m)^2 \sigma_q^2 ,$$

assuming that $\bar{q}$ remains constant. Since σ_q^2 measures the heterogeneity or "differentiation" of the total population, its decrease means that the subgroups tend to be more alike. It follows from (3) that F relative to the total population will also decrease as a result of migrations. The limiting value of any local q is $\bar{q}$.

The effects of migration on local gene frequencies is similar to that of mutations on population gene frequencies, as is shown by the following expressions:

Migration: $\Delta q = \qquad -m(q - \bar{q}) \qquad = \qquad m\bar{q}(1 - q) - m\bar{p}\cdot q \,,$

Mutation: $\Delta q = \quad -(\mu + \nu)(q - \bar{q}) \qquad = \qquad \mu(1 - q) - \nu\cdot q \,,$

Joint effect: $\Delta q = -(m + \mu + \nu)(q - \bar{q}) = (m\bar{q} + \mu)(1 - q) - (m\bar{p} + \nu)q \,.$

Therefore, in many cases the results under migration pressure may be obtained directly from those under mutation pressure merely by substituting the constants $m\bar{q}$ for μ and $m\bar{p} = m(1 - \bar{q})$ for ν and m for $\mu + \nu$ (see Chap. 23).

§ 5. Migration and Selection

In studying the joint effects of migration and selection, we assume, for the sake of simplicity, that heterozygotes are of intermediate fitness between the two homozygous types, so that $W_{Aa} = 1 - s$ and $W_{aa} = 1 - 2s$. Then the joint effect of migration and selection on gene frequency is (Wright, 1940b)

$$\Delta q = -sq(1 - q) - m(q - \bar{q}) = sq^2 - (m + s)q + m\bar{q} \,.$$

At equilibrium ($\Delta q = 0$)

$$\hat{q} = \frac{(m+s) \pm \sqrt{[(m+s)^2 - 4msq]}}{2s}, \tag{8}$$

where $\hat{q}$ is the equilibrium value for a group that has been subjected to selection of intensity s and receives m immigrants from the outside in every generation. The deviation of this equilibrium value of a group from the average value of the total population depends on the relative magnitudes of m and s in that group. Since $W_{Aa} = 1 - s$, and $W_{aa} = 1 - 2s$, a positive value of s means that the selection is against gene a, while a negative value of s implies that selection favors it. In the following this difference should always be kept in mind, as the value of $\hat{q}$ evidently depends upon whether the gene a is favorable or deleterious to the individuals. We shall consider three different situations as to the relative magnitudes of s and m and deduce approximate expressions for $\hat{q}$ in each case.

SITUATION I: $m = |s|$.—When percentage of migration and intensity of selection are of the same order of magnitude, we may let $m = |s|$ for the purpose of illustration. Then, $m + s = 2s$ or 0 according to whether s is positive or negative. Substituting in (8), we obtain

$$\hat{q} = \sqrt{\bar{q}} \quad \text{or} \quad \hat{q} = 1 - \sqrt{(1 - \bar{q})} \tag{8E}$$

for favorable (s negative) and unfavorable (s positive) genes, respectively. For example, taking $\bar{q} = 0.40$ for the total population, the equilibrium value will be

$$\hat{q} = \sqrt{0.40} = 0.6325 \quad \text{or} \quad \hat{q} = 1 - \sqrt{0.60} = 0.2254,$$

depending on whether the selection is for or against the gene. We see that in this situation the gene frequencies of local groups may be very different from each other, which implies that there will be a considerable amount of differentiation among the various groups *under differential selective forces*.

SITUATION II: $m < |s|$.—If the selection intensity is much larger than the immigration replacement proportion, the local gene frequencies will be determined largely by the direction of selection, along with only a weak diluting effect of the immigrants. Hence, we may expect that local values of q will vary widely among the various groups and also will be quite different from the population average $\bar{q}$. As an example, let us again take $\bar{q} = 0.40$, with $m = 0.01$, but $s = -0.15$ and $+0.15$, respectively. Then, (8) gives

$$q = \frac{-0.14 + \sqrt{(0.14^2 + 0.0024)}}{-0.30} = 0.9611,$$

or

$$\hat{q} = \frac{0.16 - \sqrt{(0.16^2 - 0.0024)}}{0.30} = 0.0256$$

for favorable and unfavorable genes. Here we see that the local groups differ much more than in the preceding case. There will be a high degree of local differentiation depending upon the local conditions of selection. The immigrants barely prevent the genes from becoming fixed or extinct in the group, playing a role similar to that of new mutations.

It may be shown (Ex. 6) that, when the numerical value of s is much greater than m, the equilibrium value is approximately

$$\hat{q} = 1 - \frac{m}{.s} (1 - \bar{q}), \quad \text{or} \quad \hat{q} = \frac{m}{s} \bar{q}, \tag{8S}$$

for beneficial or deleterious genes, respectively. As a check, substituting $\bar{q} = 0.40$, $m = 0.01$, $s = \pm 0.15$ in (8S), we obtain $\hat{q} = 1 - 0.60/15 = 0.960$ or $\hat{q} = 0.40/15 = 0.0267$. Both values are very close to those given before by (8).

SITUATION III: $m > |s|$.—Contrary to Situation II, if the proportion of migration in a group is much larger than the intensity of selection (whether positive or negative), the effects of immigrants will override that of selection and thus swamp the tendency toward selective differentiation. As a result, the local equilibrium values of the groups will not differ much from the average gene frequency of the total population. Thus, with $\bar{q} = 0.40$, as before, but $m = 0.15$, and $s = \pm 0.01$, we have, from (8),

$$\hat{q} = \frac{0.14 - \sqrt{(0.14^2 + 0.0024)}}{-0.02} = 0.416,$$

or

$$\hat{q} = \frac{0.16 - \sqrt{(0.16^2 - 0.0024)}}{0.02} = 0.384,$$

according to whether or not the gene is favored. The values are, however, all close to $\bar{q} = 0.40$. To obtain an approximate expression for (8) under this circumstance, we may divide the equation $\Delta q = 0$ throughout by m, thus obtaining

$$-\frac{s}{m} q (1 - q) - q + \bar{q} = 0.$$

Since q would be close to $\bar{q}$, we have, approximately,

$$\hat{q} = \bar{q} \pm \frac{s}{m} \bar{q} (1 - \bar{q}) \tag{8M}$$

for favorable and deleterious genes, respectively. That this is a good approximation formula is shown by the numerical example $\hat{q} = 0.40 \pm (0.4 \times 0.6)/15 = 0.416$ or 0.384. The larger the m relative to s, the more closely will the local gene frequencies cluster about the average value $\bar{q}$. The small selective force causes only an insignificant differentiation of the local groups. This is perhaps the most frequently encountered and the most important case in nature.

§ 6. *Equilibrium with Migrations*

Suppose that a population has been subdivided into many small groups of size N and that each is a random-mating unit by itself but that there is a certain percentage of migrations between the groups. Recall that in Chapter 15 it was shown that random mating in a small group of N individuals leads eventually to a loss of heterozygosis at the rate of approximately $1/2N$ per generation and that the ultimate fate of such a group is complete homozygosis, ignoring immigrants. The value of F in such a group increases (as the heterozygosis decreases). In fact, if F is the value in one generation, it will be increased to $1/2N + [(2N - 1)/(2N)]F$ in the next generation, assuming, for simplicity, complete random union of gametes (see formula [2] of Chap. 15).

On the other hand, the immigrants not only would prevent the groups from reaching complete homozygosis but would tend to pull the group gene frequencies toward the average value of the total population, so that σ_q^2 would be reduced to $(1 - m)^2\sigma_q^2$ in the next generation, as shown in Section 4. Hence, the value of F would also be reduced by the same proportion because of the relation (3). At equilibrium the increased value of F, owing to the limited size of the group, would be decreased by the immigrants. Therefore, the values of F between two successive generations are equal, yielding the relation (Wright, 1951)

$$F = (1 - m)^2 \left\{ \frac{1}{2N} + \frac{2N - 1}{2N} F \right\}. \tag{9}$$

This is the fundamental relation between the values of F and m under equilibrium migration conditions without selection effects. (This immigration percentage m is not to be confused with the m for correlation between mates in Chap. 14 and earlier.) It may be written in two other forms: one expressing m in terms of F, the other expressing F in terms of m. Thus,

$$(1 - m)^2 = \frac{2NF}{(2N - 1)F + 1} \tag{9m}$$

or

$$F = \frac{(1 - m)^2}{2N - (2N - 1)(1 - m)^2}. \tag{9F}$$

It is clear from these expressions, as it should be intuitively, that, the larger the value of m, the smaller will be the value of F. If immigrants are relatively few (m small), the numerator of (9F) may be treated as unity; and, writing $(1 - m)^2 = 1 - 2m$ in the denominator, (9F) reduces to approximately

$$F = \frac{1}{4Nm + 1}. \tag{9F'}$$

The distribution formula of the group gene frequencies in this equilibrium condition will be given in Chapter 23, but at this stage we already know that the variance of this distribution must be, from (3) and (9F'), approximately,

$$\sigma_q^2 = \frac{\bar{q}(1 - \bar{q})}{4Nm + 1} \tag{10}$$

for small m (Wright, 1931; Kolmogorov, 1935). A more accurate expression for σ_q^2 will be given after we consider the random fluctuations of q in small groups (see eqs. [6] and [7] of Chap. 22).

§ 7. *Isolation by Distance*

In the foregoing we have assumed, for the sake of mathematical simplicity, that a total population has been subdivided into many isolated groups with a certain proportion of migrants interchanging between them. This is sometimes known as the "island model" of isolation. At the opposite extreme from this model is that of a large population which has a continuous distribution over a wide area but in which the mating individuals are restricted to a "neighborhood" of a limited distance, so that two remote individuals have practically no chance to mate. This implicit form of subdividing a large continuous population is known as *isolation by distance* (Wright, 1943, 1951). Here we shall deal only with its most elementary theorems.

Let the size of a "neighborhood" be N, and by this we mean that the two parents of any individual are from a neighborhood consisting of N individuals. Further, let us assume that the distribution of individuals over the area is uniform, so that N is directly proportional to the area of a neighborhood. Then, the four grandparents of any individual may be considered to be drawn at random from an area of $2N$; and, in general, the ancestors of generation k may be considered as drawn at random from a territory of size kN. (If we think of a neighborhood of size N as a circular area of radius r, then the circular area of $2N$ will be of radius $r\sqrt{2}$, since the area of a circle is proportional to the square of its radius. The area of size kN will be enclosed by a circle of radius $r\sqrt{k}$. Thus, when the area of a neighborhood is enlarged nine times, the radius or distance is only lengthened three times.)

Let F_1 be the correlation between uniting gametes for a neighborhood of size N, F_2 be that for an area of $2N$, and F_k be that for a group of kN individuals; and let primes of F indicate the correlations of previous generations. Assuming complete random union of gametes, and remembering that $b^2 = \frac{1}{2}(1 + F')$, we see that the value of F for a neighborhood of a finite size is, by modification of (2) of Chapter 15,

$$F = F_1 = \frac{1}{N}\left(\frac{1+F_1'}{2}\right) + \frac{N-1}{N}F_2'.$$

Similarly,

$$F_2' = \frac{1}{2N}\left(\frac{1+F_1''}{2}\right) + \frac{2N-1}{2N}F_3'',$$

$$F_3'' = \frac{1}{3N}\left(\frac{1+F_1'''}{2}\right) + \frac{3N-1}{3N}F_4''', \quad \text{etc.}$$

If the same population structure has continued indefinitely or, in other words, if the population is in a stationary (equilibrium) state, the primes of F may be dropped, because F_k will remain the same from generation to generation. Continued substitution then gives us

$$F = \frac{1+F}{2N}\left[1 + \frac{1}{2}\left(\frac{N-1}{N}\right) + \frac{1}{3}\left(\frac{N-1}{N}\right)\left(\frac{2N-1}{2N}\right)\right.$$
$$\left. + \frac{1}{4}\left(\frac{N-1}{N}\right)\left(\frac{2N-1}{2N}\right)\left(\frac{3N-1}{3N}\right) + \ldots\right] \tag{11}$$

for some finite group with a random-mating neighborhood of the basic size N. For instance, the value of F for a territory ten times the size of the basic neighborhood would be given by summing the first nine terms of (11), assuming $F_{10} = 0$. In general, the value of F for a territory k times the basic neighborhood size N is given by summing the first $k - 1$ terms of the series (11).

Evidently, the larger the group we consider, the higher will be the value of F for that group, with a fixed basic neighborhood size N. The theoretical limit of F is unity when the considered population becomes infinite. This suggests that the sum of the infinite series within the brackets of (11) is N, as shown in Exercise 10.

Let t_i represent the ith term of the series within the brackets of (11), and $\Sigma t_i = t_1 + \ldots + t_{k-1}$, the sum of its first $k - 1$ terms. Then the value of F for a group of size kN is

$$F = \frac{1+F}{2N}[\Sigma t] \qquad \text{or} \qquad F = \frac{\Sigma t}{2N - \Sigma t}. \tag{12}$$

A simple numerical example may be helpful at this stage. Suppose that the basic random-mating neighborhood is only of size $N = 10$ and that we would like to know the value of F for a group $k = 10$ times as large. Then,

$t_1 = 1.000000$	$t_4 = 0.206625$	$t_7 = 0.110937$
$t_2 = 0.450000$	$t_5 = 0.161168$	$t_8 = 0.095683$
$t_3 = 0.285000$	$t_6 = 0.131620$	$t_9 = 0.083989$
		$\Sigma t = 2.525$

and

$$F = \frac{2.525}{20 - 2.525} = 0.1445,$$

which is the value plotted in Figure 70. When N and/or k are large, it is admittedly very tedious to calculate the sum Σt. However, an alternate form of (12), which is somewhat simpler, may be derived. Note that the kth term of the series may be written in the general form

$$t_k = \frac{1}{k}\left(1 - \frac{1}{N}\right)\cdots\left(1 - \frac{1}{(k-1)N}\right) = \frac{1}{k}\prod_{i=1}^{k-1}\left(1 - \frac{1}{iN}\right);$$

and thus the sequence relation between two consecutive terms is

$$t_k = \frac{(k-1)\,N-1}{k\,N}\,t_{k-1}. \tag{13}$$

From this relation it may be shown (Ex. 9) that the sum of the first $k-1$ terms of (11) is equal to

$$\Sigma t_i = N(1 - k t_k). \tag{14}$$

Substituting this value in (12), we obtain

$$F = \frac{\Sigma t}{2N - \Sigma t} = \frac{1 - k t_k}{1 + k t_k}. \tag{12'}$$

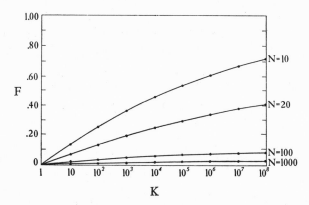

Fig. 70.—Inbreeding coefficients (F) of neighborhoods of size N for larger populations of size K times N. (After Wright, 1951.)

Let us verify (12') with our previous numerical example in which $N = 10$ and $k = 10$. By direct calculation, or using the sequence relation (13), we find that $t_{10} = (0.89)(0.083989) = 0.07475$, so that $10t_{10} = 0.7475$. Thus,

$$F = \frac{1 - 0.7475}{1 + 0.7475} = \frac{0.2525}{1.7475} = 0.1445,$$

as before. The values of F for various basic sizes N for a larger group of size kN are plotted in Figure 70. (When k is large, the value of $k t_k$ may be evaluated by the method of logarithms, and then F may be calculated from [12'].)

Since σ_q^2 of the various groups or neighborhoods measures the degree of "differentiation" (heterogeneity or variability) of a larger population, and since F is directly proportional to σ_q^2, we may use F as a measure of differentiation in a large continuous population. From the properties of the distribution function of q (which will be considered in Chap. 23), we may say that, when F is greater than $\frac{1}{3}$, which is equivalent to Nm being less than $\frac{1}{2}$ in our expression (9F'), the total population is very highly differentiated. Even when F is about 0.05, there will be important differentiation among the groups or neighborhoods. On the other hand, if F is as small as or less than 0.005, there will be only insignificant differentiation. Thus, it is apparent from Figure 70 that there is a great deal of local differentiation if the random-breeding unit (neighborhood) is as small as 10, even within an area a hundred times the basic unit size (which, it should be remembered, covers an area with a radius only ten times the length of that of the neighborhood). If the neighborhood is of size $N = 100$, differentiation becomes important only at much greater distances. If the unit size is greater than 1000, the situation is substantially the same as though there were random mating throughout the whole population. Therefore, the most important factor in isolation by distance is the size of the basic random-breeding unit.

§ 8. *Additional Considerations of Isolation*

If the distribution of a large population is continuous along a narrow belt, as along a riverbank, then the size of a group is directly proportional to distance instead of to the square root of distance, as in the case of area continuity. The results are similar to (13), (14), and (12′), except that $k - 1$ and k are replaced by $\sqrt{(k - 1)}$ and $\sqrt{k}$, respectively. The differentiation along the one-dimensional range is thus much higher, for the same distance, than in the case of area continuity. For instance, if the size of the basic random-breeding unit is less than 100, different alleles may approach fixation in different parts of a range that is only a hundred times the length of the basic unit (Wright, 1943, 1951).

Although a large population may show the same *degree* of differentiation as measured by F, the *pattern* of differentiation in the case of continuous distribution with limited size of mating neighborhood is quite different from that of separate groups with a limited proportion of immigrants. In the former case the adjacent neighborhoods are closely similar, and the differentiation is gradual as the area enlarges; in the latter case two adjacent groups may be quite different, and they are uncorrelated.

The models of separate groups ("islands") and of uniform continuity are two extreme cases. In actuality there may be all grades of an intermediate type of distribution, and their patterns of differentiation may also be of a mixed nature. Further, it is possible that, when we consider the variation between comparatively large areas, the differentiation approaches the island type; but, when we consider the variation within one such area, its differentiation approaches the continuity type.

As was pointed out previously, mathematical considerations require the use of simple models of population structure, and it is for this reason that we have assumed a continuous and uniform distribution of individuals over an area or along a narrow belt in attacking the problem of isolation by distance. Any field biologist knows that in most cases the actual distribution of any species is anything but uniform. The differential density of populations from area to area is an important complicating factor. The size N may easily be larger in an area of high density than in a sparsely populated area of equal size. If the distribution is very irregular, the differentiation of a large population may be much higher than indicated by any of the foregoing formulas.

Notes and Exercises

1. When a population is subdivided into K separate random-mating groups with gene frequencies q_i in the ith group, the proportion of heterozygotes in the total population is

$$H = \frac{2\Sigma q_i\,(1-q_i)}{K} = \frac{2\Sigma q_i - 2\Sigma q_i^2}{K}$$

$$= 2\bar{q} - 2\,(\sigma_q^2 + \bar{q}^2) = 2\,\bar{q}\,(1-\bar{q}) - 2\sigma_q^2\,.$$

2. When a population is subdivided into numerous groups with all possible values of gene frequencies, we may treat q as a continuous variable ranging from 0 to 1, with a distribution function $\phi(q)$. Thus,

$$\int_0^1 \phi\,(q)\,dq = 1\,, \qquad \int_0^1 q\,\phi\,(q)\,dq = \bar{q}\,,$$

and

$$\sigma_q^2 = \int_0^1 (q-\bar{q})^2\,\phi\,(q)\,dq = \int_0^1 q^2\phi\,(q)\,dq - \bar{q}^2\,.$$

In this continuous case Wahlund's formula holds as well:

$$H = 2\int_0^1 q\,(1-q)\,\phi\,(q)\,dq = 2\,\bar{q}\,(1-\bar{q}) - 2\sigma_q^2\,.$$

3. Referring to the results of continued sib mating (Table 36), which subdivides the total population into many isolates of size $N = 2$, we see that after three generations ($n = 3$ in Table 36) the values of q of the isolates are distributed as follows:

q......	0	0.25	0.50	0.75	1.00	Total
f.......	53	44	62	44	53	256

Verify: $\bar{q} = \frac{1}{2}$, $\sigma_q^2 = \frac{1}{8}$, $F = \frac{1}{2}$, $\sigma_q^2 = Fpq$.

4. Analyze the variance of Z (value of a metrical character with respect to which the gene effects are additive) for the five groups given in Table 78 and verify the relations given in Table 80 and expression (5).

5. It was shown in the text that, when $m = 0.01$ and $s = -0.15$, $\hat{q} = 0.9611$, with $\bar{q} = 0.40$. Verify: this value of $\hat{q}$ does make $\Delta q = 0$ (§ 5). Do the same for $\hat{q} = 0.0256$ with $s = 0.15$.

6. The approximate value of (8) is obtained by using the fact that $\sqrt{(1 \pm \epsilon)} = 1 \pm \frac{1}{2}\epsilon$, approximately, when ϵ is small in comparison with unity. If s is

numerically much larger than m, then $(m/s)^2$ may be ignored, so that the quantity with the radical sign in (8) may be written as

$$s\sqrt{\left(1+\frac{2m}{s}-\frac{4m\bar{q}}{s}\right)} \doteq s\left(1+\frac{m}{s}-\frac{2m\bar{q}}{s}\right) = s+m-2m\bar{q}.$$

Hence (8) becomes, approximately, for positive and negative s,

$$\left.\begin{aligned}\hat{q} &= \frac{(m+s)-(m+s)+2m\bar{q}}{2s} = \frac{2m\bar{q}}{2s} = \frac{m}{s}\,\bar{q} \\ \hat{q} &= \frac{(m-s)+(m-s)-2m\bar{q}}{-2s} = \frac{-2s+2m-2m\bar{q}}{-2s} = 1-\frac{m}{s}(1-\bar{q})\end{aligned}\right\} . \quad (8S)$$

7. The joint pressure of migration and mutation is still of the same form as that for migration alone. Hence the equilibrium value corresponding to (8), but with mutation effects included, may be obtained by merely substituting $m\bar{q}+\nu$ for $m\bar{q}$ and $m(1-\bar{q})+\mu$ for $m(1-\bar{q})$. Thus (Wright, 1939), when s is large,

$$\hat{q} = \frac{m\bar{q}+\nu}{s} \quad \text{or} \quad 1-\frac{m\bar{p}+\mu}{s};$$

when m is large,

$$\hat{q} = \bar{q}+\frac{1}{m}[s\bar{q}(2-\bar{q})+\mu(1-\bar{q})-\nu\bar{q}],$$

the latter being an approximate solution of the equation

$$\Delta q = -sq(1-q)-m(q-\bar{q})+\mu(1-q)-\nu q = 0.$$

8. If selection is against the recessives of a panmictic group with an intensity s, but a proportion r of recessives immigrate into the group every generation, the zygotic proportions will be p^2, $2pq$, $q^2(1-s)+r$ in the next generation. Therefore,

$$\Delta q = \frac{q-sq^2+r}{1-sq^2+r}-q = \frac{r(1-q)-sq^2(1-q)}{1-sq^2+r}.$$

If s and r are both small, so that the denominator of the above expression may be treated as unity, the equilibrium values will be either (Haldane, 1930)

$$\hat{q} = 1 \quad \text{or} \quad q^2 = \frac{r}{s}.$$

The latter equilibrium condition is stable only when $r < s$. It is obvious that, if the proportion of immigrant recessives is greater than those eliminated in every generation, the population will eventually be all recessives, and $\hat{q} = 1$ will be the final condition. This is the simplest example of *selective migration*. Haldane (1930) has also described several other cases of equilibrium between selection and migration.

9. The sequence relation (13) for two successive t's may be written in the following form (D. J. Hooton, in Wright, 1951, Appendix F):

$$kNt_k = (k-1)Nt_{k-1} - t_{k-1} \quad ;$$

$$\therefore \ (k-1)Nt_{k-1} = (k-2)Nt_{k-2} - t_{k-2}$$

$$(k-2)Nt_{k-2} = (k-3)Nt_{k-3} - t_{k-3}$$

$$\cdots \qquad\qquad \cdots$$

$$3Nt_3 = \qquad 2Nt_2 - t_2$$

$$2Nt_2 = \qquad Nt_1 - t_1$$

Adding, $kNt_k = \qquad N \ - \Sigma t_i \ (i = 1, \ldots, k-1),$

all other quantities being canceled out and the first term of the series being $t_1 = 1$. Hence,

$$\Sigma t = N - kNt_k = N(1 - kt_k). \qquad\qquad \text{i.e., } (14)$$

10. To prove that the sum of the infinite series within the brackets of (11) is N, we have only to show that $kt_k \to 0$ as k increases indefinitely, on account of the relation (14) just demonstrated. Now, write

$$kt_k = \left(\frac{N-1}{N}\right)\left(\frac{2N-1}{2N}\right)\left(\frac{3N-1}{3N}\right)\cdots$$

$$= \cfrac{1}{\left(\dfrac{N}{N-1}\right)\left(\dfrac{2N}{2N-1}\right)\left(\dfrac{3N}{3N-1}\right)\cdots}$$

$$= \cfrac{1}{\left(1+\dfrac{1}{N-1}\right)\left(1+\dfrac{1}{2N-1}\right)\left(1+\dfrac{1}{3N-1}\right)\cdots}$$

$$< \cfrac{1}{\left(1+\dfrac{1}{N}\right)\left(1+\dfrac{1}{2N}\right)\left(1+\dfrac{1}{3N}\right)\cdots}$$

$$< \cfrac{1}{1+\dfrac{1}{N}+\dfrac{1}{2N}+\dfrac{1}{3N}+\cdots} = \cfrac{1}{1+\dfrac{1}{N}\Sigma\dfrac{1}{X}},$$

where $\Sigma(1/X) = 1 + \frac{1}{2} + \frac{1}{3} + \frac{1}{4} + \ldots$. This sum is known to be divergent (its sum is "infinity"). Therefore,

$$kt_k \to 0 \quad \text{as} \quad k \to \infty \quad \text{and} \quad \Sigma t \to N.$$

11. Since the hybrid individuals between whites and Negroes are, in the United States, regarded socially as Negroes, any interbreeding between the two populations will result in a "one-way" gene flow from the white to the "Negro" population. Let q_0 be the original gene frequency of the Negro

population prior to any interbreeding with the whites and let Q denote the frequency of the same gene among the American whites. Now, let m be the fraction of the Negro gene pool that has been replaced by the "immigrated" white genes through interbreeding in each generation. Then, after the first generation of interbreeding, the gene frequency of the resulting Negro population will be changed from q_0 to

$$q_1 = (1 - m)q_0 + mQ .$$

Similarly,

$$q_k = (1 - m)q_{k-1} + mQ$$

for the kth generation of continued interbreeding. It may be desirable to express q_k in terms of q_0. Since the "weight" of q_0 is decreased by a proportion $(1 - m)$ in every generation, we have after k generations

$$q_k = (1 - m)^k q_0 + \{1 - (1 - m)^k\}Q .$$

If the original and the present American Negro gene frequencies, as well as those of the American whites, have been determined, and we are interested in finding the value of m for a specified number of generations, the above equation may be put in a more convenient form (Glass and Li, 1953):

$$(1 - m)^k = \frac{q_k - Q}{q_0 - Q}.$$

For example, the frequencies of the allele R^0 (a member of the rh series) have been found to be $q_0 = 0.630$, $q_k = 0.446$ and $Q = 0.028$. If we take a period of 275 years (1675–1950) as $k = 10$ generations, assuming 27.5 years to be one generation, we have

$$(1 - m)^{10} = \frac{0.446 - 0.028}{0.630 - 0.028} = 0.69435 ;$$

$$\therefore m = 0.0358 \quad \text{or} \quad 3.58 \text{ per cent per generation.}$$

Using this value of m, the frequencies of allele R^0 for these ten generations of American Negroes, may be "reconstructed" as follows:

Time...	0	1	2	3	4	5	6	7	8	9	10
q......	0.6300	0.6084	0.5877	0.5676	0.5483	0.5297	0.5117	0.4944	0.4777	0.4616	0.4460

The number of generations required to reduce the present 0.446 to one-tenth of q_0 (approximately the final equilibrium value of the combined population) for various values of m have also been given by Glass and Li (1953). It may be added that if m varies from generation to generation, as it probably does in actual cases, its value as determined by the foregoing method would give us the average value of m over the period of k generations.

CHAPTER 22

Small Populations and Effective Size

UNDERLYING all our discussions of Mendelian populations, except those in Chapter 15, was the assumption that the population or even the subdivided groups were large, so that a stable equilibrium value of gene frequency could persist from generation to generation under constant environmental conditions. If the size of a group is limited, however, the situation becomes more complicated, because the gene frequencies are subject to a special kind of change which is quite independent of the changes induced by mutation, selection, and migration. In this chapter we shall examine briefly the way in which gene frequencies vary in a small population.

§ 1. *Random Fluctuation of Gene Frequency*

Consider a population of N diploid monoecious individuals. Such a population may be regarded as the product of drawing $2N$ gametes at random from the population of the previous generation. If the frequency of gene a is q in the parental population, then the gene frequency of the offspring population of N individuals (which consists of a random sample from the parents) will vary, by chance, according to the binomial expansion:

$$[p(A) + q(a)]^{2N} . \tag{1}$$

The $2N + 1$ possible values of q in the offspring population of N individuals are

$$0, \quad \frac{1}{2N}, \quad \frac{2}{2N}, \quad \frac{3}{2N}, \cdots, \quad \frac{j}{2N}, \cdots, \quad \frac{2N-2}{2N}, \quad \frac{2N-1}{2N}, \quad 1 .$$

The probability that q should take the particular value $q_j = j/2N$ in the next generation is thus (Wright, 1931)

$$\binom{2N}{j} p^{2N-j} q^j = \binom{2N}{2Nq_j} p^{2Np_j} q^{2Nq_j} ,$$

which is also known as the "transition" probability of a Markov chain for this process (Feller, 1950). In brief, the gene frequency varies as a result of random sampling of a limited size. It may increase or decrease, by a considerable amount or only slightly, in the next generation. This type of change is at random. Let $\delta q = q_i - q$ denote the random deviation from the preceding generation, in contrast to the systematic deviation Δq caused by mutation, selection, and/or migration. The variance of δq in one generation is then

$$\sigma_{\delta q}^2 = \frac{q\,(1-q)}{2\,N}, \tag{2}$$

which is the variance of the distribution of q given by the expansion of (1). As a numerical illustration of the magnitude of the random fluctuation of q in a small group, let us consider a sample of $N = 50$ individuals whose parental $q = \frac{1}{2}$. The gene frequency for the 50 individuals will thus vary about the mean value $\frac{1}{2}$ with a standard deviation

$$\sigma_{\delta q} = \sqrt{\left(\frac{0.5 \times 0.5}{2 \times 50}\right)} = 0.05.$$

The probabilities of the various values that q may take are given in Table 81 (approximation by normal curve).

The distribution in Table 81 may be viewed in another way. If we consider

TABLE 81

PROBABILITY DISTRIBUTION OF q IN $N = 50$ OFFSPRING FROM
A PARENTAL POPULATION WITH $q = 0.50$

				q					TOTAL
	<0.35	0.35–0.40	0.40–0.45	0.45–0.50	0.50–0.55	0.55–0.60	0.60–0.65	0.65+	
Prob......	0.002	0.021	0.136	0.341	0.341	0.136	0.021	0.002	1.000

simultaneously a large number of loci whose frequencies are all 0.50 in the parental population, then some of the loci will have a higher, others a lower, frequency than 0.50 in the next generation because of sampling accidents. The probabilities shown in Table 81 give us the proportion of loci within the specific range. We should expect, then, that in the next generation more than 2 per cent of these loci will have a frequency between 0.60 and 0.65.

Table 81 may be interpreted in still another way. If we consider a particular locus (say, A, a) but assume that there are many small groups of the same size N with the same parental gene frequency 0.50, then the probabilities in Table 81 will give us the proportions of such groups with a value of q within the specific range. Thus, more than 2 per cent of these small groups, each of fifty individuals, will have a gene frequency between 0.60 and 0.65 in the next generation. Both viewpoints are useful for our subsequent discussions.

For sex-linked loci the variance of random deviation δq in groups of N individuals, half of them males and half females, is approximately

$$\sigma_{\delta q}^2 = \frac{2 q (1 - q)}{3 N}$$

in one generation. It is 50 per cent larger than that for autosomal genes.

Under uniparental reproduction (such as vegetative reproduction or self-fertilization in some plants), if the parental population consists of p individuals of one kind and q of another, the variance of δq for N offspring will be

$$\sigma_{\delta q}^2 = \frac{q (1 - q)}{N}, \qquad (3)$$

which is twice as large as that given by (2).

§ 2. *Final Fate of Small Groups*

The random fluctuation of q in a finite group is sometimes known as *genetic drift*, because the value of q in successive generations seems to drift about without approaching any particular value—unlike the situation described for systematic changes. As long as the value of q is between $1/2N$ and $(2N - 1)/2N$, the drift of q is in both directions. Whatever the initial value of q, it may assume almost any value after a number of generations of random mating. If q eventually becomes small due to cumulative random deviations, it still may be increased in the next generation or decreased to a still lower value; and, indeed, the gene may be lost altogether in the next generation due to accidents of random sampling. Once a gene is lost from a population ($q = 0$) or fixed ($q = 1$), however, there will no longer be any variation of q in subsequent generations. The points $q = 0$ and 1 are like "dead ends" at which the variation of q stops. It is an irreversible process (Fig. 71).

We see from (2) that, when q is near 0 or 1, the magnitude of its chance variation is smaller than when it is of intermediate value. But the chance factor operates with greater finality in the former than in the latter case, because genes with very low or high frequency are in danger of extinction or fixation in subsequent generations.

Since intermediate values of q may reach the end points 0 and 1, but never the other way round, the gene frequency of a small population (with any initial value) will be ultimately either zero or unity if it is let alone for a sufficiently long time (in terms of generations). In other words, the population will then consist of either all AA or all aa individuals, even though random mating has been the practice. The significance of this process in evolution will be discussed in the last section of this chapter.

§ 3. *Decay of Variability*

The process by which a small group eventually reaches complete homozygosis (ignoring effects of mutation and migration) is known as the "decay" of variability, because in this process the group loses its capacity to change genetically. We shall investigate the rate of this decay as follows.

1. First of all, we notice from Table 81 that the parental gene frequency ($q = 0.50$) spreads out over a wide range in the next generation. If this process of spreading continues for a number of generations, the distribution of q (among many groups for the same locus or for various loci in the same group) will be practically uniform (Fig. 72); there is no reason why any particular value of q should be more frequent than others, since the spreading-out is a random process. For a uniform distribution its mean value is $\bar{q} = \frac{1}{2}$.

2. The frequencies of the two terminal classes ($q = 0, 1$) increase from generation to generation, but all the other classes are equally numerous (the fre-

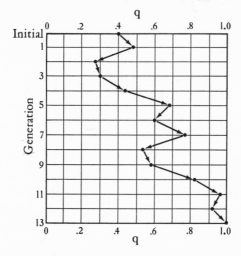

FIG. 71.—Random variation of q in a small population leads to ultimate extinction or fixation of a gene. The smaller the population, the more rapidly will it reach the end points.

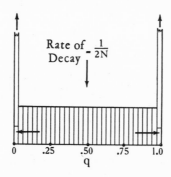

FIG. 72.—Distribution of q among small groups. The fixation and loss of genes are each proceeding at the rate $1/4N$ per generation, so that the total rate of decay is $1/2N$ in the absence of mutation, selection, or migration. (After Wright, 1931.)

quency of the subterminal classes is slightly less than that of the middle classes, but we shall ignore this small difference), although their absolute frequencies gradually decrease. Hence, the variance of q, *excluding the two terminal classes*, is

$$\sigma_q^2 = \frac{\Sigma f (q - \frac{1}{2})^2}{\Sigma f},$$

in which the summation includes $2N - 1$ terms, and f is the frequency of a class. If the form of the distribution of q (excluding terminal classes) remains the same in successive generations, the variance σ_q^2 will also remain the same.

3. This variance, however, will be increased in the next generation by the spreading-out of each frequency class as a result of random sampling. The variance from the spreading of a single class is that given by (2). The average value for all the classes is the increment of σ_q^2 in the next generation:

$$\Delta\sigma_q^2 = \frac{\Sigma q (1 - q) f}{2 N \Sigma f} = \frac{-\Sigma (q^2 - q + \frac{1}{4} - \frac{1}{4}) f}{2 N \Sigma f}$$

$$= \frac{-\Sigma (q - \frac{1}{2})^2 + \frac{1}{4}\Sigma f}{2 N \Sigma f} = \frac{1}{2 N} (\frac{1}{4} - \sigma_q^2).$$

The increased variance $\sigma_q^2 + \Delta\sigma_q^2$ includes the *newly* fixed loci in that generation.

4. Now, let κ be the rate of fixation (including extinction) of genes per generation. Since the distribution of q is uniform, the rates at which q becomes 0 and 1 are equal, both being $\frac{1}{2}\kappa$ per generation. The contribution of these κ newly fixed genes to the increased variance described above is $\frac{1}{4}\kappa$, because each gene contributes $\frac{1}{4}$, as shown in the accompanying calculation.

q	f	fq	fq^2
0.........	$\frac{1}{2}$	0	0
1.........	$\frac{1}{2}$	$\frac{1}{2}$	$\frac{1}{2}$
Sum.......	1	$\frac{1}{2}$	$\frac{1}{2}$

Variance $= \frac{1}{2} - (\frac{1}{2})^2 = \frac{1}{4}$

5. The remaining $(1 - \kappa)$ unfixed genes still have a variance σ_q^2, as the form of their distribution remains the same (uniform). Hence, we obtain the relation (Wright, 1931, 1939a, p. 15)

$$\sigma_q^2 + \Delta\sigma_q^2 = \frac{1}{4}\kappa + (1 - \kappa)\sigma_q^2.$$

Substituting the value of $\Delta\sigma_q^2$ as given in Subsection 3, and simplifying, the above equation reduces to

$$\left(\kappa - \frac{1}{2 N}\right)(\sigma_q^2 - \frac{1}{4}) = 0.$$

Therefore, $\kappa = 1/2N$ per generation, and the rate of fixation is $\frac{1}{2}\kappa = 1/4N$ at each end. Figure 72 illustrates this situation.

6. If we let f_t be the frequency of unfixed loci (height in Fig. 72) after t generations of random variation, we have

$$f_t = f_0 e^{-t/2N} \to 0 \quad \text{as} \quad t \to \infty \;.$$

The results of this section are the same as those reached in Chapter 15 for the decrease of heterozygosis in a finite random-breeding group. The loss or fixation of a gene means the loss of a heterozygote. But the demonstration given here is based on a consideration of the variance of q and makes no use of path coefficients. It will be remembered that the rate $\kappa = 1/2N$ is exact for complete random union of gametes, including the possibilities of self-fertilization. If the latter is excluded, the rate $1/2N$ is still a very good approximation for a moderate value of N. The exact distribution of q for some very special cases ($N = 2$ or 3) has also been given by Wright (1931).

§ 4. *Random Fluctuation with Inbreeding or Subdivision*

Although inbreeding and subdivision have similar effects on the zygotic proportions in the total population, the variances of the random deviation δq in these two cases are different and will be treated separately.

Inbreeding.—It will be recalled that a population with an inbreeding coefficient F may be regarded as consisting of an F inbred component and a $(1 - F)$ random-mating component (Table 42). Let $\bar{q}$ be the gene frequency of the population of size N. Then, from (2) and (3), its sampling variance is

$$\sigma_{\delta q}^2 = \frac{\bar{q}\,(1 - \bar{q})}{2\,N}\,(1 - F) + \frac{\bar{q}\,(1 - \bar{q})}{N}\,F = \frac{\bar{q}\,(1 - \bar{q})\,(1 + F)}{2\,N}, \quad (4)$$

being larger than the "standard" case (2) by a proportion F.

Subdivision.—If a total population is subdivided into K random-breeding groups, each of size N, the sampling variance for each group is $q_i(1 - q_i)/2N$, where q_i is the gene frequency of the ith group. Hence, its average value over the K groups is

$$\sigma_{\delta q}^2 = \frac{1}{K} \sum_i \frac{q_i\,(1 - q_i)}{2\,N} = \frac{2\Sigma q_i\,(1 - q_i)}{4\,N\,K}\;.$$

But $2\Sigma q_i(1 - q_i)/K$ is the proportion of heterozygotes in the total population and thus is equal to $2\bar{q}(1 - \bar{q})(1 - F)$, as shown in Chapter 20. Substituting, we obtain (Wright, 1943)

$$\sigma_{\delta q}^2 = \frac{\bar{q}\,(1 - \bar{q})\,(1 - F)}{2\,N}, \quad (5)$$

which is smaller than the "standard" case (2) by a proportion F for the same size and the same gene frequency.

The variance due to the "random deviations" of gene frequencies, as given in this chapter, should not be confused with the variance of a metrical character described in previous chapters.

§ 5. *Variance of* q *with Migrations*

For a subdivided population it was shown (Chap. 21) that $\sigma_q^2 = \bar{q}(1 - \bar{q})F$. In deriving this relation, we regarded each group gene frequency as a constant; consequently, it is true only when each group is large. When the groups are small, the above formula does not allow for the contribution to variance made by the random fluctuation of gene frequencies in the groups. The average value of this contribution is equal to that given by (5). Since the variation between groups and that within groups are independent, the variance of q, including the effects of δq in the groups, will be

$$\sigma_q^2 = \bar{q}\,(1 - \bar{q})\,F + \frac{\bar{q}\,(1 - \bar{q})}{2\,N}\,(1 - F)\,, \tag{6}$$

which is equivalent to an expression given by Wright (Ex. 4). It is seen that, when $F = 0$, it reduces to $\bar{q}(1 - \bar{q})/2N$, as given by (2) for the case of random distribution.

Substituting (9F) of Chapter 21 in the above equation (6), and simplifying, we obtain an expression for σ_q^2 in terms of m instead of F under equilibrium conditions:

$$\sigma_q^2 = \frac{\bar{q}\,(1 - \bar{q})}{2\,N - (2\,N - 1)\,(1 - m)^{\,2}}\,. \tag{7}$$

This formula was obtained by Wright through another procedure (Ex. 2). When there is no isolation whatever ($m = 1$), the expression (7) reduces to (2) again. When there is complete isolation ($m = 0$), and thus every group is fixed, the variance between the groups becomes $\bar{q}(1 - \bar{q})$. When m is small, the expression (10) of Chapter 21, $\bar{q}(1 - \bar{q})/(4Nm + 1)$, is a good approximation of (7).

§ 6. *The Effective Size of a Population*

In a natural population the total number of individuals of all ages may be very large, but not every individual reaches sexual maturity and mates. Even those that mate do not necessarily leave offspring that survive to maturity in the next generation. No matter what their genotypes may be, those that leave no offspring will have nothing to do with the genetic composition of the next generation. The number of actual progenitors (breeding size) responsible for the genetic constitution of the next generation may be much less than the number of individuals living at any time in a population. Further, the breeding size may be much larger than what is known as the "effective" size of a population, an expression that will be defined in the next paragraph.

In an "ideal" population there are N breeding individuals, half of them females and half males, mating at random, and the variance of the random deviation of gene frequencies is $q(1 - q)/2N$, and the rate of decay is $1/2N$. We use this as the "standard" quantity with which others are to be compared; and the actual breeding size is reduced to a number equivalent to the number of individuals in the ideal population. This number is then called the *effective size* of the breeding group, a designation that will be made clear by considering the following four situations:

Unequal numbers of sexes.—Let N_0 and N_1 be the number of female and male parents, respectively. Reviewing the contents of Chapter 15 and, particularly, comparing its expressions (10) and (10') for the ultimate rates of decrease in heterozygosis, we see that approximately

$$\frac{N_0 + N_1}{8 N_0 N_1} = \frac{1}{2\tilde{N}}; \qquad \therefore \tilde{N} = \frac{4 N_0 N_1}{N_0 + N_1}, \qquad (8)$$

where $\tilde{N}$ stands for the effective size of the group of $N_0 + N_1$ breeding individuals. For example, suppose that there are 280 breeding females and 40 breeding males in a random-mating group. Heterozygosis in this group of 320 breeding individuals will decrease at the same rate as if there were only

$$\frac{4 (280) (40)}{280 + 40} = 140$$

breeding individuals in the group equally divided between the sexes. Inequality of the numbers of the two sexes always reduces the breeding size to a smaller effective size. It should be noted that the effective size depends much more on the sex that is fewer in number than on the other sex. Thus, with a limited number of males but a very large number of females, $\tilde{N}$ will be only slightly larger than $4N_1$. Another derivation of (8), based on the consideration of random deviations of q, is given in Exercise 7.

Similarly, for sex-linked genes, we have (referring to eq. [12] of Chap. 15)

$$\frac{N_0 + 2 N_1}{9 N_0 N_1} = \frac{1}{2\tilde{N}}; \qquad \therefore \tilde{N} = \frac{9 N_0 N_1}{2 N_0 + 4 N_1}.$$

Reproductive inequalities among individuals.—Up to this point we have assumed that gametes produce the next generation wholly at random from the parental population. This condition is, however, rarely fulfilled in natural populations. The number of surviving offspring left by different parents may vary tremendously, either through the pressure of selection or from accidental causes. The variation in number of offspring also tends to reduce the effective size of the breeding group. Let k be the number of gametes left by a parent and N be the actual number of parents. There will be Σk gametes, where the summation is over the N parents. The mean number of gametes per parent is $\bar{k} = \Sigma k/N$; and the variance of k is

$$\sigma_k^2 = \frac{\Sigma (k - \bar{k})^2}{N - 1} = \frac{1}{N - 1} \{\Sigma k^2 - N\bar{k}^2\};$$

$$\therefore \Sigma k^2 = (N - 1) \sigma_k^2 + N\bar{k}^2.$$

Since there are $N\bar{k}$ gametes, there will be $N\bar{k}(N\bar{k}-1)/2$ possible pairs of gametes. For the gametes of one particular parent there are $k(k-1)/2$ possible pairs; therefore the total number of pairs of gametes from the same parent is $\Sigma k(k-1)/2$. The proportion of pairs of gametes derived from the same parent among all possible pairs of gametes is

$$\frac{\Sigma k\,(k-1)}{N\bar{k}\,(N\bar{k}-1)} = \frac{(N-1)\,\sigma_k^2 + N\bar{k}\,(\bar{k}-1)}{N\bar{k}\,(N\bar{k}-1)}.$$

Now, in the ideal population of $\tilde{N}$ monoecious individuals with complete random union of gametes (including self-fertilization), the proportion of gamete pairs derived from the same parent is $1/\tilde{N}$. Equating these two equivalent proportions, we obtain

$$\tilde{N} = \frac{N\bar{k}\,(N\bar{k}-1)}{(N-1)\,\sigma_k^2 + N\bar{k}\,(\bar{k}-1)}. \tag{9}$$

(The above demonstration is based on a personal communication from Wright, in 1951, to J. F. Crow, who made it available to the writer.)

When gametes are drawn wholly at random from the parents, so that the number k forms a Poisson series with $\sigma_k^2 = \bar{k}$, the general formula (9) reduces to $\tilde{N} = N$, regardless of the actual value of $\bar{k}$. As we would expect, the effective size is equal to the breeding size of a group when there is random sampling of gametes. It becomes clear that, when $\sigma_k^2 > \bar{k}$, as is probably the case in most natural populations, the effective size will be smaller than the breeding size.

Another special case is that in which $\bar{k} = 2$, so that the breeding size of the group remains the same in successive generations. Then $\sigma_k^2 = \Sigma(k-2)^2/N$; and it should be noted that we use N here in the denominator instead of $N-1$ on account of the specified mean value. Substituting 2 for $\bar{k}$ and $N\sigma_k^2$ for $(N-1)\sigma_k^2$ in the general formula (9), we obtain (Wright, 1938c, 1940b) the frequently encountered formula

$$\tilde{N} = \frac{4N-2}{\sigma_k^2 + 2}. \tag{10}$$

It may be shown (Ex. 5) that, with random sampling of $2N$ gametes, the effective size is also equal to the breeding size. If N is large, there is here an approach to a Poisson distribution of k.

Periodic depletion in breeding size.—It often happens in nature that population size varies tremendously from generation to generation, as in different seasons of a year or in other cyclic variations. If there is a regular cycle of a few generations, an approximately equivalent population number can be found. Since the sampling variance is cumulative, the *average* sampling variance for a cycle of t generations with population numbers $N_1, N_2, \ldots, N_t$ is approximately

$$\frac{q\,(1-q)}{t} \left\{ \frac{1}{2N_1} + \frac{1}{2N_2} + \cdots + \frac{1}{2N_t} \right\}.$$

Equating this quantity to that of the ideal population, viz., $q(1 - q)/2\tilde{N}$, we obtain the effective size as (Wright, 1939a, p. 22)

$$\frac{1}{\tilde{N}} = \frac{1}{t}\left[\frac{1}{N_1} + \ldots + \frac{1}{N_t}\right]. \tag{11}$$

In other words, the effective size is the harmonic mean of the population sizes of the various generations of the cycle. For example, if there are four generations with effective sizes 20, 100, 800, and 5000, their average effective size is only 65, which is much closer to the minimum number than to the maximum of the cycle. The above formula can be applied only if the number of generations is so small that the amount of approach toward equilibrium (determined by selection and mutation pressures) during the period of large population sizes does not destroy the cumulative character of the sampling variance during successive generations of small population sizes.

The change in population size may not be regular or cyclic but may be a great reduction in size on rare occasions. One such great reduction in size may alter the gene frequencies so much as to nullify the previous effects of selection and mutation; and thereafter the gene frequencies may be directed toward a new point of equilibrium. The actual occurrence of cycles and of occasional great reductions in population size has been discussed especially by Elton (1924, 1942). He has concluded that chance deviations in the character of survivors at times of least numbers may have significant evolutionary effects.

Reduction due to inbreeding.—Comparing the sampling variance (4) with that of the ideal case (2), we see that the effective size of an inbred population is

$$\tilde{N} = \frac{N}{1+F}. \tag{12}$$

Thus, in the extreme case where $F = 1$, the effective size is half the actual population number as shown by (3).

§ 7. *Summary and Discussion*

In this chapter we have examined for the first time the variation of gene frequencies due to random deviation as a result of sampling accidents from one generation to the next. This deviation is appreciable in small populations and will lead eventually to random fixation of all loci. In such small populations the effects of new mutations are negligible. The rate of decay of variability (rate of loss of heterozygosis or rate of fixation of loci) is $1/2N$ per generation, where N stands for the effective size of the population. The effective size may be much smaller than the actual breeding size, which, in turn, may be much smaller than the number of living individuals in a population. Therefore, an apparently large population may have the characteristics of a small population when considered from the standpoint of random deviation of gene frequencies.

As a consequence of the above process, small isolated populations with identical initial gene frequencies will diverge further and further apart as time goes on. After a sufficiently large number of generations they will be quite different in their genetic compositions, even if the environmental conditions are the same for all these groups. This process permits considerable "differentiation" of isolated local groups. This type of differentiation, resulting from random variation and fixation of genes, occurs at random and thus is of no adaptive significance. Some genes may be unfavorable under certain conditions and yet be fixed by chance against the selection pressure. In brief, the factor of chance variation dominates the change in gene frequencies of small groups, and the selection force may be completely ineffective.

It is true that a species which consists of a very large number of individuals is usually distributed over a wide region; but such a species does not necessarily constitute a homogeneous, free interbreeding population because of the many discontinuities in the actual distribution. In fact, the organisms over a large region are usually distributed in small patches rather than continuously and uniformly. (There will be some isolation by distance even if they are uniformly distributed.) The work of Anderson (1936) on the distribution of *Iris* illustrates this point clearly. These discontinuities and irregularities in distribution subdivide a large species into a great number of small isolates, each subject to random variation of gene frequencies.

The differentiation of local forms of snails, such as *Achatinella* on Hawaii (particularly on the island of Oahu) and *Partula* on Tahiti and Moorea, provides an excellent example of the random fixation of genes in small populations (for references see Dobzhansky, 1951). The snails in every valley, or even in different parts of a valley, all vary as to color, size, and shape of the shell, dextrality and sinistrality, etc. These variations are not consistent with any systematic change in the environmental conditions of the valleys. It is impossible to explain this extreme diversity of local forms by the principle of "survival of the fittest." Many other examples of this kind have been reviewed and well discussed by Dobzhansky (1951). However, it should be said that nonselective differentiation is not necessarily nonadaptive. Since the process of differentiation is largely at random, some adaptive types may be fixed, by chance, along with nonadaptive types.

Small populations in which every locus has been fixed have no genetic variability left. When environmental conditions change, such populations will be unable to go through genotypic reorganizations to meet a new situation. Therefore, no matter how favorable a fixed type may be under present conditions, its ultimate fate in the long process of evolution probably is extinction. This is why partial isolation (with migrations among the groups to prevent complete fixation and yet to permit considerable differentiation) furnishes much more favorable conditions for evolutionary success. It provides a delicate balance between immediate adaptation and future flexibility.

Unfortunately, in most cases it is difficult to obtain direct information on the effective sizes of natural populations. Some indirect estimates of the magnitude of N have been made by Wright *et al.* (1942), but much more remains to be done in this area of investigation. Finally, it may be said that there is no clear-cut line between "large" and "small" populations. They are of all sizes. Moreover, the effective size of a population is in certain respects relative to the selection intensity and mutation rates. This point will be discussed more fully in the next chapter.

Notes and Exercises

1. Perform the following experiment: Put 50 black and 50 white marbles into an urn, from which draw 10 marbles at random (without replacement, to save time) and note the numbers of black and white marbles in the sample. Suppose that there are 3 blacks and 7 whites. Then put 30 black and 70 white marbles in a new urn, from which again draw a sample of 10 at random and note the numbers of blacks and whites, say, 2 and 8. Then put 20 black and 80 white marbles into a new urn, from which withdraw a random sample of 10 marbles again and note its numbers of blacks and whites. Continue this process until all 10 marbles in your sample are black or white. Note the number of operations (generations) required to reach this result. Compare your result with those of other students in the class. What is your conclusion?

2. The variance σ_q^2 reduces to $(1 - m)^2\sigma_q^2$ in the next generation on account of migrations among the groups. In stationary distribution of gene frequencies (where the variance remains of the same magnitude from generation to generation) the decrease in variance must have been compensated by the sampling variance of the new gene frequency including immigrants, $q + \Delta q = q - m(q - \bar{q})$. Now, for each group of size N, its sampling variance is $(q + \Delta q)(1 - q - \Delta q)/2N$. Let $\phi(q)$ be the distribution function of q among the groups. Then the *average* value of this sampling variance for all the groups is

$$\overline{\sigma_{\delta q}^2} = \frac{1}{2N} \int_0^1 [q - m(q - \bar{q})][1 - q + m(q - \bar{q})]\phi(q)\,dq.$$

The integrand may be written as

$$q(1 - q) + 2mq(q - \bar{q}) - m(q - \bar{q}) - m^2(q - \bar{q})^2,$$

which may be integrated easily term by term. It will be recalled (Chap. 20, Ex. 2) that $\int q(1 - q)\phi(q)dq$ is $\bar{q}(1 - \bar{q}) - \sigma_q^2$. Further, $\int(q - \bar{q})\phi(q)dq$ is zero; and $\int q(q - \bar{q})\phi(q)dq = \int(q - \bar{q})^2\phi(q)dq = \sigma_q^2$. Therefore, on integrating, we obtain

$$\overline{\sigma_{\delta q}^2} = \frac{\bar{q}(1 - \bar{q}) - \sigma_q^2 + 2m\sigma_q^2 - m^2\sigma_q^2}{2N} = \frac{\bar{q}(1 - \bar{q}) - (1 - m)^2\sigma_q^2}{2N},$$

which is the contribution to variance due to random deviations. Hence, in stationary state, we have the following relation (Wright, 1943):

$$\sigma_q^2 = (1-m)^2\sigma_q^2 + \frac{\bar{q}(1-\bar{q}) - (1-m)^2\sigma_q^2}{2N}.$$

Solving for σ_q^2 from this equation, we obtain our expression (7).

3. If we make no allowance for random deviations of q of the groups, then $(1-m)^2\sigma_q^2 = \bar{q}(1-\bar{q})F$. Hence, $\sigma_q^2 = \bar{q}(1-\bar{q})F/(1-m)^2$. Equating this value to (7), we obtain

$$\frac{\bar{q}(1-\bar{q})F}{(1-m)^2} = \frac{\bar{q}(1-\bar{q})}{2N - (2N-1)(1-m)^2},$$

which yields our expression (9F) of Chapter 21.

4. If we express σ_q^2 (7) in terms of F instead of $(1-m)^2$ by substituting (9m) of Chapter 21, we get at once

$$\sigma_q^2 = \frac{\bar{q}(1-\bar{q})[(2N-1)F+1]}{2N}, \qquad\qquad \text{i.e., (6)}$$

which is the original form given by Wright (1943).

5. Our formula (10) may be directly derived as follows: If the mean number of gametes contributed per parent is $\bar{k}=2$, we have $N\sigma_k^2 = \Sigma(k-2)^2 = \Sigma k^2 - 4N$ and $\Sigma k = 2N$. There are $2N(2N-1)/2$ possible ways of pairing the $2N$ gametes, including self-fertilization, but of these only $\Sigma k(k-1)/2$ come from the same parent. Therefore the proportion of self-fertilization is

$$\frac{\Sigma k(k-1)}{2N(2N-1)} = \frac{N\sigma_k^2 + 4N - 2N}{2N(2N-1)} = \frac{\sigma_k^2+2}{4N-2}.$$

Equating this to $1/\tilde{N}$ of the ideal case of $\tilde{N}$ monoecious individuals with complete random union of gametes, we obtain the effective size as given by (10). Furthermore, for each gamete the probability that it comes from a certain parent is $1/N$ and that it does not come from that same parent is $(N-1)/N$. If the sample of $2N$ gametes is drawn wholly at random, the distribution of k should be given by the expansion of

$$\left(\frac{1}{N} + \frac{N-1}{N}\right)^{2N}$$

with variance

$$\sigma_k^2 = 2N\left(\frac{1}{N}\right)\left(\frac{N-1}{N}\right) = \frac{2(N-1)}{N}.$$

Substituting this value of variance in (10), we obtain $\tilde{N} = N$, as expected (Wright, 1939a, p. 21). If N is large, the distribution of k approaches a Poisson series, and $\sigma_k^2 \to 2 = \bar{k}$.

6. If every parent contributes exactly the same number of gametes to the next generation, $k = \bar{k}$ and $\sigma_k^2 = 0$, our general formula (9) then becomes

$$\tilde{N} = \frac{N\bar{k} - 1}{\bar{k} - 1}.$$

In particular, when $k = \bar{k} = 2$, $\tilde{N} = 2N - 1$, nearly twice as large as the actual breeding size. In the extreme case $k = \bar{k} = 1$, we have $\tilde{N} = \infty$. This is equivalent to an indefinitely large population, because here no two gametes could possibly come from the same parent. The case of constant k for all parents is, however, highly improbable in nature.

7. The effective size as given by (8) for unequal numbers of males and females may be derived from the following considerations: the sampling variance of the $2N_0$ gametes which produced the N_0 females is approximately $q(1 - q)/2N_0$, and, similarly, for those which produce males it is approximately $q(1 - q)/2N_1$. The effective gene frequency of the population (females and males), being $q = \frac{1}{2}(q_0 + q_1)$, the approximate sampling variance may be written

$$\sigma_{\delta q}^2 = \frac{1}{4}(\sigma_{\delta q_0}^2 + \sigma_{\delta q_1}^2) = \frac{q(1 - q)}{4}\left[\frac{1}{2N_0} + \frac{1}{2N_1}\right].$$

Equating this value to the "standard" quantity $q(1 - q)/2\tilde{N}$, we obtain (8).

8. If there is a cycle of six generations with population sizes 10, 10^2, ..., 10^6, show that the average effective size is only 54.

9. An example of random deviation of gene frequencies in a small religious isolate (Old German Baptist Brethren) with an approximate effective size $N = 90$ has been reported by Glass et al. (1952). The student may find it interesting reading in conjunction with the contents of our Chapters 21–23. A good general review of the evidences of genetic drift in human populations has been given by Glass (1954).

CHAPTER 23

Stationary Distributions of
Gene Frequencies

UNDER constant environmental conditions the gene frequencies of an indefinitely large population will remain constant from generation to generation at certain stable equilibrium points determined by the counteracting but systematic pressures of selection, migration, and mutation. In finite populations, however, the gene frequencies may be expected to fluctuate at random from the accidents of sampling. The tendency toward a stable equilibrium point due to systematic pressures (Δq), and the tendency to drift away from that point due to random deviations (δq), should eventually result in a certain stationary (of constant form) distribution of gene frequencies. The distribution of q under equilibrium conditions was mentioned several times in earlier chapters, and now a study of the explicit functions of this type of distribution is in order. It will give us a more complete description of the total population under various circumstances, and it is a central problem in population genetics.

The stationary distribution of a gene frequency may be viewed in three different ways. First, it may be taken as the relative frequencies of the values of q of a particular locus over a large number of generations, all conditions being constant. Second, it may be considered as the probability distribution of the frequencies of all loci (subject to systematic pressures of the same magnitude) of one generation in a single population. Finally, we may imagine that there are a large number of isolated or partially isolated groups of the same size and subject to the same systematic pressures; it would then be the expected distribution of values of q of a particular gene at a given time among these groups. Although these three views are mathematically equivalent, the last interpretation appears the easiest to understand. The approach adopted in this chapter was selected with this last view in mind.

The following analogy will help to clarify the concept of stationary distributions. Suppose we measure the height of 10,000 fathers and find it normally distributed, with the mean 5.7 feet and the standard deviation 0.60 foot. The sons are in general not of the same height as their fathers. But, when we measure the height of these 10,000 mature sons, we may find that their height is also normally distributed, with the same mean value and standard deviation. Although perhaps no father-and-son pair have identical height, the distribution of height in these two generations is nevertheless the same. Now, the value of q in any one group may not remain the same in the next generation, but the distribution of q among all the groups remains the same in an equilibrium state. It is this distribution function we shall study in this chapter.

§ 1. *Statistical Memoranda*

For the benefit of the student who is not familiar with them, we shall first review some of the elementary properties of the beta and gamma functions.

1. The integral

$$\Gamma (n) = \int_0^\infty e^{-x} x^{n-1} dx$$

converges if n is positive; and it is called the *gamma function*, a function of n. In particular, if n is a positive integer, it may be shown by repeated integration by parts that

$$\Gamma(n) = (n - 1)\Gamma(n - 1) = (n - 1)! \qquad (1)$$

And it is for this reason that the gamma function is also known as the factorial function. It interpolates between the values of factorials when n is not an integer.

2. The integral

$$B (n, m) = \int_0^1 x^{n-1} (1 - x)^{m-1} dx \qquad (2)$$

also converges if n and m are both positive; and it is called the *beta function*, a function of n and m. It may be shown that the beta and gamma functions are connected by the relation

$$B (n, m) = \frac{\Gamma (n) \Gamma (m)}{\Gamma (n + m)}. \qquad (3)$$

Example:

$$B (4, 3) = \frac{\Gamma (4) \Gamma (3)}{\Gamma (7)} = \frac{3! 2!}{6!} = \frac{1}{60}.$$

3. If x is a continuous variable with values ranging from 0 to 1 and is distributed with probability density

$$\phi (x) = \frac{x^{n-1} (1 - x)^{m-1}}{B (n, m)} = \frac{\Gamma (n + m)}{\Gamma (n) \Gamma (m)} x^{n-1} (1 - x)^{m-1}, \qquad (4)$$

so that

$$\int_0^1 \phi (x) \, dx = 1$$

because of the relation (2), then x is said to be a *beta variate* (of the first kind) with parameters n and m; and its distribution (4) is a *beta distribution* (of the first kind). It belongs to Karl Pearson's Type I curve. Example:

$$\phi(x) = \frac{x^3(1-x)^2}{B(4,3)} = 60x^3(1-x)^2.$$

4. Since $B(n, m)$ is a constant in (4), the *form* of this distribution may be studied simply by plotting the curve $y = x^{n-1}(1-x)^{m-1}$. The shape of the curve depends upon the actual values of the parameters n and m. For instance, if n and m are each greater than unity, the curve will have a mode. Putting $dy/dx = 0$, we obtain the equation

$$(n-1)x^{n-2}(1-x)^{m-1} - x^{n-1}(m-1)(1-x)^{m-2} = 0$$

or

$$(n-1)(1-x) - x(m-1) = 0.$$

Therefore,

$$\dot{x} = \frac{n-1}{n+m-2} \tag{5}$$

is the modal value of x. In the above numerical example the modal value of x is $(4-1)/(7-2) = \frac{3}{5} = 0.60$. When $n = m$ and both are greater than unity, the distribution (4) becomes symmetrical, and its mode occurs at the point $\dot{x} = \frac{1}{2}$.

5. The shape of the curve at both ends is also important. If $n > 2$, the curve touches the x-axis at the origin ($x = 0$). If $1 < n < 2$, it is tangent to the y-axis at the origin. Finally, if $0 < n < 1$, the curve is asymptotic to the y-axis. Similar remarks hold for the shape of the curve near the other end ($x = 1$), according to the value of m.

6. The *mean* value of x of the beta distribution (4) is

$$\bar{x} = E(x) = \int_0^1 x\,\phi(x)\,dx$$

$$= \int_0^1 \frac{x^n(1-x)^{m-1}dx}{B(n,m)} = \frac{B(n+1,m)}{B(n,m)} = \frac{n}{n+m} \tag{6}$$

from the relations (3) and (1). Similarly,

$$E(x^2) = \frac{B(n+2,m)}{B(n,m)} = \frac{n(n+1)}{(n+m)(n+m+1)}.$$

Hence, the variance of x is

$$\sigma_x^2 = E(x^2) - \bar{x}^2 = \frac{nm}{(n+m)^2(n+m+1)}. \tag{7}$$

The student will find these simple theorems very helpful in reading the rest of this chapter. As a preliminary exercise, he should plot the following curves ($0 < x < 1$):

$$y = x^9(1-x)^4; \quad y = x^{1/2}(1-x)^2; \quad y = x^{-1/2}(1-x)^2$$

and verify some of the above formulas, after introducing the appropriate numerical values of $B(n, m)$. An excellent account of the beta and gamma distributions is to be found in Weatherburn's *A First Course in Mathematical Statistics* (1949), chapter viii.

§ 2. *General Distribution Formula*

The derivation of the general formula for the distribution of q previously was based upon the conditions that the mean and variance of q in the next generation must be equal to those of the preceding generation if the distribution is stationary. Recently, Wright (1952*a*) has given us a more rigorous demonstration based upon the fact that, if the distribution curve remains the same from generation to generation, all of its moments (about the mean) will also remain

TABLE 82

PROPERTIES OF q, Δq, AND δq

	Gene Frequency	Random Deviation
Range....................	$0 < q < 1$	$-q < \delta q < 1 - q$
Class frequency.............	$f(q)$	$g(\delta q)$
Total frequency............	$\Sigma f(q) = 1$	$\Sigma g(\delta q) = 1$
Mean....................	$\Sigma q \cdot f(q) = \bar{q}$	$\Sigma \delta q \cdot g(\delta q) = 0$
Variance.................	$\Sigma (q - \bar{q})^2 f(q) = \sigma_q^2$	$\Sigma (\delta q)^2 g(\delta q) = \sigma_{\delta q}^2$
Sum of products............	$\Sigma\Sigma (q - \bar{q})(\delta q) f(q) g(\delta q) = 0$ $\Sigma\Sigma (\Delta q)(\delta q) f(q) g(\delta q) = 0$	

the same. The following treatment is taken from his 1952 article. Those who do not care for the details of integral calculus may inspect the final results, (14) and (15), directly.

Preliminary remarks.—The gene frequency in each group is subject simultaneously to two kinds of changes, systematic and random; therefore, the distribution must be a function of Δq and δq. If $f(q)$ and $g(\delta q)$ be the class frequencies of q and δq, respectively, then we obtain the relations shown in Table 82, about which several obvious remarks may be made. Suppose that the gene frequency of a certain group is q in one generation. As a consequence of random deviation, it may become smaller (in which case we say δq is negative) or larger (whereupon δq is positive) in the next generation. Therefore the range of δq is from $-q$ to $1 - q$ as indicated in Table 82. The sum (and thus the mean) of these random deviations is of course zero. Its mean square is the variance $\sigma_{\delta q}^2$. Furthermore, being a random value, the sum of products of δq with Δq or $(q - \bar{q})$ should all be zero (bottom of Table 82); in other words, these two kinds of changes are assumed to be uncorrelated.

The fundamental equation.—If q is the gene frequency of a group in one generation, the nth moment about the mean of the distribution in this generation is $\Sigma(q - \bar{q})^n f(q)$, where the summation covers all the class values of q. In the next generation the class gene frequency will be $q + \Delta q + \delta q$, because of the two kinds of changes, so that the deviation from mean becomes $(q - \bar{q}) + (\Delta q + \delta q)$. Since the nth moment in the next generation should remain the same as that of the previous generation, we obtain the fundamental equation

$$\sum_q \sum_{\delta q} [(q - \bar{q}) + (\Delta q + \delta q)]^n f(q) g(\delta q) = \sum_q (q - \bar{q})^n f(q). \quad (8)$$

The relation holds for the moment of any order ($n = 1, 2, 3, \ldots$). Expanding the left-hand member in powers of $(q - \bar{q})$ and $(\Delta q + \delta q)$, we note that the first term cancels the right-hand member. Thus, (8) becomes

$$\sum_q \sum_{\delta q} \left[n (q - \bar{q})^{n-1} (\Delta q + \delta q) + \frac{n(n-1)}{2} (q - \bar{q})^{n-2} (\Delta q + \delta q)^2 + \ldots \right] f(q) g(\delta q) = 0.$$

Neglecting terms involving $(\Delta q)^2$, $(\delta q)^3$, $(\Delta q)(\delta q)^2$, and their higher powers, and using the simplifying relations given in Table 82, the equation reduces to

$$\sum_q [(q - \bar{q})^{n-1} \Delta q f(q)] + \frac{n-1}{2} \sum_q [(q - \bar{q})^{n-2} \sigma^2_{\delta q} f(q)] = 0. \quad (9)$$

Approximation by integration.—As noted in the previous chapter, the values of q can take only the values $0, 1/2N, \ldots, j/2N, \ldots, (2N - 1)/2N, 1$, in a group of N diploid individuals with minimal steps of $1/2N$. When N is moderately large, it is convenient to regard q as a continuous variable and substitute integration for summation, writing $\phi(q)dq$ for $f(q)$ where $\phi(q)$ is the desired distribution function of q. This process gives good approximations except for some distortions at the terminal classes ($q = 0$ or 1). With the transformation $\Delta q \phi(q) dq = d\chi(q)$, our equation (9) becomes

$$\int_0^1 (q - \bar{q})^{n-1} d\chi(q) + \frac{n-1}{2} \int_0^1 (q - \bar{q})^{n-2} \sigma^2_{\delta q} \phi(q) \, dq = 0. \quad (10)$$

Its first term, on integrating by parts, becomes

$$[\chi(q)(q - \bar{q})^{n-1}]_0^1 - (n-1) \int_0^1 \chi(q)(q - \bar{q})^{n-2} dq.$$

Substituting in (10) and letting $n = 1$, we obtain

$$[\chi(q)]_0^1 = 0 \quad \text{or} \quad \chi(1) = \chi(0).$$

But, in general, the quantity

$$[\chi(q) \cdot (q - \bar{q})^{n-1}]_0^1 = \chi(1) \cdot (1 - \bar{q})^{n-1} - \chi(0) \cdot (-\bar{q})^{n-1}$$

$$= \chi(1)[(1 - \bar{q})^{n-1} - (-\bar{q})^{n-1}] = (n-1) \chi(1) \int_0^1 (q - \bar{q})^{n-2} dq.$$

Substituting all these in (10), it becomes, ignoring the common factor $(n-1)$,

$$\int_0^1 (q - \bar{q})^{n-2} \{ \chi(1) - \chi(q) + \tfrac{1}{2}\sigma_{\delta q}^2 \phi(q) \} \, dq = 0. \qquad (11)$$

This is the last version of our original equation (8).

Solution for distribution function $\phi(q)$.—In terms of our original condition that all moments remain unchanged in successive generations, equation (11) should be true whatever the value of n. Being so, its integrand within the braces must vanish:

$$\chi(q) - \chi(1) = \tfrac{1}{2}\sigma_{\delta q}^2 \phi(q) . \qquad (12)$$

This is the key equation from which an expression for $\phi(q)$ in terms of Δq and $\sigma_{\delta q}^2$ may be found. To do this, let us take the differential of the logarithm of its left-hand member and then make the appropriate substitutions:

$$d \log \{ \chi(q) - \chi(1) \} = \frac{d\chi(q)}{\chi(q) - \chi(1)} = \frac{\Delta q \phi(q) \, dq}{\tfrac{1}{2}\sigma_{\delta q}^2 \phi(q)} = \frac{2\Delta q \, dq}{\sigma_{\delta q}^2} .$$

Integrating,

$$\log \{ \chi(q) - \chi(1) \} = 2 \int \frac{\Delta q \, dq}{\sigma_{\delta q}^2} + \text{const.}$$

Therefore

$$\chi(q) - \chi(1) = C' e^{2\int(\Delta q/\sigma_{\delta q}^2) dq} , \qquad (13)$$

where C' is a constant. Equating the two expressions for $\{\chi(q) - \chi(1)\}$ of (12) and (13), we get the desired distribution function

$$\phi(q) = \frac{C}{\sigma_{\delta q}^2} e^{2\int(\Delta q/\sigma_{\delta q}^2) dq} , \qquad (14)$$

where $C(= 2C')$ is a constant such that

$$\int_0^1 \phi(q) \, dq = 1 .$$

This is the general formula for the distribution of a gene frequency when a steady state (under the joint actions of Δq and δq) has been reached.

Since $\sigma_{\delta q}^2 = q(1-q)/2N$ for groups of *effective size* N, the general formula (14) may be written

$$\phi(q) = \frac{C}{q(1-q)} e^{4N\int[\Delta q/q(1-q)] dq} , \qquad (15)$$

where the C is another constant (being $2N$ times the previous one), to make the total probability unity. It should be said that the distribution function applies to groups of constant size, for which Δq is small in any one generation, since we neglected terms involving $(\Delta q)^2$, etc., in (9). Although δq is indeterminate in magnitude and direction, its variance $\sigma_{\delta q}^2$ is finite and determinate. Now we shall study the specific forms of (15) under various circumstances in which the expression for Δq is specified.

§ 3. *Distribution with Small Systematic Pressure*

If the groups are completely isolated and are so small that the effects of mutation are negligible and the selection is totally ineffective as compared with the relatively large random deviations of q, we may take $\Delta q = 0$ as an approximation. Under this circumstance the distribution formula (15) becomes very nearly (Fig. 73)

$$\phi\,(q)\;=\;\frac{C}{q\,(1-q)}=C\,q^{-1}\,(1-q)^{\,-1}, \tag{16}$$

excluding the two terminal classes in which $q = 0$, 1. This distribution is **U**-shaped, which means that most of the genes have their q value near 0 or 1 and

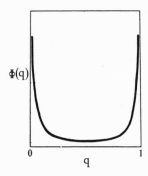

$\Phi(q)$

0   1

q

FIG. 73.—Distribution of q for small populations (16) in which systematic pressure is negligible: $\phi(q) = Cq^{-1}(1 - q)^{-1}$.

that only a few genes have intermediate q values. This conforms with the results of the preceding chapter, where it was shown that isolated small groups tend to reach complete homozygosis in a sufficiently long period of time. It is only the very occasional mutations from the homallelic classes that make the stationary distribution possible.

Since the range of q in (16) is from $q_1 = 1/2N$ to $q_2 = (2N - 1)/2N = 1 - q_1$, the value of C may be first roughly determined by the relation

$$\frac{1}{C}=\int_{q_1}^{q_2}\frac{d\,q}{q\,(1-q)}=\left[-\log_e\frac{1-q}{q}\right]_{q_1}^{q_2}=2\log_e\,(2\,N-1)\,.$$

But the actual values of q are at minimal steps of an interval of $1/2N$ rather than continuous, so that the more accurate value of C should be determined by the summation

$$\Sigma\,\frac{1}{q\,(1-q)}=\Sigma\,\frac{1}{q}+\Sigma\,\frac{1}{1-q}=2\Sigma\,\frac{1}{q}\,.$$

The difference between the true value of the summation $\Sigma(1/q)$ and its approximate value given by the integral $\int(1/q)dq$, for $0 < q < 1$, is

$$\Sigma \frac{1}{q} - \int \frac{dq}{q} = 0.577 = \gamma \,,$$

where γ is known as Euler's constant. With this correction, we have $1/C = 2 \log (2N - 1) + 2(0.577)$. Hence, (16) becomes (Wright, 1931)

$$\phi (q) = \frac{1}{2 \left[\log (2N - 1) + 0.577\right]} \; q^{-1} (1 - q)^{-1}, \qquad (16')$$

discounting the two terminal classes.

One point should be repeated here. The distribution takes the approximate form (16) when Δq is very small (so that random deviations dominate the situation) but not quite absolutely zero; for, if it were zero, there would be no stationary distribution to speak of, and the situation would be reduced to the case represented in Figure 72. There the distribution is uniform, but the absolute frequencies decrease by $1/2N$ per generation, with an ultimate fate of complete fixation.

§ 4. *Distribution under Mutation Pressures*

Next, let us consider the distribution under recurrent mutation pressures from both directions. The effect of mutation is appreciable only when the population is fairly large. Then, $\Delta q = \mu(1 - q) - \nu q$ as stated in equation (5) of Chapter 18. Substituting this value, the exponential quantity of (15) becomes

$$4N \int \frac{\mu (1 - q) - \nu q}{q (1 - q)} \, dq = 4N \int \left(\frac{\mu}{q} - \frac{\nu}{1 - q}\right) dq$$

$$= 4N\mu \log q + 4N\nu \log (1 - q) = U \log q + V \log (1 - q) \,,$$

where, for brevity, we write the constants $4N\mu = U$ and $4N\nu = V$. Hence, the distribution function (15) takes the form (Fig. 74)

$$\phi (q) = \frac{C}{q (1 - q)} \; e^{U \, \log q + V \, \log(1-q)}$$

$$= \frac{C}{q (1 - q)} \; q^U (1 - q)^V = C q^{U-1} (1 - q)^{V-1}, \qquad (17)$$

which is a simple beta distribution (4). Here, the constant

$$C = \frac{1}{B (U, V)} = \frac{\Gamma (U + V)}{\Gamma (U) \, \Gamma (V)} \,.$$

The formula (17) again gives good approximations for moderately large populations, except for the two terminal classes. The mean and variance of this distribution may be found easily by direct application of (6) and (7). Thus,

$$\bar{q} = \frac{U}{U+V} = \frac{4N\mu}{4N\mu + 4N\nu} = \frac{\mu}{\mu+\nu}. \qquad (17\text{M})$$

It will be recalled that this is also the stable equilibrium value $\hat{q}$ under mutation pressures from both directions. Because of the random deviations occurring simultaneously in each group, the value of q will not stay constant but will vary with a variance

$$\sigma_q^2 = \frac{UV}{(U+V)^2(U+V+1)} = \frac{\bar{q}(1-\bar{q})}{U+V+1} = \frac{\bar{q}(1-\bar{q})}{4N(\mu+\nu)+1}, \qquad (17\text{V})$$

since $U/(U+V) = \bar{q}$ and $V/(U+V) = 1 - \bar{q}$. This gives us a far more complete picture of the total population than that obtained from the chapters

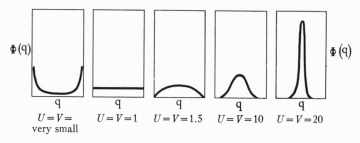

$$\phi(q) = Cq^{U-1}(1-q)^{V-1} = C[q(1-q)]^{4N\nu-1}$$

$\Phi(q)$

q	q	q	q	q
$U=V=$	$U=V=1$	$U=V=1.5$	$U=V=10$	$U=V=20$
very small				

FIG. 74.—Distribution of q under mutation pressures (17), assuming $\mu = \nu$

in which mutation and random deviation were treated separately. Now we see that the consequence of the joint effect of these factors is that group gene frequencies will vary, about the stable equilibrium point as their mean, with a finite variance. Naturally, the smaller the N, the larger will be the variance. This leads us to examine the various forms of distribution (17) corresponding to the magnitude of the effective size N (Fig. 74).

Some of the properties of the beta distribution have already been pointed out in Subsections 4 and 5. If $4N\mu$ and $4N\nu$ are both much smaller than unity, the distribution (17) will be U-shaped and similar to (16). If they are equal to unity, $\phi(q) = C$, a uniform distribution. When $4N\mu$ and $4N\nu$ are each greater than unity, however, there will be a mode in the distribution. The modal value of q, according to (5), is (Wright, 1931)

$$\dot{q} = \frac{4N\mu - 1}{4N(\mu+\nu) - 2}. \qquad (17 \text{ mode})$$

When N is so large that $4N\mu$ and $4N\nu$ are much larger than unity, the distribution will be clustered closely about its mean value with a small variance. For the sake of simplicity, we have assumed that $\mu = \nu$, so that the curves in Figure 74 are symmetrical with mean $\bar{q} = 0.50$. It becomes clear from these distribution forms that a population will be considered "small" when its effective size is such that $4N\mu$ and $4N\nu$ are less than unity. On the other hand, if they are much greater than unity (at least greater than 2), the population will be considered "large," because the group gene frequencies do not deviate much from their mean value. Finally, if $4N\mu$ and $4N\nu$ are between 1 and 2, the population size may be termed "intermediate," and the variation of group gene frequencies is still considerable.

§ 5. *Distribution under Migration Pressure*

When there is migration, the immigrants tend to pull the group gene frequencies toward the general mean $\bar{q}$ of the entire population with $\Delta q = -m(q - \bar{q})$. At the same time the random-sampling accidents tend to make them drift away from that point, so that an eventual stationary distribution of q will be established. The exact expression for $\sigma^2_{\delta q}$ was given in Exercise 2 of Chapter 22, where the effects of new immigrants into the group were accounted for. Here, however, we may take $\sigma^2_{\delta q} = q(1 - q)/2N$ as an approximation when the percentage of immigrants m is small. Then the distribution function may be found by making the following substitutions (p. 302) in formula (17):

$$m \text{ for } (\mu + \nu), \quad m\bar{q} \text{ for } \mu, \quad m\bar{p} \text{ for } \nu.$$

Proceeding exactly as before, we find that

$$\phi(q) = C q^{4Nm\bar{q}-1} (1 - q)^{4Nm\bar{p}-1}. \tag{18}$$

This is also a simple beta distribution with $U = 4Nm\bar{q}$, and $V = 4Nm\bar{p}$. Everything said about (17) applies also to (18). In particular, the mean of this distribution is the gene frequency of the entire population, as expected. Its variance may be directly obtained from (17V). Thus,

$$\sigma^2_q = \frac{\bar{q}(1 - \bar{q})}{4Nm + 1}. \tag{18V}$$

This last expression is in agreement with (10) of Chapter 21 for small m. Exercise 2 at the end of this chapter gives a more detailed consideration of $\sigma^2_{\delta q}$ for the case in which the percentage of immigrants is not very small.

In the simple case where $\bar{p} = \bar{q} = \frac{1}{2}$, the forms of the distribution (18) are the same as those shown in Figure 74 with

$$\phi(q) = C[q(1 - q)]^{2Nm-1} \tag{18\frac{1}{2}}$$

according to whether the quantity $2Nm$ (or, in general, $4Nm\bar{q}$ and $4Nm\bar{p}$) is less than unity, between 1 and 2, or much larger than unity. It is obvious that, when m is of any magnitude at all, the group gene frequencies will vary only slightly from each other and will cluster about the general mean. In most partially isolated groups in nature, the magnitude of m is probably greater than that of the mutation rates. In completely isolated groups, however, the distribution reduces to (16) again.

§ 6. *Distribution under Selection Pressure*

The distribution under selection pressure is more complicated because there are so many different types of selection, as we saw in Chapter 19. However, we shall consider first the general case from which some simple special cases may be deduced later. The general expression for selection pressure, as given in (19) of Chapter 19, is

$$\Delta q = \frac{q\,(1-q)}{2\bar{W}}\,\frac{d\bar{W}}{d q}\,,$$

where $\bar{W}$ is the average "fitness" of the population as a whole. Substituting this value in the exponential quantity of (15), we obtain

$$4N\int\left[\frac{q\,(1-q)}{2\bar{W}}\,\frac{d\bar{W}}{d q}\right]\frac{d q}{q\,(1-q)} = 2N\int\frac{d\bar{W}}{\bar{W}} = 2N\log\bar{W}.$$

Hence, the distribution formula under selection pressure alone becomes

$$\phi\,(q)\;=\;\frac{C}{q\,(1-q)}\;e^{2N\,\log\bar{W}}=\frac{C\bar{W}^{2N}}{q\,(1-q)}\,,\qquad(19)$$

whose explicit form depends upon the explicit expression of Δq or $\bar{W}$. These, in turn, depend upon the type of selection operating in the population. In reading the following special cases, it may be well to remember that, if ϵ is a small quantity in comparison with unity, $\log_e(1-\epsilon)=-\epsilon$, and $(1-\epsilon)^{2N}=e^{-2N\epsilon}$, approximately.

Intermediate heterozygotes.—When $W_{AA}=1$, $W_{Aa}=1-s$, and $W_{aa}=1-2s$, we have $\bar{W}=1-2sq$ for a random-mating population (Table 69); and, if $2sq$ is a small quantity, $\Delta q=-sq(1-q)$, approximately, where q is the frequency of the *unfavorable* gene. Hence, the distribution formula becomes (Fig. 75)

$$\phi(q) = C(1-2sq)^{2N}q^{-1}(1-q)^{-1} = Ce^{-4Nsq}q^{-1}(1-q)^{-1}.\quad(19.1)$$

If there were no random deviations involved, the stationary state would be $q=0$, and there would be practically no distribution of q. With random deviations, most of the unfavorable genes would still be near the zero point if the selection intensity were appreciable. But some of them might assume other values, and, indeed, a few of them might even be near the $q=1$ point if the group were small enough. Therefore the form of (19.1) will be J-shaped for intermediate values of $4Ns$. In Figure 75 we assumed $4Ns = 5$. If s or N or both are so small that $4Nsq$ is considerably smaller than unity, the factor e^{-4Nsq} will be very nearly equal to 1; and the distribution (19.1) will approach the form of (16) again, as expected. On the other hand, if selection is strong or the population is large, e^{-4Nsq} will be nearly zero; and most of the q's will be in the neighborhood of zero. (*Note.*—In many of Wright's papers this factor has been written e^{4Nsq}. This is because he takes $\Delta q = sq(1 - q)$, in which the s itself represents a negative quantity. Wright's q may also be interpreted as the frequency of the favorable gene.)

Unfavorable recessives.—When dominance is complete and $W_{aa} = 1 - s$, we have $\Delta q = -sq^2(1 - q)$, approximately, and $\bar{W} = 1 - sq^2$. Hence, the distribution function will be

$$\phi(q) = C(1 - sq^2)^{2N}q^{-1}(1 - q)^{-1} = Ce^{-2Nsq^2}q^{-1}(1 - q)^{-1}. \quad (19.2)$$

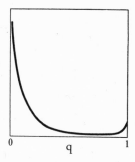

Fig. 75.—Distribution (19.1), with $4Ns = 5$. $\phi(q) = Ce^{-5q}/q(1 - q)$

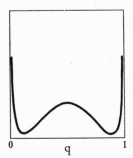

Fig. 76.—Distribution (19.3), with $4Ns = 10$. $\phi(q) = Ce^{-10q(1-q)}/q(1 - q)$

The form of this distribution is more or less similar to that of the previous one (19.1).

Superior heterozygotes.—For simplicity, let us assume that homozygotes AA and aa have equal fitness (which we take as unity) and that $W_{Aa} = 1 + s$, so that the stable equilibrium point is $\hat{q} = \frac{1}{2}$. Then $\bar{W} = 1 + 2spq$ and $\Delta q = spq(1 - 2q)$. Hence (Fig. 76)

$$2\int \frac{\Delta q}{\sigma^2_{\delta q}}\, dq = 4N s \int (1 - 2q)\, dq = 4N s\, (q - q^2)\,;$$

$$\therefore \phi(q) = C e^{4Nsq(1-q)} q^{-1} (1 - q)^{-1}. \quad (19.3)$$

When the population is of intermediate size, the distribution is as shown in Figure 76; it is symmetrical with $\bar{q} = \hat{q} = \frac{1}{2}$ and has a mode at the same point. But, when q is either very low or very high, there is a considerable chance of fixation by random-sampling accidents.

§ 7. *Distribution under Joint Pressures*

Having investigated the distributions of gene frequencies under separate systematic pressures, we turn now to the more realistic cases in which there are joint pressures of two or more factors. In such cases the distributions vary according to the relative magnitude of the effective size of the groups, on the one hand, and the rate of mutation, the selection intensity, and the proportion of migration, on the other. Only a few simple examples will be given in this section.

Mutation and migration.—Since the expression of Δq for mutation pressure is of the same form as that for migration pressure, their joint systematic effect on gene frequency will still be of that same form; thus

$$\Delta q = \mu p - \nu q + m\bar{q}\cdot p - m\bar{p}\cdot q = (\mu + m\bar{q})p - (\nu + m\bar{p})q .$$

Proceeding exactly as in Section 4, we see that $\phi(q)$ will still be a simple beta distribution similar to (17) and (18), except that now

$$U = 4N(\mu + m\bar{q}) \quad \text{and} \quad V = 4N(\nu + m\bar{p}) . \tag{20}$$

Therefore, in the following, we shall investigate only the joint effects of mutation and selection, which may thus be considered as a general case.

Mutation and selection.—Comparing the distribution formula under mutation pressure (17) with that under selection pressure (19), we note that s (included in $\bar{W}$) appears in a separate factor from those involving μ and ν (included in U and V). Therefore, the distribution function under the joint pressures of mutation and selection is the product of the corresponding separate functions, $\sigma_{\delta q}^2$ being a common factor. This will be made clear by writing out their joint systematic effects

$$\Delta q = \mu (1 - q) - \nu q + \frac{q (1 - q)}{2\bar{W}} \frac{d\bar{W}}{d q} ;$$

$$4N \int \frac{\Delta q}{q (1 - q)} \, d q = 4N\mu \log q + 4N\nu \log (1 - q) + 2N \log \bar{W} ;$$

$$\phi (q) = C\bar{W}^{2N} q^{U-1} (1 - q)^{V-1} , \tag{21}$$

where $U = 4N\mu$ and $V = 4N\nu$. If U and V take the values indicated in (20), the above distribution formula includes also the effects of migration. Thus formula (21) is virtually as general as (15), and all the specific formulas given earlier may be derived by assigning particular values to $\bar{W}$, U, and V. For instance, in the case of no selection, we have $s = 0$ and $\bar{W} = 1$, and (21) reduces to (17) or (18). On the other hand, if there is no mutation or migration,

$U = V = 0$, and (21) reduces to (19). The various forms of (21) depend upon the values of $\bar{W}$, U, and V. The following are a few examples.

(i) Without dominance, $\bar{W} = 1 - 2sq$ and (Fig. 77)

$$\phi(q) = Ce^{-4Nsq}q^{4N\mu-1}(1 - q)^{4N\nu-1} . \tag{21.1}$$

It will be recalled that, if $\mu = \nu$ without selection, the distribution is symmetrical with $\bar{q} = \frac{1}{2}$. Now, with selection against a, its mean frequency is pushed below the middle point to an extent depending upon the intensity of selection— even if the mutation rates are still equal. If s is small, (21.1) reduces to (17) approximately.

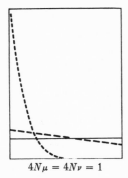
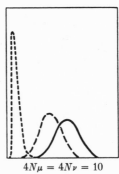

$$4N\mu = 4N\nu = 1 \qquad\qquad 4N\mu = 4N\nu = 10$$

FIG. 77.—Distribution of q in the case of no dominance (21.1), assuming mutation rates to be constant and equal ($\mu = \nu$). In each case the solid line represents least selection, $s = \mu/10$; the broken line, moderate selection, $s = \mu$; and the dotted line, strong selection, $s = 10 \mu$. If $4N\mu$ and $4N\nu$ are much less than unity, the curve will be U-shaped as in Figure 73; the selection effects merely make the U slightly less symmetrical. (Wright, 1939a.)

(ii) For recessive deleterious genes, $\bar{W} = 1 - sq^2$, and

$$\phi(q) = Ce^{-2Nsq^2}q^{4N\mu-1}(1 - q)^{4N\nu-1} . \tag{21.2}$$

This is a form commonly met with in discussions concerning the distribution of gene frequencies. If q is being kept at a low level by selection, the effect of reverse mutations νq is negligible, so that the distribution of a *rare* recessive gene is approximately

$$\phi(q) = Ce^{-2Nsq^2}q^{4N\mu-1}(1 - q)^{-1} . \tag{21.3}$$

It may be recalled that the equilibrium value is $\hat{q} = \sqrt{(\mu/s)}$ in such a case (eq. [2] of Chap. 20). Its form of distribution is similar to that of the following extreme case.

(iii) For recessive lethals, $\bar{W} = 1 - q^2$. Since lethal genes are rare, the reverse mutation effect may be neglected ($4N\nu = 0$). Thus, (21) takes the form (Fig. 78)

$$\phi(q) = C(1 - q^2)^{2N}q^{4N\mu-1}(1 - q)^{-1} . \tag{21.4}$$

Its equilibrium value is $\hat{q} = \sqrt{\mu}$, as stated in (2L) of Chapter 20. Its distribution forms in small, medium, and large populations are shown in Figure 78.

§ 8. *Joint Distribution of Gene Frequencies*

So far we have derived formulas for distributions of gene frequencies only for single pairs of genes, with constant selection coefficients. That is, we have assumed that the effect on fitness of one locus is independent of all other loci. A more adequate treatment requires that we take into account factor interactions. For instance, with respect to two pairs of genes, it may be that only the double recessive (*aabb*) is disadvantageous (with $W = 1 - s$), while the other eight genotypes are all normal. Or, if the gene effects are additive with respect to a metrical character, only those of medium size are favored by selection (Chap. 19, Ex. 17). In brief, the selective value of a genotype depends on the particular combination of genes rather than on the presence or absence of a particular

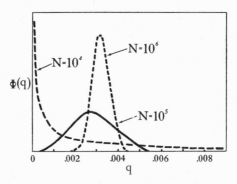

FIG. 78.—Distribution (21.4) of a rare recessive lethal gene, with $\mu = 10^{-5}$. Note that the mean $\bar{q} = \sqrt{\mu} = \sqrt{0.00001} = 0.00316$ in large populations and becomes increasingly small as N decreases. (Wright, 1937, 1939a.)

allele. The problem of joint distribution of several gene frequencies has been treated by Wright in a number of articles (e.g., Wright, 1939a, Sec. V, "The Frequencies of Interacting Factors"). Here we cannot deal with this subject as exhaustively as we did with the frequencies of single pairs of genes. The following brief account is not intended to be a detailed analysis; it provides only an introduction to the concept of joint distribution.

As we have seen, whether the effective size of a population is large or small is relative to selection intensities and mutation rates. If these differ widely from locus to locus, a population may be "small" with respect to one gene and "large" with respect to another. Therefore, the joint distribution of several gene frequencies may assume very complicated forms. In the examples shown in Figure 79 it was assumed, for easy plotting of the distribution surface, that mutations and reverse mutations for the two loci are all the same. The joint distribution formula for just two pairs of genes is, considering only selection and mutation pressures,

$$\phi\,(q_1,\ q_2)\ = C\overline{W}^{2N} \cdot q_1^{U_1-1}\,(1-q_1)^{\,V_1-1} \cdot q_2^{U_2-1}\,(1-q_2)^{\,V_2-1}\,,$$

where $U_1 = 4N\mu_1$, etc., and $\bar{W}$ is the average fitness of the population (of nine genotypes). This is an extension of (21) and may be extended to the case of k pairs of genes. Some of the forms of the distribution surface for small, medium, and large populations are shown in Figure 79. Various other forms may be obtained by assigning particular values to U, V, and $\bar{W}$. For k pairs of genes the joint distribution, $\phi(q_1 \ldots q_k)$, would be represented by a "surface" in $k + 1$ dimensional space. The important point to remember here is that the surface would be very irregular in shape and consist of numerous peaks of various heights.

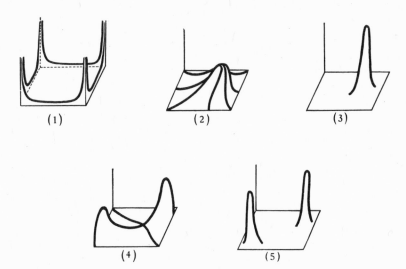

Fig. 79.—Joint distribution of the frequencies of two pairs of genes. The vertical axis is $\phi(q_1, q_2)$, while the square bottom represents the q_1-q_2-plane.

(1) Population small: genes mostly fixed. The genotypes $AABB(0, 0), AAbb(0, 1), aaBB(1, 0), aabb(1, 1)$ are most frequent.

(2) Population of medium size. Here it is assumed that only the double recessive (*aabb*) is inferior with fitness value $W = 1 - s$, so that $\bar{W} = 1 - sq_1^2 q_2^2$. The selection intensity and mutation rates are assumed to be of the same order of magnitude.

(3) Population large under the same conditions as (2). The distribution surface becomes a narrow and tall cone on top of the equilibrium point $(\hat{q}_1, \hat{q}_2)$.

(4) Population medium. Here it is assumed that the two pairs of genes have equal and additive effects on a metrical character on which adverse selection acts according to the square of the deviation from the mean and that all mutation rates are equal. The saddle-shaped line shows the frequencies along the diagonal connecting the two favorable types $AAbb$ and $aaBB$. The other line refers to the frequencies connecting the extreme (unfavorable) types $AABB$ and $aabb$. The entire surface assumes the shape of the back of a double-humped camel.

(5) Population large under the same conditions as (4). The surface then has two widely separated and steep peaks over the favorable points.

(All figures are adapted from unpublished notes of Dr. J. F. Crow.)

§ 9. *Some Implications for Evolution: A Summary*

The concept of the distribution of gene frequencies is both useful and important in any discussion of biological evolution at the populational rather than the individual level; and the change in gene frequency must be considered as an elementary step in that process. The distribution forms of the frequencies depend upon the relative magnitudes of the various agents which bring about changes in gene frequency. Broadly speaking, however, the distributions fall into three main types according to the effective size of the populations (Fig. 80).

In large random-mating populations all gene frequencies remain at a certain stable equilibrium point which is determined by the counteracting but systematic pressures of mutation, selection, and migration. Thus, the distribution of q

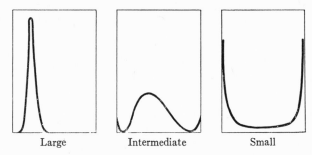

| Large | Intermediate | Small |

FIG. 80.—Three main types of distribution of q according to the effective size of populations. (Wright, 1932.)

is I-shaped. When all genes reach their equilibrium points, there can be no further genetic change in the composition of a population under constant environmental conditions, and evolution may come to a standstill. Only when environmental conditions change will the selective values of the various genotypes vary accordingly, and with them the values of the equilibrium points. At such times the gene frequencies will move toward new equilibrium points. Evolution in such large random-mating populations may be said to be guided by intragroup selection. But this process is sometimes so slow that it may be unfavorable for evolutionary changes.

In small and completely isolated populations the gene frequencies diverge from their equilibrium points at random, and hence most of the genes eventually are fixed or lost by chance, yielding a random combination of genes. The distribution of q in such populations is U-shaped. The result is largely nonadaptive differentiation of small local varieties, because random deviation is the dominating factor—not selection. Since most of such randomly fixed combinations of genes will not be of the types most favored by selection, and since small population groups completely lack genetic plasticity, their ultimate fate is probably extinction.

In populations of intermediate size, selection is effective to some extent in determining the direction of evolutionary change; but at the same time there is also considerable random fluctuation of gene frequencies. This condition is more favorable, from the evolutionary point of view, than either the very large or the very small populations already discussed. The most favorable condition is, however, that in which a large population is subdivided into numerous *partially isolated* groups (with migrations between them). Then, all the evolutionary forces—mutation, selection, migration, and random deviation—may be at work simultaneously. Under such conditions there will be differentiation among the partially isolated groups, some of it adaptive and some nonadaptive, depending upon the relative influence of migration and selection in each group. Complete fixation in any group will be prevented by the interchange of individuals between the groups. The selection effect, varying from one locality to another, may be said to be intergroup, which is much more efficient than intragroup selection in one large population. If the groups are small, some of them will be eliminated by selection, while others will flourish. When a group grows large, it may be subdivided again into partially isolated groups. Hence, this condition provides a trial-and-error mechanism under which the systems of gene frequencies may finally reach their most favorable equilibrium points. The species (the total population) may evolve continuously even without substantial changes in environmental conditions. If conditions do change, the total population, with its diversified and flexible subgroups, will be able to cope with the new situation instead of facing extinction.

From the preceding discussion it is clear that there is no one all-important factor in evolutionary change. The type of change in a population depends on what Wright calls the "breeding structure" of that population (N, F, m, s, μ, ν, q). The effective size of a population, inbreeding, isolation, migration, selection, mutation, and the absolute value of gene frequency may all be important in different cases. The most favorable condition for evolutionary advance is that in which all these forces are balanced against one another in certain ways under certain conditions rather than that in which one factor dominates the situation all the time.

The process of evolutionary change may be further elucidated by considering the average fitness of a population. It will be recalled that $\bar{W}$ is a function of gene frequencies and that the effect of selection is to adjust the value of q so that $\bar{W}$ is at a maximum. The simplest example is that in which heterozygotes are favored by selection (Chap. 19, Ex. 9), and $\bar{W} = 1 - s_1(1 - q)^2 - s_2 q^2$, which attains its maximum at the point $\hat{q} = s_1/(s_1 + s_2)$. Similarly, if two pairs of genes are concerned, $\bar{W}$ will be a function of two gene frequencies (see Chap. 19, § 12). Geometrically, if we represent q_1 in one dimension and q_2 in another, and the value of $\bar{W}$ by a third dimension, the values of $\bar{W}$ will form a surface in the three-dimensional space, there being a value of $\bar{W}$ corresponding to each point in the $q_1 q_2$ plane. The effect of selection is to adjust the values of q_1 and q_2

so that a pair of values $(\hat{q}_1, \hat{q}_2)$ will make $\bar{W}$ a maximum. There may be more than one maximum point in the $\bar{W}$ surface, and the points are not necessarily of equal height. To which of the maximum points the population will attain depends on the circumstances of selection as well as the gene frequencies at that time.

Now, if we consider 100 loci simultaneously, and represent $\bar{W}$ by another dimension, the values of $\bar{W}$ will form a surface in the 101-dimensional space, there being a value of $\bar{W}$ corresponding to each point in the 100-dimensional subspace. There will be many maximum points ("peaks") in this surface. The effect of selection is to find a point $(\hat{q}_1, \ldots, \hat{q}_{100})$ which will make $\bar{W}$ attain one of its maximum values. This is known as Wright's "peak-valley" model, in which the $\bar{W}$ surface has been represented by a topographical "map" showing its peaks and valleys in the general "field" of possible gene combinations (Wright, 1932, 1939a). With this picture in mind, the discussion in the preceding paragraphs may be reformulated as follows.

A large random-mating population with a system of gene frequencies close to the point $(\hat{q}_1, \ldots, \hat{q}_{100})$ occupies a peak of the $\bar{W}$ surface and its vicinity. With increased selection intensity or reduced mutation rates (so that $4Ns$ and $4N\mu$ are very large), the fitness of the population as a whole will be improved, and thus the population will occupy a smaller neighborhood around a peak of the adaptive surface. On the other hand, if selection is lessened, the population will occupy a larger neighborhood around the peak; that is, a greater variation about the point $(\hat{q}_1, \ldots, \hat{q}_{100})$. There is a high degree of stability for a large species.

A change of environmental conditions means a change in the topography of the field of gene combinations: peaks may become valleys as the favorable gene combinations become unfavorable, and vice versa. The effect of selection is to lead the population from a valley to its nearest peak, which means that the system of gene frequencies will move gradually toward a new equilibrium point determined by the new environment.

A very small population, or one with close inbreeding, will yield finally a random combination of genes, so that the population may occupy almost any point in the field with any value of $\bar{W}$. The chances are that such populations would only rarely land on any peak at all.

A population of intermediate size would wander around a peak at random and probably would occupy a place on the surface not too far from the nearest peak. Such a population would not move down from a peak to a valley, but there is some chance that it might encounter a gradient leading to another peak and shift its allegiance to that. Here, then, is a trial-and-error mechanism by which in time a species might work its way to the higher parts of the general field. The rate of progress, however, would be extremely slow, since change of gene frequency per generation is very small (of the order of mutation rates).

Finally, let us consider the case of a species subdivided into many local, partially isolated groups. Each group, with its fluctuating gene frequencies, will occupy a considerable field of gene combinations, and thus the total population will spread over a very wide area on the surface of adaptation. Although each of these local races may shift continually in a primarily nonadaptive fashion, there will nevertheless be broad adaptive differentiation among the large regions if the conditions of selection vary in different parts of the whole range. The rate of movement of gene frequencies may be much larger than in the preceding case, since the change per generation now is of the order of migration proportions (instead of mutation rates). With a wide area of occupation and a relatively high rate of movement, there is a good chance that some one race will come under the influence of another peak; in other words, this one race would turn out to have acquired a "preadaptation." If this second peak is a higher one (corresponding to a superior adaptation), this race will expand in numbers and by cross-breeding with other groups, as well as by actual displacement of these, will pull the species as a whole toward the new position. In this way subdivision of a large species into partially isolated local groups provides a highly efficient mechanism for trial and error in the field of gene combinations and for evolutionary advance by intergroup selection.

For more detailed discussions the reader is referred to Wright's original articles. An excellent nonmathematical presentation of this whole concept is that of Dobzhansky (1951). In brief, the evolutionary process depends on a continually shifting but never obliterated state of balance between factors of persistence and those of change; and the most favorable condition for this process is to be found in a subdivided structure in which isolation and cross-communication continue in proper balance.

In closing, a word should be said about the rival teleological and mechanical theories of evolution. We have seen that even so-called "preadaptation" may have a mechanical basis. In discussing the evidences of the precision of genetic adaptation through natural selection, Muller (1948) points out that organisms starting with similar needs but different genetic make-up nevertheless tend to develop the same characters, even to the utmost degree of precision. This can be explained only on the ground of selective advantage of the characters concerned. This result of selection resembles that of conscious profiting by experience. It is as though a goal were aimed at, regardless of the means of its attainment. It is therefore justifiable, in this sense, to regard the organism teleologically. Hence, Muller concludes: "Teleology, of a sort, is a part of 'mechanism' after all."

Notes and Exercises

1. Since $0.577 = \log_e 1.78$, approximately, the constant factor in (16) may be written as, with moderate N,

$$\frac{1}{C} = 2 \left[\log 2N + \log 1.78\right] = 2 \log 3.56N.$$

2. When Δq is a linear function of q, the variance of q may be more accurately determined (than indicated by [17V] and [18V]) in the following manner. Let $\Delta q = -c(q - \bar{q})$, where c is a constant. For stationary distributions, although q in one generation becomes $q + \Delta q + \delta q$ in the next generation, the variance of the distribution remains the same; thus the following equation

$$\sigma_q^2 = \int_0^1 (q - \bar{q})^2 \phi(q) \, dq = \int_0^1 (q + \Delta q - \bar{q})^2 \phi(q) \, dq$$
$$+ \int_0^1 \frac{q(1-q)}{2N} \phi(q) \, dq,$$

approximately, assuming δq is independent of $q + \Delta q$. The first term of the right-hand side of the above equation represents the portion of variance contributed by the new gene frequencies, taking into account Δq but not the random deviations. Since the new systematic deviation is

$$q + \Delta q - \bar{q} = q - c(q - \bar{q}) - \bar{q} = (1 - c)(q - \bar{q}),$$

the first term reduces to

$$(1 - c)^2 \int_0^1 (q - \bar{q})^2 \phi(q) \, dq = (1 - c)^2 \sigma_q^2. \tag{i}$$

The second term, representing the contribution of random deviations to the variance, is easy to integrate:

$$\int_0^1 \frac{q(1-q)}{2N} \phi(q) \, dq = \frac{\bar{q}(1 - \bar{q}) - \sigma_q^2}{2N}. \tag{ii}$$

Substituting (i) and (ii) in the original equation, we obtain

$$\sigma_q^2 = \frac{\bar{q}(1 - \bar{q})}{2N + 1 - 2N(1 - c)^2} = \frac{\bar{q}(1 - \bar{q})}{1 + 4Nc - 2Nc^2},$$

where

$c = \mu + \nu$ for mutation pressure,

$c = m$ for migration pressure,

$c = m + \mu + \nu$ for joint migration and mutation pressures.

Note that this expression for σ_q^2 is very nearly, but not exactly, equal to (7) of Chapter 22 for the case $c = m$. This is so because the contribution of random deviations to variance is not exactly $\int [q(1 - q)/2N] \phi(q) dq$, as assumed here, but is $\int [(q + \Delta q)(1 - q - \Delta q)/2N] \phi(q) dq$, as explained in Exercise 2 of Chapter 22. The present expression, however, is an improvement of (17V) and (18V). The three derivations of σ_q^2 are summarized as follows for comparison:

CONTRIBUTIONS FROM		VARIANCE OF q OF STATIONARY DISTRIBUTION
Systematic Deviation	Random Deviation	
$(1-2c)\sigma_q^2$	$\dfrac{\bar{q}(1-\bar{q})-\sigma_q^2}{2N}$	$\sigma_q^2=\dfrac{\bar{q}(1-\bar{q})}{1+4Nc}$
$(1-c)^2\sigma_q^2$	$\dfrac{\bar{q}(1-\bar{q})-\sigma_q^2}{2N}$	$\sigma_q^2=\dfrac{\bar{q}(1-\bar{q})}{1+4Nc-2Nc^2}$
$(1-c)^2\sigma_q^2$	$\dfrac{\bar{q}(1-\bar{q})-(1-c)^2\sigma_q^2}{2N}$	$\sigma_q^2=\dfrac{\bar{q}(1-\bar{q})}{2N-(2N-1)(1-c)^2}$

3. Plot the curves (18), assuming $\bar{q}=\frac{1}{2}$ in the entire population, for the cases $Nm = 0.05, 0.50, 5,$ and 50. (See Fig. 81.)

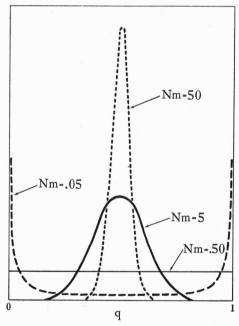

FIG. 81.—Distribution of q under migration pressure alone (18), assuming $\bar{q} = 0.50$. $Nm = 0.50$ is equivalent to $4Nm\bar{q} = 1$, etc. (Wright, 1940a, b.)

4. Putting $V = 4N\nu = 1$ in (17), we have

$$\phi(q) = \frac{\Gamma(U+1)}{\Gamma(U)\,\Gamma(1)}\,q^{U-1} = 4N\mu \cdot q^{4N\mu-1}.$$

This is an approximate distribution when the mutations are largely of one direction. Plot the curve $\phi(q) = 4q^3$ as an example.

5. Plot the distribution curve (21.1) in large populations with $4N\mu = 4N\nu = 5$ and strong selection without dominance, $4Ns = 40$. Note that $\hat{q} = \mu/s = \frac{5}{40} = \frac{1}{8}$, approximately, which is also very near the modal value of the curve. (See Fig. 82.)

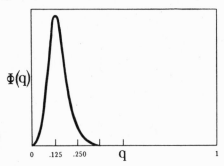

Fig. 82.—Distribution (21.1): $\phi(q) = Ce^{-40q}q^4(1-q)^4$

6. In the general case of slow zygotic selection, where the adaptive values of the three genotypes are all different, we may write $\Delta q = q(1-q)(-s+tq)$, where t may be negative or positive, depending upon the degree of dominance (eq. [20] of Chap. 19). Show that the distribution formula in this case becomes

$$\phi(q) = Ce^{-4Nsq+2Ntq^2}q^{U-1}(1-q)^{V-1}.$$

7. In Chapter 6 we investigated the equilibrium conditions for self-sterility alleles. In the simplest case, in which there were only three such alleles, it was shown that the equilibrium value of the gene frequency is $\hat{q} = \frac{1}{3}$ for each of the alleles (S_1, S_2, S_3). If the population is not in equilibrium, the gene frequencies will change toward their stable equilibrium value at the rate

$$\Delta q = \frac{1}{2}(1-3q)$$

per generation. Taking $\sigma^2_{\delta q} = q(1-q)/2N$ for populations of effective size N, and ignoring the effects of mutation and migration, show that the stationary distribution formula is

$$\phi(q) = \frac{\Gamma(6N)}{\Gamma(2N)\,\Gamma(4N)}\, q^{2N-1}(1-q)^{4N-1},$$

a beta distribution. Also show that the mean value of q is equal to its equilibrium value ($\bar{q} = \hat{q} = \frac{1}{3}$) and that the modal value and variance are, respectively,

$$\hat{q} = \frac{2N-1}{6N-2} \doteq \frac{1}{3}; \qquad \sigma^2_q = \frac{2}{9(6N+1)} \doteq \frac{1}{27N}.$$

The more general distributions for the case of more than three alleles, and allowing for mutations and migrations, may be found in Wright (1939*b*).

8. The mode of the general distribution (15) may be found by solving the equation $d\phi(q)/dq = 0$, but it is simpler to work with the logarithm of the distribution function; thus

$$L = \log \phi\,(q)\, = 4N\!\int \frac{\Delta q\,dq}{q\,(1-q)} - \log q\,(1-q) + \text{const}.$$

$$\frac{dL}{dq} = \frac{d\log \phi\,(q)}{dq} = \frac{4N\cdot\Delta q}{q\,(1-q)} - \frac{1-2q}{q\,(1-q)} = 0.$$

For example, the joint effects of mutation and selection without dominance is

$$\Delta q = -sq(1-q) + \mu(1-q) - \nu q\,.$$

Substituting in the equation $dL/dq = 0$, and noting that $1-2q = (1-q)-q$, we obtain (Wright, 1931)

$$-4Ns + \frac{4N\mu}{q} - \frac{4N\nu}{1-q} - \frac{1}{q} + \frac{1}{1-q} = 0$$

or

$$-4Ns + \frac{4N\mu-1}{q} - \frac{4N\nu-1}{1-q} = 0\,.$$

In particular, when the effects of reverse mutations are negligible, the equation becomes

$$4Ns = \frac{4N\mu-1}{q}\,;$$

$$\therefore\quad \hat{q} = \frac{4N\mu-1}{4Ns} \doteq \frac{\mu}{s}\,,$$

indicating that the modal value is very near its equilibrium value for large populations.

9. The general distribution function (14) is equivalent to the following differential equation, which is known as the Fokker-Planck equation in physics:

$$\frac{\partial}{\partial q}\,[\Delta q\cdot\phi\,(q)] = \frac{1}{2}\frac{\partial^2}{\partial q^2}\,[\sigma_{\delta q}^2\phi\,(q)] \qquad\qquad \text{(A)}$$

(Kolmogorov, 1935; Wright, 1945). This may be independently derived from the condition that the distribution of q remains the same in successive generations in spite of the changes Δq and δq. However, for our present purpose, which is to show (14) to be a solution of (A), we merely have to integrate (A) twice with respect to q. The first integration gives

$$\Delta q\cdot\phi\,(q)\, = \frac{1}{2}\frac{\partial}{\partial q}\,[\sigma_{\delta q}^2\phi\,(q)] + \text{const}. \qquad\qquad \text{(B)}$$

At this stage it is interesting to note that the left-hand member of (B),

$\Delta q \cdot \phi(q)$, represents the fraction of the distribution that tends to be carried past a given value of q by the systematic pressure Δq in each generation. Since the distribution is stationary, the right-hand side

$$\frac{1}{2} \frac{\partial}{\partial q} [\sigma_{\delta q}^2 \phi(q)] = \frac{1}{4N} \frac{d}{dq} [q(1-q) \phi(q)]$$

must be the fraction of the distribution which tends to be scattered away in the opposite direction by random deviations in each generation.

To facilitate the second integration, we rewrite (B) as follows:

$$\frac{\Delta q}{\sigma_{\delta q}^2} [\sigma_{\delta q}^2 \phi(q)] = \frac{1}{2} \frac{d}{dq} [\sigma_{\delta q}^2 \phi(q)]$$

$$\frac{2(\Delta q)}{\sigma_{\delta q}^2} = \frac{\frac{d}{dq} [\sigma_{\delta q}^2 \phi(q)]}{\sigma_{\delta q}^2 \phi(q)}.$$

Integrating,

$$2 \int \frac{\Delta q}{\sigma_{\delta q}^2} dq = \log [\sigma_{\delta q}^2 \phi(q)] + \text{const.} ;$$

$$\therefore \quad \sigma_{\delta q}^2 \phi(q) = C e^{2\int(\Delta q/\sigma_{\delta q}^2)dq} ,$$

which is our general distribution formula (14).

References

ANDERSON, E. 1936. The species problem in *Iris*. Ann. Missouri Bot. Garden, **23**: 457–509.

BARTLETT, M. S., and HALDANE, J. B. S. 1934. The theory of inbreeding in autotetraploids. J. Genetics, **29**:175–80.

———. 1935. The theory of inbreeding with forced heterozygosis. *Ibid.*, **31**:327–40.

BERNSTEIN, F. 1925. Zusammenfassende Betrachtungen über die erblichen Blutstrukturen des Menschen. Ztschr. f. Abstamm-. u. Vererbungslehre, **37**:237–70.

———. 1930a. Über die Erblichkeit der Blutgruppen. *Ibid.*, **54**:400–426.

———. 1930b. Fortgesetzte Untersuchungen aus der Theorie der Blutgruppen. *Ibid.*, **56**:233–73.

BOORMAN, K. E. 1950. An analysis of the blood types and clinical condition of 2000 consecutive mothers and their infants. Ann. Eugenics, **15**:120–34 .

BOYD, W. C. 1950. Genetics and the Races of Man. Boston: Little, Brown & Co.

BRYCE, L. M., JAKOBOWICZ, R., MCARTHUR, N., and PENROSE, L. S. 1950. Blood-group frequencies in a mother and infant sample of the Australian population. Ann. Eugenics, **15**:271–75.

BUNAK, V. V. 1936. Changes in the mean values of characters in mixed populations. Ann. Eugenics, **7**:195–206.

CASTLE, W. E. 1903. The laws of heredity of Galton and Mendel and some laws governing race improvement by selection. Proc. Am. Acad. Arts & Sc., **39**:223–42.

CAVALLI, L. L. 1950. The analysis of selection curves. Biometrics, **6**:208–20.

CHETVERIKOV, S. S. 1926. On certain features of the evolutionary process from the point of view of modern genetics. J. Exper. Biol. (Moscow), **2**:3–54.

COTTERMAN, C. W. 1937a. The detection of sex-linkage in families collected at random. Ohio J. Sc., **37**:75–81.

———. 1937b. Indication of unit factor inheritance in data comprising but a single generation. *Ibid.*, pp. 127–40.

———. 1941. Relatives and human genetic analysis. Scient. Monthly, **53**:227–34.

———. 1947. A weighting system for the estimation of gene frequencies from family records. Contr. Lab. Vert. Biol., Univ. Michigan, No. 33, pp. 1–21.

COTTERMAN, C. W., and SNYDER, L. H. 1937. Studies in human inheritance. XVII. Gene frequency analysis of double recessive inheritance involving one autosomal and one sex-linked gene substitution. Genetica, **19**:537–52.

CROW, J. F. 1948. Alternative hypotheses of hybrid vigor. Genetics, **33**:477–87.

———. 1952. Dominance and overdominance. *In* J. W. GOWEN (ed.), Heterosis, pp. 282–97. Ames: Iowa State College Press.

———. 1954. Breeding structure of populations. II. Effective population number. *In* KEMPTHORNE *et al.* (eds.), Statistics and Mathematics in Biology, pp. 543–56. Ames: Iowa State College Press.

CROW, J. F., and ROBERTS, W. C. 1950. Inbreeding and homozygosis in bees. Genetics, **35**:612–21.

DA CUNHA, A. B. 1949. Genetic analysis of polymorphism of color pattern in *Drosophila polymorpha*. Evolution, **3**:239–51.

DAHLBERG, G. 1929. Inbreeding in man. Genetics, **14**:421–54.

———. 1938. On rare defects in human populations with particular regard to inbreeding and isolate effects. Proc. Roy. Soc. Edinburgh, **58**:213–32.

———. 1948*a*. Mathematical Methods for Population Genetics. New York: Interscience Publishers.

———. 1948*b*. Genetics of human populations. *In* Advances in Genetics, **2**:69–98. New York: Academic Press.

DOBZHANSKY, TH. 1943. Genetics of natural populations. IX. Temporal changes in the composition of populations of *Drosophila pseudoobscura*. Genetics, **28**:162–86.

———. 1947. Genetics of natural populations. XIV. A response of certain gene arrangements in the third chromosome of *Drosophila pseudoobscura* to natural selection. *Ibid.*, **32**:142–60.

———. 1950. Genetics of natural populations. XIX. Origin of heterosis through natural selection in populations of *Drosophila pseudoobscura*. *Ibid.*, **35**:288–302.

———. 1951. Genetics and the Origin of Species. 3d ed. New York: Columbia Univ. Press.

DOBZHANSKY, TH., and LEVENE, H. 1948. Genetics of natural populations. XVII. Proof of operation of natural selection in wild populations of *Drosophila pseudoobscura*. Genetics, **33**:537–47.

———. 1951. Development of heterosis through natural selection in experimental populations of *Drosophila pseudoobscura*. Am. Naturalist, **85**:247–64.

DOBZHANSKY, TH., and QUEAL, M. L. 1938*a*. Genetics of natural populations. I. Chromosome variation in populations of *Drosophila pseudoobscura* inhabiting isolated mountain ranges. Genetics, **23**:239–51.

———. 1938*b*. Genetics of natural populations. II. Genic variation in populations of *Drosophila pseudoobscura* inhabiting isolated mountain ranges. *Ibid.*, pp. 463–84.

DOBZHANSKY, TH., and WRIGHT, S. 1941. Genetics of natural populations. V. Relations between mutation rate and accumulation of lethals in populations of *Drosophila pseudoobscura*. Genetics, **26**:23–51.

DUBININ, N. P. 1946. On lethal mutations in natural populations. Genetics, **31**:21–38.

EAST, E. M., and JONES, D. F. 1919. Inbreeding and Outbreeding. London and Philadelphia: J. B. Lippincott Co.

EAST, E. M., and MANGELSDORF, A. J. 1925. A new interpretation of the hereditary behaviour of self-sterile plants. Proc. Nat. Acad. Sci., **2**:166–71.

ELTON, C. 1924. Periodic fluctuations in the numbers of animals: their causes and effects. J. Exper. Biol., **2**:119–63.

———. 1942. Voles, Mice, and Lemmings: Problems in Population Dynamics. Oxford: Clarendon Press.

EMIK, L. O., and TERRILL, C. E. 1949. Systematic procedures for calculating inbreeding coefficients. J. Hered., **40**:51–55.

FABRICIUS-HANSEN, V. 1939. Blood groups and MN types of Eskimos in East Greenland. J. Immunol., **36**:523–30.

————. 1940. Blood groups and MN types of Eskimos in West Greenland. *Ibid.*, **38**: 405–11.

FELLER, W. 1950. An Introduction to Probability Theory and Its Applications. New York: John Wiley & Sons.

FINNEY, D. J. 1948*a*. The estimation of gene frequencies from family records. I. Factors without dominance. Heredity, **2**:199–218.

————. 1948*b*. The estimation of gene frequencies from family records. II. Factors with dominance. *Ibid.*, pp. 369–89.

FISH, H. D. 1914. On the progressive increase of homozygosis in brother-sister matings. Am. Naturalist, **48**:759–61.

FISHER, R. A. 1918. The correlation between relatives on the supposition of Mendelian inheritance. Trans. Roy. Soc. Edinburgh, **52**:399–433.

————. 1922. On the dominance ratio. Proc. Roy. Soc. Edinburgh, **42**:321–41.

————. 1930*a*. The Genetical Theory of Natural Selection. Oxford: Clarendon Press.

————. 1930*b*. The distribution of gene ratios for rare mutations. Proc. Roy. Soc. Edinburgh, **50**:205–20.

————. 1936. The measurement of selective intensity. Proc. Roy. Soc., London, B, **121**:58–62.

————. 1937. The wave of advance of advantageous genes. Ann. Eugenics, **7**:355–69.

————. 1939. Stage of development as a factor influencing the variance in the number of offspring, frequency of mutants, and related quantities. *Ibid.*, **9**:406–8.

————. 1940. The estimation of the proportion of recessives from tests carried out on a sample not wholly unrelated. *Ibid.*, **10**:160–70.

————. 1949. The Theory of Inbreeding. London and Edinburgh: Oliver & Boyd.

————. 1951. Standard calculations for evaluating a blood group system. Heredity, **5**:95–102.

FISHER, R. A., and MATHER, K. 1943. The inheritance of style length in *Lythrum salicaria*. Ann. Eugenics, **12**:1–23.

GARBER, M. J. 1951. Approach to genotypic equilibrium with varying percentages of self-fertilization and cross-fertilization. J. Hered., **42**:299–300.

GEIRINGER, H. 1944. On the probability theory of linkage in Mendelian heredity. Ann. Math. Stat., **15**:25–57.

————. 1945. Further remarks on linkage theory in Mendelian heredity. *Ibid.*, **16**: 390–93.

————. 1948. On the mathematics of random mating in case of different recombination values for males and females. Genetics, **33**:548–64.

————. 1949*a*. Contribution to the linkage theory of autopolyploids. Bull. Math. Biophysics, **11**:59–82.

————. 1949*b*. Contribution to the linkage theory of autopolyploids. *Ibid.*, pp. 197–219.

————. 1949*c*. Chromatid segregation of tetraploids and hexaploids. Genetics, **34**: 665–84.

————. 1949*d*. On some mathematical problems arising in the development of Mendelian genetics. J. Am. Stat. Assoc., **44**:526–47.

GLASS, B. 1950. The action of selection on the principal Rh alleles. Am. J. Human Genetics, **2**:269–78.

GLASS, B. 1954. Genetic changes in human populations, especially those due to gene flow and genetic drift. *In* Advances in Genetics, **6**:95–139. New York: Academic Press.

GLASS, B., and LI, C. C. 1953. The dynamics of racial intermixture—an analysis based on the American Negro. Am. J. Human Genetics, **5**:1–20.

GLASS, B., SACKS, M. S., JAHN, E. F., and HESS, C. 1952. Genetic drift in a religious isolate: an analysis of the causes of variation in blood group and other gene frequencies in a small population. Am. Naturalist, **86**:145–59.

HALDANE, J. B. S. 1924–32. A mathematical theory of natural and artificial selection. Proc. Cambridge Phil. Soc., **23**:19–41, 158–63, 363–72, 607–15, 838–44; **26**:220–30; **27**:131–42; **28**:244–48.

————. 1930. Theoretical genetics of autopolyploids. J. Genetics, **22**:359–72.

————. 1932. The Causes of Evolution. London: Harper & Bros.

————. 1935. The rate of spontaneous mutation of a human gene. J. Genetics, **31**:317–26.

————. 1936. The amount of heterozygosis to be expected in an approximately pure line. *Ibid.*, **32**:375–91.

————. 1937*a*. Some theoretical results of continued brother-sister mating. *Ibid.*, **34**:265–74.

————. 1937*b*. The effect of variation on fitness. Am. Naturalist, **71**:337–49.

————. 1939*a*. The spread of harmful autosomal recessive genes in human populations. Ann. Eugenics, **9**:232–37.

————. 1939*b*. The equilibrium between mutation and random extinction. *Ibid.*, pp. 400–405.

————. 1940. The conflict between selection and mutation of harmful recessive genes. *Ibid.*, **10**:417–21.

————. 1942. Selection against heterozygosis in man. *Ibid.*, **11**:333–40.

————. 1948. The theory of a cline. J. Genetics, **48**:277–84.

————. 1949*a*. Parental and fraternal correlations for fitness. Ann. Eugenics, **14**:288–92.

————. 1949*b*. The association of characters as a result of inbreeding and linkage. *Ibid.*, **15**:15–23.

————. 1949*c*. The rate of mutation of human genes. *In* Proc. Eighth Internat. Cong. Genetics (supplement to Hereditas), pp. 267–73. Lund: Berlingska Boktryckeriet.

HALDANE, J. B. S., and MOSHINSKY, P. 1939. Inbreeding in Mendelian populations with special reference to human cousin marriage. Ann. Eugenics, **9**:321–40.

HARDY, G. H. 1908. Mendelian proportions in a mixed population. Science, **28**:49–50.

HOGBEN, L. 1931. The genetic analysis of familial traits. I. Single gene substitutions. J. Genetics, **25**:97–112.

————. 1932*a*. The genetic analysis of familial traits. II. Double gene substitutions, with special reference to hereditary dwarfism. *Ibid.*, pp. 211–40.

————. 1932*b*. The genetic analysis of familial traits. III. Mating involving one parent exhibiting a trait determined by a single recessive gene substitution with special reference to sex-linked conditions. *Ibid.*, pp. 293–314.

————. 1932*c*. The factorial analysis of small families with parents of undetermined genotype. *Ibid.*, **26**:75–79.

———. 1932d. Filial and fraternal correlations in sex-linked inheritance. Proc. Roy. Soc. Edinburgh, 52:331–36.

———. 1933. A matrix notation for Mendelian populations. Ibid., 53:7–25.

———. 1946. An Introduction to Mathematical Genetics. New York: W. W. Norton & Co.

IKIN, E. W., PRIOR, A. M., RACE, R. R., and TAYLOR, G. L. 1939. The distributions in the A_1A_2BO blood groups in England. Ann. Eugenics, 9:409–11.

JENNINGS, H. S. 1914. Formula for the results of inbreeding. Am. Naturalist, 48: 693–96.

———. 1916. The numerical results of diverse systems of breeding. Genetics, 1:53–89.

———. 1917. The numerical results of diverse systems of breeding, with respect to two pairs of characters, linked or independent, with special relation to the effects of linkage. Ibid., 2:97–154.

KALMUS, H., and SMITH, C. A. B. 1948. Production of pure lines in bees. J. Genetics, 49:153–58.

KEMP, W. B. 1929. Genetic equilibrium and selection. Genetics, 14:85–127.

KOLMOGOROV, A. 1935. Deviations from Hardy's formula in partial isolation. Compt. rend. Acad. d. sc. de l'U.R.S.S., 3(7):129–32.

LANDSTEINER, L., and LEVINE, P. 1928. On individual differences in human blood. J. Exper. Med., 47:757–75.

LAWRENCE, W. J. C. 1931. The genetics and cytology of Dahlia variabilis. J. Genetics, 24:257–306.

LERNER, M. I. 1950. Population Genetics and Animal Improvement. London: Cambridge Univ. Press.

LEVENE, H. 1949a. On a matching problem arising in genetics. Ann. Math. Stat., 20: 91–94.

———. 1949b. A new measure of sexual isolation. Evolution, 3:315–21.

———. 1953. Genetic equilibrium when more than one ecological niche is available. Am. Naturalist, 87:331–33.

LEVIT, S. G. 1936. The problem of dominance in man. J. Genetics, 33:410–34.

LI, C. C. 1948. Note on estimation of the amount of inbreeding from random samples of a natural population. Chinese J. Agric., 1:43–52.

———. 1953a. A direct proof of the relation between genotypic mating correlation and gametic uniting correlation in equilibrium populations. J. Heredity, 44:39–40.

———. 1953b. On an equation specifying equilibrium populations. Science, 117: 378–79.

———. 1953c. Is Rh facing a crossroad? A critique of the compensation effect. Am. Naturalist, 87:257–61.

———. 1953d. Some general properties of recessive inheritance. Am. J. Human Genetics, 5:269–79.

———. 1954. Some methods of studying human genetics, I–IV. Methods in Medical Research, 6:1–38.

LI, C. C., and HORVITZ, D. G. 1953. Some methods of estimating the inbreeding coefficient. Am. J. Human Genetics, 5:107–17.

LI, C. C., and SACKS, L. 1954. The derivation of joint distribution and correlation between relatives by the use of stochastic matrices. Biometrics, 10:347–60.

LOTKA, A. J. 1925. Elements of Physical Biology. Baltimore: Williams & Wilkins Co.

LUSH, J. L. 1945. Animal Breeding Plans. 3d. ed. Ames: Iowa State College Press.

———. 1946. Chance as a cause of changes in gene frequency within pure breeds of livestock. Am. Naturalist, 80:318–42.

MALÉCOT, G. 1944. Sur un problème de probabilités en chaine que pose génétique. Comp. rend. Acad. d. sc., 219:379–81.

———. 1948. Les Mathématiques de l'hérédité. Paris: Masson & Cie.

MATHER, K. 1935. Reductional and equational separation of the chromosomes in bivalents and multivalents. J. Genetics, 30:53–77.

———. 1936. Segregation and linkage in autotetraploids. Ibid., 32:287–314.

———. 1942. The balance of polygenic combinations. Ibid., 43:309–36.

———. 1943. Polygenic inheritance and natural selection. Biol. Rev., 18:32–64.

———. 1946. Dominance and heterosis. Am. Naturalist, 80:91–96.

———. 1949. Biometrical Genetics. New York: Dover Publications.

———. 1951. The Measurement of Linkage in Heredity. 2d ed. London: Methuen & Co.

MOREE, R. 1950. A modification of the Hardy-Weinberg Law. Science, 111:691–92.

MULLER, H. J. 1948. Evidence of the precision of genetic adaptation. The Harvey Lectures, Series 43, pp. 165–229. Springfield, Ill.: Charles C Thomas.

———. 1950. Our load of mutations. Am. J. Human Genetics, 2:111–76.

NEEL, J. V., and SCHULL, W. 1954. Human Heredity. Chicago: Univ. Chicago Press.

OWEN, A. R. G. 1952. A genetical system admitting of two stable equilibria. Nature, 170:1127–28.

———. 1953. A genetical system admitting of two distinct stable equilibria under natural selection. Heredity, 7:97–102.

PÄTAU, K. 1938. Die mathematische Analyse der Evolutionsvorgänge. Ztschr. f. Abstamm-. u. Vererbungslehre, 76:220–28.

PEARSON, K. 1904. On a generalized theory of alternative inheritance, with special references to Mendel's laws. Phil. Trans. Roy. Soc., A, 203:53–86.

PENROSE, L. S. 1935. The detection of autosomal linkage in data which consist of pairs of brothers and sisters of unspecified parentage. Ann. Eugenics, 6:133–38.

———. 1939. Some practical considerations in testing for genetic linkage in sib data. Ohio J. Sc., 39:291–96.

———. 1946. A further note on the sib-pair linkage method. Ann. Eugenics, 13:25–29.

———. 1949. The meaning of "fitness" in human populations. Ibid., 14:301–4.

———. 1951. Genetics of the human race. In L. C. DUNN (ed.), Genetics in the 20th Century, pp. 393–99. New York: Macmillan Co.

PHILIP, U. 1938. Mating systems in wild populations of Dermestes vulpinus and Mus musculus. J. Genetics, 36:197–211.

RIFE, D. C. 1938. Simple modes of inheritance and the study of twins. Ohio J. Sc., 38:281–93.

———. 1950. An application of gene frequency analysis to the interpretation of data from twins. Human Biol., 22:136–45.

———. 1951a. A method for analyzing multiple allelic inheritance. J. Heredity, 42:105–6.

———. 1951b. A method for testing two-factor inheritance. Ibid., p. 162.

ROBBINS, R. B. 1917. Some applications of mathematics to breeding problems. I. Genetics, **2**:489–504.

———. 1918*a*. Some applications of mathematics to breeding problems. II. *Ibid.*, **3**: 73–92.

———. 1918*b*. Some applications of mathematics to breeding problems. III. *Ibid.*, pp. 375–89.

———. 1918*c*. Random mating with the exception of sister by brother mating. *Ibid.*, pp. 390–96.

ROBERTSON, A. 1952. The effect of inbreeding on the variation due to recessive genes. Genetics, **37**:189–207.

ROMASHOV, D. D., and ILYINA, E. D. 1942. Analysis of fox populations after Hardy's formula. Doklady Acad. Sc., U.R.S.S., **37**:193–96.

SCHMALHAUSEN, I. I. 1949. Factors of Evolution: The Theory of Stabilizing Selection. Trans. I. DORDICK. New York: Blakiston Co.

SNYDER, L. H. 1929. Blood Grouping in Relation to Clinical and Legal Medicine. Baltimore: Williams & Wilkins Co.

———. 1932. Studies in human inheritance. IX. The inheritance of taste deficiency in man. Ohio J. Sc., **32**:436–40.

———. 1934. Studies in human inheritance. X. A table to determine the proportion of recessives to be expected in various matings involving a unit character. Genetics, **19**:1–17.

———. 1947*a*. Studies in human inheritance. XXX. A gene frequency analysis of maternal-fetal incompatibility. J. Immunol., **56**:281–85.

———. 1947*b*. The principles of gene distribution in human populations. Yale J. Biol. & Med., **19**:817–33.

———. 1951. The Principles of Heredity. 4th ed. Boston: D. C. Heath & Co.

SNYDER, L. H., and COTTERMAN, C. W. 1936. Studies in human inheritance. XIII. A table to determine the expected proportion of females showing a sex-influenced character corresponding to any given proportion of males showing the character. Genetics, **21**:79–83.

SPENCER, W. P. 1947. On Rh gene frequencies. Am. Naturalist, **81**:237–40.

SRB, A. M., and OWEN, R. D. 1952. General Genetics. San Francisco: W. H. Freeman & Co.

STANTON, R. G. 1946. Filial and fraternal correlations in successive generations. Ann. Eugenics, **13**:18–24.

STERN, C. 1943. The Hardy-Weinberg Law. Science, **97**:137–38.

———. 1950. Principles of Human Genetics. San Francisco: W. H. Freeman & Co.

STEVENS, W. L. 1938. Estimation of blood group gene frequencies. Ann. Eugenics, **8**: 362–75.

———. 1950. Statistical analysis of the ABO blood groups. Human Biol., **22**:191–217.

———. 1952. Statistical analysis of the ABO system in mixed populations. *Ibid.*, **24**: 12–24.

STRANDSKOV, H. H. 1941. The distribution of human genes. Scient. Monthly, **52**: 203–15.

———. 1942. The genetics of human populations. Am. Naturalist, **76**:156–64.

———. 1950. Genetics and the origin and evolution of man. Cold Spring Harbor Symp. Quant. Biol., **15**:1–11.

TAYLOR, G. L., and PRIOR, A. M. 1938. Blood groups in England. II. Distribution in the population. Ann. Eugenics, 8:356–61.

———. 1939. The distribution of the M and N factors in random samples of different races. *Ibid.*, 9:97–108.

WAHLUND, S. 1928. Zusammensetzung von Populationen und Korrelationserscheinungen von Standpunkt der Vererbungslehre aus betrachtet. Hereditas, 11:65–106.

WEATHERBURN, C. E. 1949. A First Course in Mathematical Statistics. London: Cambridge Univ. Press.

WEINBERG, W. 1908. Über den Nachweis der Vererbung beim Menschen. Jahresh. Verein f. vaterl. Naturk. in Württemberg, 64:368–82.

———. 1909. Über Vererbungsgesetze beim Menschen. Ztschr. Abst. u. Vererb., 1: 277–330.

WELLISCH, S., and THOMSEN, O. 1930. Ueber die Vier-Gen-Hypothese Thomsens. Hereditas, 14:50–52.

WENTWORTH, E. N., and REMICK, B. L. 1916. Some breeding properties of the generalized Mendelian population. Genetics, 1:608–16.

WIENER, A. S. 1943. Blood Groups and Transfusion. 3d ed. Springfield, Ill.: Charles C Thomas.

———. 1950. Heredity of the Rh blood types. IX. Observations in a series of 526 cases of disputed parentage. Am. J. Human Genetics, 2:177–97.

WRIGHT, S. 1921a. Correlation and causation. J. Agric. Research, 20:557–85.

———. 1921b. Systems of mating, I–V. Genetics, 6:111–78.

———. 1922a. Coefficients of inbreeding and relationship. Am. Naturalist, 56:330–38.

———. 1922b. The effects of inbreeding and crossbreeding on guinea pigs. III. Crosses between highly inbred lines. U.S. Dept. Agric. Bull. 1121.

———. 1923a. The theory of path coefficients. Genetics, 8:239–55

———. 1923b. Mendelian analysis of the pure breeds of livestock. I. The measurement of inbreeding and relationship. J. Hered., 14:339–48.

———. 1931. Evolution in Mendelian populations. Genetics, 16:97–159.

———. 1932. The roles of mutation, inbreeding, crossbreeding, and selection in evolution. Proc. Sixth Internat. Cong. Genetics (Ithaca), 1:356–66.

———. 1933a. Inbreeding and homozygosis. Proc. Nat. Acad. Sc., 19:411–19.

———. 1933b. Inbreeding and recombination. *Ibid.*, pp. 420–33.

———. 1934. The method of path coefficients. Ann. Math. Stat., 5:161–215.

———. 1935a. The analysis of variance and the correlation between relatives with respect to deviations from an optimum. J. Genetics, 30:243–56.

———. 1935b. Evolution in populations in approximate equilibrium. *Ibid.*, pp. 257–66.

———. 1937. The distribution of gene frequencies in populations. Proc. Nat. Acad. Sc., 23:307–20.

———. 1938a. The distribution of gene frequencies under irreversible mutation. *Ibid.*, 24:253–59.

———. 1938b. The distribution of gene frequencies in populations of polyploids. *Ibid.*, pp. 372–77.

———. 1938c. Size of population and breeding structure in relation to evolution. Science, 87:430–31.

———. 1939a. Statistical Genetics in Relation to Evolution, pp. 1–64. Paris: Hermann & Cie.

———. 1939*b*. The distribution of self-sterility alleles in populations. Genetics, **24**: 538–52.

———. 1940*a*. The statistical consequences of Mendelian heredity in relation to speciation. *In* J. S. HUXLEY (ed.), The New Systematics, pp. 161–83. London: Oxford Univ. Press.

— ———. 1940*b*. Breeding structure of populations in relation to speciation. Am. Naturalist, **74**:232–48.

———. 1942. Statistical genetics and evolution. Bull. Am. Math. Soc., **48**:223–46.

———. 1943. Isolation by distance. Genetics, **28**:114–38.

———. 1945. The differential equation of the distribution of gene frequencies. Proc. Nat. Acad. Sc., **31**:382–89.

———. 1946. Isolation by distance under diverse systems of mating. Genetics, **31**: 39–59.

———. 1948. On the roles of directed and random changes in gene frequency in the genetics of populations. Evolution, **2**:279–94.

———. 1949*a*. Adaptation and selection. *In* G. L. JEPSEN *et al.* (eds.), Genetics, Paleontology, and Evolution, pp. 365–89. Princeton, N.J.: Princeton Univ. Press.

———. 1949*b*. Population structure in evolution. Proc. Am. Phil. Soc., **93**:471–78.

———. 1951. The genetical structure of populations. Ann. Eugenics, **15**:323–54.

———. 1952*a*. The theoretical variance within and among subdivisions of a population that is in a steady state. Genetics, **37**:312–21.

———. 1952*b*. The genetics of quantitative variability. *In* E. C. R. REEVE and C. H. WADDINGTON (eds.), Quantitative Inheritance, pp. 5–41. London: H.M. Stationery Office.

WRIGHT, S., and DOBZHANSKY, TH. 1946. Genetics of natural populations. XII. Experimental reproduction of some of the changes caused by natural selection in certain populations of *Drosophila pseudoobscura*. Genetics, **31**:125–56.

WRIGHT, S., DOBZHANSKY, TH., and HOVANITZ, W. 1942. Genetics of natural populations. VII. The allelism of lethals in third chromosome of *Drosophila pseudoobscura*. Genetics, **27**:363–94.

WRIGHT, S., and MCPHEE, H. C. 1925. An approximate method of calculating coefficients of inbreeding and relationship from livestock pedigrees. J. Agric. Research, **31**:377–83.

YULE, G. U., and KENDALL, M. G. 1950. An Introduction to the Theory of Statistics. 14th ed. New York: Hafner Publishing Co.

Index